PSYCHOLOGY

and the

PHILOSOPHY of SCIENCE

CENTURY PSYCHOLOGY SERIES

Richard M. Elliott, Kenneth MacCorquodale,
Gardner Lindzey, & Kenneth E. Clark
Editors

Psychology and the Philosophy of Science was
first published as Part II of the author's *Philosophy and the Science of Behavior*, winner of
the 1965 Century Psychology Award and published in 1967.

RPmac

MERLE B. TURNER
SAN DIEGO STATE COLLEGE

PSYCHOLOGY

and the

PHILOSOPHY of SCIENCE

1967

New York

APPLETON-CENTURY-CROFTS

DIVISION OF THE MEREDITH CORPORATION

698–1

Library of Congress Card Number: 69–13071

This book was copyrighted © 1967 by Meredith Publishing Company as part of *Philosophy and the Science of Behavior.*

PRINTED IN THE UNITED STATES OF AMERICA

E88881

ACKNOWLEDGMENTS

Acknowledgments are made to the following sources for quotations and figures used in this book.

Page 18   Quotes from *The Value of Science* by Henri Poincaré, Dover Publications, Inc., New York.

Page 18   Quote from *Science and Hypothesis* by Henri Poincaré, Dover Publications, Inc., New York.

Pages 22–23   Quotes from P. A. M. Dirac, *Quantum Mechanics* (3rd ed.). London: Oxford University Press, 1947.

Pages 25, 26, 83, 102–103   Quotes from P. Duhem, *The Aim and Structure of Physical Theory.* Princeton, N.J.: Princeton University Press, 1954.

Page 36   Quote from MODERN LEARNING THEORY by William K. Estes et al., Copyright 1954, by Appleton-Century-Crofts, Inc. Reprinted by permission of Appleton-Century-Crofts.

Pages 38, 39, 40   Quotes from PSYCHOLOGY: A STUDY OF SCIENCE, Vol. II by S. Koch. Copyright 1959. McGraw-Hill Book Company. Used by permission.

Pages 49, 50   Quotes from P. K. Feyerabend, "Explanation, Reduction and Empiricism," in *Minnesota Studies in the Philosophy of Science,* Vol. III, edited by H. Feigl and G. Maxwell. Minneapolis, Minnesota: University of Minnesota Press, 1962.

Pages 52–53   Quote from C. I. Lewis, "A Pragmatic Conception of *a priori,*" in *Journal of Philosophy,* 1923, Vol. 20, pp. 169–177.

Page 53   Quote from *Mind and the World Order* by C. I. Lewis, Dover Publications, Inc., New York.

Page 54   Quote from K. Koffka, *Principles of Gestalt Psychology.* New York, Harcourt, Brace & World, 1935.

Page 55   Quote from F. Hayek, *The Sensory Order.* Chicago: Chicago University Press, 1952; London: Routledge and Kegan Paul Ltd., 1952.

Page 66   Quote from *Foundations of Science* by Norman R. Campbell, Dover Publications, Inc., New York.

Pages 94, 162   Quotes from: PRINCIPLES OF BEHAVIOR by Clark L. Hull. Copyright 1943, by D. Appleton-Century Company, Inc. Reprinted by permission of Appleton-Century-Crofts.

iv

Page 102   Quote from Suppes and Atkinson, *Markov Learning Models for Multi-person Interaction* (Stanford, Stanford University Press, 1960), p. 279.

Pages 113, 116   Quotes from C. Hempel and P. Oppenheim, "Studies in the Logic of Explanation," in *Philosophy of Science*, 1948, Vol. 15, pp. 135–175.

Page 115   Quote from M. Scriven, "Explanation, Prediction and Laws," in *Minnesota Studies in the Philosophy of Science*, Vol. III, edited by H. Feigl and G. Maxwell. Minneapolis, Minnesota: University of Minnesota Press, 1962.

Page 121   Quotes from C. D. Broad, *Mind and its Place in Nature*. London: Routledge and Kegan Paul Ltd., 1925.

Page 122   Quote from E. Nagel, *The Structure of Science*. New York: Harcourt, Brace & World, 1961.

Page 128   Quote from PRINCIPLES OF TOPOLOGICAL PSYCHOLOGY by K. Lewin. Copyright 1936. McGraw-Hill Book Company. Used by permission.

Pages 135, 136   Quotes from Henri Bergson: AN INTRODUCTION TO METAPHYSICS, copyright © 1949, 1955 by the Liberal Arts Press, Inc., reprinted by permission of the Liberal Arts Press Division of the Bobbs-Merrill Company, Inc.

Page 155   Quote from: THE BEHAVIOR OF ORGANISMS by B. F. Skinner. Copyright 1938, by D. Appleton-Century Company, Inc. Reprinted by permission of Appleton-Century-Crofts.

Page 158   Quote from P. Bridgman, "Remarks on the Present State of Operationism," in *Scientific Monthly*, 1954, Vol. 79, pp. 224–226.

Pages 158–159   Quote from A. Eddington, *Space, Time and Gravitation*. New York: Cambridge University Press, 1920.

Pages 161, 162   Quote from J. H. Woodger, *Language and Biology*. New York: Cambridge University Press, 1952.

Page 162   Quote from C. L. Hull, *Essentials of Behavior*. New Haven, Conn.: Yale University Press, 1951.

Pages 167–168   Quotes reprinted and illustration redrawn from *The Structural Basis of Behavior* by J. A. Deutsch by permission of the University of Chicago Press. © 1960 by the University of Chicago.

Pages 194–195   Quote from K. Spence, *Behavior and Conditioning*. New Haven, Conn.: Yale University Press, 1956.

Page 196   Illustration redrawn from Richard T. Weidner, Robert L. Sells, ELEMENTARY MODERN PHYSICS, © Copyright 1960, Allyn and Bacon, Inc., Boston. Reprinted with permission.

Page 206   Quotes from G. Ryle, *The Concept of Mind*. New York: Barnes & Noble, 1949; London: Hutchison Publishing Group Ltd., 1949.

PREFACE

THE PRESENT BOOK examines certain aspects of behavioristic psychology in the context of the philosophy of science. Quite obviously the treatment must be limited. The subject matter of experimental and theoretical psychology is much too diversified to be subjected to extensive critical analysis. Here the argument is necessarily a restricted one, concentrating as it does on stimulus-response paradigms and on learning where psychologists have presumed to a theory worthy of the name.

As a science psychology presents neither the formal maturity nor the quandary which has characterized modern physics. As a result, one hears the claim that psychology is not ready for its philosophy. Or, more often, one hears that philosophical analysis has little to contribute to the skills that the behavioral scientist must bring to his experimental problems. Such reactions are reasonable ones only if the psychologist has little to question concerning first principles or concerning the basics of his language. Frequently, however, the behaviorist overlooks the fact that his scientific credo was born in philosophical ferment; that whenever he defends the data of behavior as being the proper subject matter for the language of his science, he is making a commitment which is to be defended not as a subject of science but as one of philosophy in a technical sense. The logical positivists learned long ago that anti-metaphysics, and all the protestations, lead nowhere if not to metaphysics. And the behaviorist who restricts the data language of his science to public observation, doing so out of his commitment to clarity, to communicability, and to systemic efficiency, shows his own philosophical hand as surely as the philosopher who often waits until his major work is done before he pens his prolegomena.

Experience, and the data and language of experience, become the focal issues for the psychologist who would look critically at his own science. The contemporary behaviorist frequently vacillates between a radical, naive empiricism and facile operationism. Having been encouraged to disdain philosophy, he has to a large extent been unaware of the difficulty of analyzing the language of experience itself. He has been prepared neither to recognize how unobvious, how debatable is so simple a thing as a fact, nor to articulate as first principles that one cannot divest the fact of its theoretic attribute or divorce theory of its apperceptive function.

In brief, a theme of this book is that theory is integral with all behavioral science—that, more explicitly, scientific fact cannot be rendered independent of theory. Yet beyond this, some maintain that theory is not wholly the subject of an arbitrary option as befits the taste of the practitioner. Nor is one open to just any kind of operational license. To the criteria of parsimony and comprehensiveness in selecting from among our theoretical languages, we must add and emphasize that of reduction. The questions of alternative theoretical conceptions will be resolved by reducing the terms of one science to those of a more basic science. In some such sense there is a real convergence in scientific endeavor. It is in the reduction that one finds whatever sense of scientific realism is philosophically defensible.

Acknowledgments are due many people who contributed directly or indirectly to this work. I am indebted to the staff of Appleton-Century-Crofts for their editorial assistance and to Miss Mary Dowse, Mrs. Helen Ledbetter, and Mrs. Lynn White for the travails of typescript.

I am especially indebted to David Hawkins for the sense of realism that is invasive of pragmatism, to R. B. Braithwaite for the formal analysis of scientific thinking, to the late Norwood R. Hanson for the conceptual prescription of fact and theory, and to Charles L. Sherman, my first mentor in philosophy, for the Kantian critique of empiricism. I wish to express my appreciation to Stanley Weissman for his critical reading of selected parts of the manuscript.

I am grateful to the Department of Psychology, the Moral Sciences Faculty and the trustees of the University of Cambridge for use of library resources during the writing of this book.

M. B. T.

CONTENTS

ix

CHAPTER 1

Introduction

THE PROBLEMS of psychology are the problems of other sciences. Systematically treated, they follow the resumé of the philosophy of science. They are the problems of data, of theory, and of inference. Where solutions to the problems are not immediately forthcoming, procedural agreements and rules may arise which permit either the inspired novitiate or the drudging veteran to get on with his work. In a word, most of us become uncritical positivists, with little inclination to consider the matter further. Still, problems of meaning, of construction, of explanation remain obtrusive. On occasion each one of us slips into his own chair, if only to rest. The positive moments become less positive, and we wonder what kind of science, what knowledge, can be built on a critical empiricism.

There was a time not too long ago when psychology was the maidservant of philosophy. Its major function was to tidy up the household of epistemology. But that was changed by the irascible behaviorists. They emancipated us from traditional philosophy. They freed us once, but not for all, from the skeins of mentalism, from the tangles of volition, feeling, and imageless thought. Thus by taking behavior, and only behavior, as the source of its data, psychology was to become a science such as physiology, or even physics. It would have no need of metaphysics. It would renounce its grandparentage, as indeed it did, and turn to positivism and operationism for familial support. But unfortunately they, the science of behavior and positivism, were siblings, and boasts of allegiance came at a time when positivism itself was temporizing its proprietary claims on dogmatic objectivity.

Philosophically speaking, the critical issues were epistemic ones. What, for example, constitutes meaningful discourse? Whereof may we speak sense? What are the boundaries of defensible knowledge? These proved to be rather tiresome questions. However, the success of the

1

physical sciences had led to a vigorous reaffirmation of the logico-empirical foundations of knowledge. A meaningful statement is one that is amenable to truth analysis. It must be capable of a truth evaluation. If what a statement asserts can be known to be true, and what it asserts is true, then the statement is unequivocally meaningful. Likewise, if what a statement asserts can be known to be false, and what it asserts is false, then that statement is meaningful by virtue of its falsification. Thus the function of philosophy is critical. Critical philosophy should enable us to determine whether our statements are subject either to verification or to falsification. Should a statement prove to be neither verifiable nor falsifiable nor true by its purely logical status, then it is meaningless. Thus all statements stand as judged in the court of critical analysis.

The focal problem of philosophy is meaning. Language, the instrument of meaning, has both a syntactical and a semantic structure. The syntax of a language is the set of rules for forming and manipulating word symbols. In short, it is the grammar of the language. On the other hand, the semantics of the language concerns matters of meaning—how we assign meaning to symbols and to sentences. For efficient communication we need consistent and comprehensive rules for manipulating symbols and statements. However, given a syntactically rigorous language, the problem of meaning devolves upon the signification that we give to individual terms and sentences. The critical task for philosophy then becomes that of ascertaining which sentences and arguments are meaningful and which are not. In brief, two categories of sentences are judged to be meaningful. The first are statements which are meaningful by virtue of their satisfying the rules of logic for forming and transforming complexes of symbols. Such statements may be empty of empirical content. The second are statements which are meaningful by virtue of their being true reports of empirical states of affairs. Hence, the logico-empirical foundations of our scientific knowledge.

If confining oneself to matters of public fact and to matters of logic were all there is to science, then perhaps scientists and philosophers could remain as sanguine and as dogmatic as some of their early pronouncements made them out to be. For example, if prescribing the limits for admissible data was the only question, then, indeed, for the psychologist behavioral data are acceptable, whereas reports taken to signify introspected states of consciousness are not. Few scientists, however, are content with collecting data. They also feel the need to interpret the data. They seek explanations. They construct theories. Yet, theories are more than summaries of data and more than mere calculating devices. Invariably, theories contain statements which are neither purely logical nor purely empirical. They embody hypothetical terms which are only indirectly related to data. As we shall see, a very large critical literature attends to this issue and cracks the dogmatic shell of empiricism. The task of adjudicating meaning has become complicated. At least one class of scientific statements, namely statements about hypothetical entities, is problematic. No easy decision as to the semantic status of such statements can be reached, for they are neither purely logical nor strictly empirical.

Probably no one can fully appreciate the problems and analyses which belong to the philosophy of science without placing them in the context of modern empiricism. The roots of empiricism go wide and deep, but in our efforts to trace them we inevitably come to focus on Locke, Berkeley, and Hume. The idea of the empirical foundations of knowledge was, of course, not new with them—the origins go back to antiquity—but with these English philosophers we find empiricism emerging as a systematic critical philosophy. From them we draw the few basic textual themes that are to occupy our contemporary philosophers of experience.

First, empiricism rejects rationalism as an indubitable means to knowledge about the world. There are no innate ideas concerning the world which are independent of the contents of experience (Locke), no intuitional means which assure us of non-empirical access to knowledge. Second, the concept of necessity belongs alone to logic. It makes no sense at all for us to deny a necessary conclusion in the logic of formal, content-less, propositions. However, to deny the truth of a non-formal empirical proposition is itself to propose an empirical possibility (Hume). Third, empiricism emphasizes that experience alone gives content to knowledge (Berkeley). Ideas of "substance," of "universals," of "causal relation" have no meaning independent of the phenomenal context out of which they are constructed. These ideas do not allude to entities as such. Rather, they are reducible to the data of experience which point in no direct way to any such purported entities. (This is the thesis of phenomenalism.) Fourth, empiricism is a critical philosophy. By analyzing the nature of the support of propositions, empiricism led to the rejection of all ideas which were without empirical foundations. For Locke this meant the rejection of a rationalism based on innate ideas and intuition. For Berkeley this meant the rejection of ideas of universals, of the infinitely divisible, and of causal agents intermediating between events. And for Hume it meant the rejection of practically the whole of metaphysics.

The path from English empiricism to modern logical empiricism is by no means a direct one. The effort of Immanuel Kant to secure a metaphysical foundation for empiricism stands along the way as one of the most original achievements in all of the history of philosophy. According to Kant, experience alone is not sufficient for the construction and relatedness of ideas. What is required, in addition, is a synthetic principle, the agent of unique processing, which the mind contributes. Both the unification of perception into phenomenal entities and the relatedness of ideas, as in the case of causality, are contributed by the processing capacities of the mind. The content of ideas, *per se,* is indeed contributed by experience, but the structure of that experience is imposed by the mind. Thus, Kant maintained that the empiricists were correct in reducing the properties of objects to their empirical constituents, but empiricism alone was not enough—the spatio-temporal processing of phenomena must be attributed to the *a priori* capacities of the mind. Science, therefore, was to be ever built upon its enduring base of Newtonian space and time. That, at least, was the indubitable contribution of the pristine mind.

At the turn of the century, however, physical science was in ferment. Efforts to verify the absolute Newtonian spatio-temporal frame had failed. Mathematicians and scientists alike experimented with new geometries and new physical assumptions in order to resolve their quandaries of relativity. As a result new empiricists, operating as much from scientific as from philosophical backgrounds, sided with Hume. They could be heard in America, in England, and on the Continent. In America we find the pragmatism of Peirce and James and later C. I. Lewis, and in England the logical atomism of Russell and Wittgenstein. But perhaps nowhere was reaffirmation of empiricism so vocal as in that dedicated group known as the Vienna Circle. These logical positivists paid their tribute to Hume. Their credo was the verification theory of meaning: "The meaning of a proposition is the method of its verification." Or, in the words of the English disciple, A. J. Ayer, ". . . to give the meaning of a proposition is to give the conditions under which it would be true and those under which it would be false" (1934, p. 337).

Thus the positivists set the tenor of empiricistic critique. Two types of propositions are to be regarded as meaningful. *Analytic* propositions, the propositions of logic and mathematics, are true by virtue of the conventions of this logic. They are *a priori* true since, granting the syntactical system, there is no means by which we can render these propositions invalid. *Synthetic,* or empirical, propositions are true and hence meaningful by virtue of their being true reports of experience. They are contingent and posterior to experience rather than necessary and prior. Furthermore, only these two types of propositions are admissible to legitimate discourse. Kant was in error—there is no possibility of synthetic *a priori* propositions, the truth of which is both contingent and at the same time necessary.

In brief the intent of the positivists was to espouse the true logical empiricism. The paradigms of meaningful discourse were to be drawn from science. But no sooner were commitments to the new empiricism made than problems began to arise. The laws of scientific disciplines are universal generalizations; their extension is unlimited, their quantification of application is universal. No finite amount of observation is sufficient to establish the truth of the universal proposition. Therefore, our utilization of laws in a chain of inference requires an element of convention, an element of pragmatic conjecture, which fails the rigid test of verification.

Other problems exist as well. Both historical propositions and predictive propositions allude to events to which we have no access. Then how can they be meaningful? Some propositions (the counterfactual conditionals) express hypotheses which very likely will never be put to test. ("If we do not inoculate, the disease will surely spread.") And what of the propositions postulating the hypothetical entities which play such important roles in our highly developed theories? What of our genes, our atomic ingredients of matter, our S-R bonds? The evidence for these is by no means so direct, by no means so accessible, as the counting of beans in a pot. Even where empiricists felt the most secure, doubts intruded. How can we be sure that the confrontation of the sensory input, the indubitable data, is sufficient support for propositions expressed in the vernacular of existence?

If this bill of particulars against empiricism, as such, is insufficient, we can turn to the domain of pure logic for further refutation. Even in the asceptic refinements of logic, difficulties arose. For a logical system, such as that of arithmetic, to be regarded as unexceptionable, we should be able to demonstrate that it has two properties: consistency and completeness. A logical system is *consistent* if it is not possible both to demonstrate the truth and to demonstrate the falsity of a proposition (theorem) within the system. A logical system is *complete* if for any well constructed proposition in the system (theorem) it is possible to demonstrate either its truth (validity) or its falsity. By ingenious indirection Kurt Gödel (1931) was able to demonstrate that for presumably consistent systems it was impossible to satisfy the second of these two requirements. The completeness of logical systems such as arithmetic was impossible to establish. Moreover, Church (1936) was able to show that it is impossible to construct any device, any algorithm, for ascertaining which theorems of the system are provable and which are not.

Alas, then, the positivists stand judged by their own precepts. If all which does not pass the rigid censor of verification is to be judged nonsense, then much of our scientific pretensions must go the way of metaphysics. Indeed, this has been the argument. However, it must be emphasized that the logical empiricists were not unaware of the pitfalls they had laid for themselves. Their own exercises in self-critique had, in fact, turned up the difficulties of their simplistic doctrine. The doctrine itself must be modified to accommodate the element of convention, of assumption, of the corpus of premise which was essential to scientific inference. The retreat from a dogmatic logical empiricism did not signify a return to rationalism or to intuitionism. But it did signify an acknowledgment of the predicament spelled out by Immanuel Kant. Scientific knowledge without prior presumption is superficial. However, for our contemporary empiricist, the presumption is not one of innate propensity; rather it is to be regarded as the *inventive* contribution of the scientific mind (cf. N1.1).

NOTES

NOTE 1.1

The present work is part of a longer one by the same author, *Philosophy and the Science of Behavior,* which includes a survey of the British empiricists, logical empiricism, and logical atomism. The critique of empiricism is there spelled out in greater detail.

Since in the present selection reference is made to the logical atomism of Bertrand Russell and Ludwig Wittgenstein, brief note should be taken of its doctrine of the perfect proposal for a logical empiricism. Let us consider a universe of atomic propositions, such that for any particular we can assign a property and such that the truth of the proposition is indubitably ascertained through observation. Then for an adequate logic such as that of *Principia Mathematica* (Whitehead and Russell, 1913) all possible relations, all possible compounding of molecular propositions, are rendered possible by explicit logical operations performed upon these atomic propositions. The truth of any molecular proposition will then be a function of (an "extension" of) these atomic propositions. In his remarkable *Tractatus Logico-Philosophicus,* Wittgenstein (1922) proposed that such a schema would achieve a perfect propositional picturing of the world. What can be said of the world can be said by such a propositional system. Necessarily this implies that all meaningful propositions must be constructible as extensions of a finite set, however large, of atomic propositions. Then, however, the difficulties which confronted the Continental positivists (those of universals, hypothetical entities, and so on) were also difficulties to obscure the hopes for an ideal language and for an ideal propositional picturing of reality.

CHAPTER 2

The Contents of Science

PHILOSOPHIC INVESTIGATIONS of the foundations, limits, and possibilities of knowledge have brought us to the front of scientific empiricism. The way has not been easy, it has not always been free of misgivings. But from Locke to Kant to Wittgenstein we have been assured that the important problems of knowledge have been dissolved. It remains only for the scientist to get on with his work, to marshal fact and law and theory, and thence to cut the heart out of metaphysics. This is a sanguine picture, to say the least. After all, no layman need eavesdrop in order to learn of the scandals of science. The difficulties are advertised freely. Yet they are not difficulties that send us into epistemological retreat. Nor need they invite us to reconsider intuitionism as a significant alternative to empiricism.

ON THE QUEST OF SCIENCE

What is it then that gives to science its endowment of epistemic privilege? One will not be much rewarded here by reviewing descriptions of what science is, or even descriptions of what it is that scientists do. Rather, he comes more directly to face the special status of science by considering what are the aims of science and what, at least, are the pretensions of its achievements. Whatever science is, its commitment to logic and observation have earned for it the fullest measure of public support. Its systematized knowledge, its methodological explorations of first principles, its reliance upon data seem somehow to bring to the person answers often more satisfying than any others he receives. As a rule, he does not question the "findings" of science. Facts, it would appear, are indubitable, even though they may not tell all the observer wants to know. But what is more impor-

7

tant, science provides a kind of closure to curiosity; it gives answers that put an end to the person's search for meanings and explanations.

Observations and data, law, theory, and the rare synthesis of one theory within another theory: all these give comfort to the curious. These are the rewards of science. What is more, they provide answers to our incipient ontological enquiries. Whether the problem being considered is the machinery that makes the clock go round or the cosmologist's search for the origins of the universe, or whether it is even the psychologist's looking for the mechanism of perceptual constancy, the specific quest is always the same—a description of the world "as it really is." On first impression, we all seem to be realists. When the child sees the internal mechanism of the clock with its springs and gears, he is satisfied that there is no mystery to the rotating hands. If the cosmologist pursues the retreating galaxies for one more clue to an evolving universe, he is likely to think of himself as learning what the universe is, or was, really like. And if the psychologist sees perceptual invariance emerging from neural integration over equivalence classes of input, he is likely to put aside his heuristic devices and proclaim the truth as to the real nature of perception. Such satisfying states of knowledge have this in common: they bring the inquirer close to some kind of microstructure that lies concealed behind the larger phenomenon. That microstructure is what reality is.

By temperament, then, it would seem that scientists at first are realists. For them, the quest itself is real. True explanations lie behind the confusion, uncertainty, and unknowns concerning man's present state of knowledge. Although the most recent theories are subject to revision, or may yield to entirely new formulations, and even though each new experiment may provide only tentative conclusions, the postulate of terminal truth appears to be implicit—as if the quest should end eventually with apodictic success and allow the researcher to move on to other inquiries.

I say only at first brush with fact and theory do scientists appear to be realists. For soon doubt creeps into the picture. The road to scientific progress is bestrewn with the "debris of antiquated ideas." Concepts that once were held with confidence become the discarded relics of many presumptive worlds. The psychologist's entelechies, his instincts and faculties, join the calorics, the electric fluids, and aethers in our museums of scientific heirlooms. Nowadays we are more amused than impressed to learn that Newton could retire early from his memorable career in science because he felt the important truths were known, or to learn that Kant could proclaim that the absolute nature of time and space are forever embedded in the perceiving mind, or to learn that even today some scientists pronounce that the frontiers of microphysics are exhausted with only a few details remaining to be added. We are much too sensitive to the fragility of our theories and, alas, of our convictions to invest much faith in enduring scientific conceptions.

But there is another factor that is even more disconcerting to the naive realist. As the grain of microstructure is further refined, the hypotheses become further and further removed from the data that are their support. In physics there are technological and perhaps logical barriers to penetrating the hypothesized microstructures. All palpable properties of the material world evaporate. Cloud chamber tracks, scintillations, and Geiger counts are distant cousins to the postulated "entities" which compose the flesh of a theoretical calculus. Rather than a corpus we have a wraith incarnate in a deductive system, looking much more like an "idea" than any of the familiar grains of sand.

In psychology the logical barriers to microknowledge may not exist, but technology still does not permit our probing the fine structure of the nervous system. Like the physicist, the psychologist may turn to invention, indeed, even preferring it, say, to crude excursions into neuroanatomy. A system can be built with hypothetical entities having no more initial credence than the prospect that their theoretical role may lead to the deduction of confirmable hypotheses. It may even be that microphysiology is an encumbrance, since so little of it is known. Thus, a feeling of emancipation comes to a theorist who can say that theoretical constructs "need have no truth character at all" (Kendler, 1952). And among other strategies, he may proceed, as the cyberneticist does, to sketch out functional components of a system of behavior without specifying how any one of the components necessarily implements that function. Only the eventual output counts.

CONVENTIONALISM VERSUS REALISM

We have breathed this air of conventionalism before. Science should not be so pretentious. It should be more modest in its aims, and leave to metaphysics all matters of ontology. The caution comes from positivism itself. Statements about the real world are hardly ever subject to test; either direct verification of an hypothesis is impossible, or the assumptions of verification are in doubt. Tests of theoretical constructs are always in terms of material implications, i.e., of if–then propositions. Therefore, the confirmation of the consequent is never sufficient to establish the truth of the theoretical antecedent. Only disconfirmation is straightforward. Furthermore, all tests of hypotheses are subject to qualifications. One always makes assumptions which, themselves, are not subject to test in the given experiment. If the assumptions are suspect, they may be subject to revision, with a subsequent discard or a reinterpretation of the original data. Thus test results are seldom conclusive.

In brief the conventionalistic character of assumptions and theoretical terms suggests to us that the scientist may be more concerned with predictive ingenuity than he is with "truth" or "the real," neither of which have proved enduring or accessible. In the words of Poincaré, certain conventions prove convenient for describing the processes underlying events. We should no more ask whether they are true than "ask if the metric system is true, and if the old weights and measures are false; if Cartesian co-ordinates are true and polar co-ordinates false" (1905, p. 50; and cf. N2.1).

The story is more familiar in physics than it is in psychology. This is because physics has a large number of formal theories that postulate theoretical entities only indirectly related to observation. Quite frequently the psychologist avoids speculating about internal processes intervening between observable states of the organism, between stimulus and response. Or, if he engages in any conceptual activities, he is likely to adopt constructs that are explicitly reducible to sets of observation terms such that the given construct is no more than a convenient means of designating a complex of data. Only rarely does he venture into the realm of microstructure wherein theoretical entities are postulated to explain behavior, not in terms of what is observed and given, but in terms of what might be in order that the data of behavior should be what they are. Now in physics the story is different. We come much more quickly to face problems of microstructure. Molar descriptions will not suffice, nor will the correlations of a crude empirical chemistry. We need to enter the smallest structure of matter in order to ascertain what it is that determines the binding and disintegrative properties of matter.

As is well known, the fine-grain constructs are "as-if" entities; they are not observed but are betrayed, as it were, by events quite gross on the observational scale. The structure of the hydrogen atom was initially inferred from scintillations on zinc sulphide screens, and from spectrograms. No nucleus, no electron of the atom was ever photographed, just tell-tale tracks in the ionized gas of a cloud chamber. Nor has the fine structure of a crystalline solid been photographed; all we have are gross patterns of reflected light. We say that the theoretical entities are "as-if" constructs, because the data suggest that it is *as if* there was such an atomic structure, or that it is *as if* atoms are arranged in Bragg planes (cf. N2.2). One cannot say that a theoretical construct is definitely true, for alternative constructions of theoretical entities may serve just as well to suggest the events. And it may be that no experiment can decide the issue among alternatives.

When he enters the labyrinths of mathematics, the physicist doubtless gives little thought to any hard-core reality. As Dirac has said, the physicist must get over thinking in terms of pictures and concrete models, and rather accept his constructs as possessing significance only in the context of an abstract, unconcretized mathematical model (cf. N2.3). He seems hardly concerned with questions such as: what is the world really like? or, where is the electron at this very moment? or, is a smallest particle hard like a grain of sand? Philosophers in turn have wondered whether theoretical constructs picture facts at all and whether the physicist has not entered into a world of disciplined fictionizing.

We need, therefore, to have another look at realism, or at least at the ontological status of theoretical terms. Are we playing games? Are we inventing convenient prediction machines? Or, do our constructs take the measure of a more substantial world? Second thoughts are likely to be sobering. An increasing number of empiricists maintain that existence propositions (these propositions have always been problematic) are not uniquely different from propositions about hypothetical entities (cf. N2.4). We attribute existence to an object if there is a set of observations which is taken as testimony to the real, not illusory, presence of the object. In other words, existence prescribes evidential bases for asserting the object. But then, are not theoretical terms used in just this kind of context? To assert the theoretical entity is to prescribe a set of observations which are evidential to the entity. In fact, it is very likely that the theory incorporating the theoretical entity has, through deductive inference, led precisely to the search for some evidential support in behalf of that entity. Photographs are not the objects they report, but they are evidential bases for objects occupying some slice of time and space. If we observe that the hands of a clock move and hear the ticking of the clock's escapement, we are satisfied as to the existential status of its mechanical guts. The existential extension of our world at any given time exceeds our immediate data. Perceptually, we process only minimal cues, the rest of the construction is done by inference. One cannot conceive what it would be like to perceive each and every detail of the composite event—not only, for example, to witness another person's smile, but to perceive the state of each and every cell that composes that person's being. Even the smile is evidence for an hypothesis—an hypothesis, say, about some interpersonal attitude. That attitude is no less real because it cannot be pointed to directly, as we can "point to" the worm in the case of the jumping bean.

We are led then to reconsider the status of our theoretical terms. The descent into microstructure has meant that we have had to give up formulating existential propositions in terms of simple empiric equivalences. The data suggest what we would assert, but only indirectly; yet, the data-inference rubric itself spells out what it is we mean to assert by our maintaining existential status for our theoretical constructs. Could we separate the data from the hypothesis, the case might be more clear-cut for separating the two into exclusive epistemic classes. But this cannot be done. The state of one's knowledge, his hypothesis, if you will, indicates how the complex of data input is to be processed—what, for example, is to be the figure and what, the ground. It takes training, i.e., hypothesis, to read an electro-encephalogram, just as the star in the cloud chamber photograph can only be existentially read by a person conversant in the field of cosmic ray research. The student who is new to his science is blind to the facts put before him. He has to learn to see what is in the microscope, he has to learn to detect the significant patterns in an oscilloscope—just as a music student must learn to detect harmonic structure in a musical composition. One does not just open his eyes and see, he brings with him perceptual hypotheses. Otherwise, he remains blind to facts.

One other comment should be made before we leave this preview on theoretical entities. Existence and existential status carry overtones of permanence. The evidential basis of our data should not signify one thing at one phase of hypothesis and another thing at another. The rhythmic pattern of the electro-encephalogram, for example, cannot be the evidential basis for *both* spontaneous electro-cortical response *and* mechanical vibrations of the brain substance. The red-shift in the galactic spectrum cannot indicate *both* a static *and* an expanding universe. The state of our knowledge determines how we interpret the data, what hypothesis we bring to them, and consequently, what the real world is like at any given time. Why speak of the real world or existential status at all? Why not accept the predicament and acknowledge all constructions to be ephemeral? And what of alternative theoretical entities bound to the same data complexes? These are sticky ontological problems. However, much of their apparent difficulty resides in our naive commitment to simple empirical equivalences (again, like our looking for the worm in the jumping bean). Nevertheless, hypotheses do affect what we perceive and hypotheses do determine how we construct entities out of data. A good hypothesis is one that serves to crystallize data into the meaningful configuration we call the entity. One does not claim permanence for his entities but only that in any given historical context those "entities" serve unambiguously and consistently as approximations to the real. To be sure our ideas, even the most basic ones like those of force and motion, are subject to modification with the changing state of our knowledge. Yet they change not so much because we were mistaken but because at any given time the data and hypothesis are such that just this particular construction should be given to the world and not another. One does not catalogue his textbooks of biology and physics as fiction because he knows in time their hypotheses will be outmoded. There is an element of time-boundedness in existence, and in truth, just as Margenau and Whitehead, for example, have pointed out.

LAWS OF NATURE

When scientists speak the word "nature" they often do so with just a touch of reverence, as if "she" is that cosmic entity hiding a treasury of secrets for us to share piece by experimental piece. And it is not always clear whether or not they are speaking metaphorically. What are laws? On initial inspection the question resolves to whether nature, the cosmic entity, conforms to some *a priori* set of regularities which do in fact detail the cosmic processes, or to whether laws are man-created generalizations which facilitate both his description of his world and his predictions concerning specifiable events in certain familiar surrounds. Are laws true descriptions? Or are they conventions? No doubt our metaphorical predilections commit us to think of laws in terms of cosmic decrees. Events must obey laws; indeed, they have no alternative. However, one need not think of decrees and cosmic agents to support this view. Mechanists and determinists may arrive at such a position merely by assuming that lawfulness is a characteristic of the given universe.

Now it takes but little reflection for us to reject this metaphysical point of view. The scientist inclines more toward methodology than metaphysics. He may proceed as if he believes there are cosmic regularities, but his belief is hardly more than a procedural agreement. The history of his subject reveals that laws are subject to revision, disconfirmation, and withdrawal. They are more like hypotheses than decrees. He uses them to predict, not necessarily to command. An event that violates a law of nature is still an event. It is the law that must yield.

In this context, two comments from the philosophy of science are worthy of attention. One, the certainty that man finds compelling belongs only to logic. Events themselves, though their relations may be expressed in a language of rigorous syntax, are not compelled to follow any prescribed pattern. As we have seen, a purely empirical contingency is the basis of Humean skepticism. And two, laws are adopted as instruments of understanding and prediction. In this context they have been called "inference tickets" (Ryle, 1949; Kneale, 1949); but happy as the phrase may be, this is not quite the appropriate metaphor. Rather, laws are the credentials which enable the scientist to justify asserting his expectations. Laws, therefore, assume a personal reference. They are the expressions of our states of knowledge, they are not ontological contracts held to be binding upon nature.

The issues here are not so poignantly drawn in psychology as they are in physics. Psychologists need little persuasion as to the provisional character of their laws. Laws of learning, of reinforcement, contiguity, and recency, for example, are hardly more than empirical surveys of certain classes of learning experiments. The fact that a law like that of reinforcement has only limited extension over the range of all possible learning situations is implicit in the prevalence of two-factor learning theories. And the Weber-Fechner law, $S = k \log R$, offers a classic example of the well-tempered law.

As is well known, the Weber–Fechner law, which prescribes that perceived intensity over scales such as loudness or brightness varies directly with the logarithm of the intensity of the physical stimulus, holds only for the intermediate range of intensity. The law breaks down at the extremes.

That is to say, the law is a useful generalization over a certain range of stimuli but not over others. It is for the psychophysicist to determine the range of application by experiment, and not to pronounce, as Fechner did, that some underlying principle of nature had been defined (cf. N2.5).

Laws are useful, then, as devices of inference, but they are to be tempered, as it were, by the search for their extensions. Thus, like theoretical constructions, they have a conventional character; they are inventions that serve as hypotheses concerning events. But as before, one need not conclude that laws are thereby unreal. To say a law is true is merely to say that there is a class of events for which the lawlike statement serves as a convenient summarization.

THEORIES

If, ontologically speaking, theoretical entities and laws have only a contextual status, then theories, too, can be interpretably real only in the context of convention and procedural agreements. Is a theory a picture of the world? Is it some description of actual events? Or is it a model and deductive system by means of which we infer lawful relations among observables? A theory could, of course, be both a picture of an actual world *and* a deductive system. Yet, if we are not careful we will impart to our naive phenomenology the properties of the deductive system. This temptation to reify fails us in matters concerning laws and hypothetical entities. All the more reason, then, that it should fail for theory.

Though ultimately concerned with data, theories begin with conventions, laws, and rules of inference. Only somewhat belatedly does a dictionary tie the theory to the world of experiment. The foremost considerations are that the theory be consistent and comprehensive. It must protect against generating contradictory hypotheses; it must have a secure foundation in tested scientific traditions. But of the truth of a theory, one may only speak with reservation. Theories are useful and they are "contextually true," but only to the extent they generate well-confirmed hypotheses. Their extension is empirically determined and provisional. They make no claim to an absolute truth status that would enable us to prejudge the world and retire from the ontological quest.

Yet, at some critical point each well-supported theory may be disconfirmed. The false hypothesis condemns it; and the temptation may be great to declare the theory false and ourselves, in that moment of humble reckoning, mistaken. To succumb abjectly, however, would itself be a mistake. The history of science would show us that no theory can be true in any lasting sense, for no theory endures without modification. Should we then presume that science can make no claims for any special epistemic resource?

The mistake here is to confuse enduring logical truths with contingent factual ones. One expects that logical truths will endure throughout all time; he cannot conceive what it would mean to say that the laws of arithmetic or those of syllogistic inference might be disconfirmed, for data have no part in logic. This is not true, however, in the domain of fact and theory. It is the nature of fact that it should be subject to revision. To the scientific empiricist, fact is inseparable from theory. It is an hypothesis, a conjecture germinated in theory, which guides the scientist in his search for evidence. What kind of world one finds is determined by what kind of structure that world is assumed to have. Rather than facts standing alone to be discovered at the blink of an eyelid, they emerge only in conceptual focus. They are the product of the theory and its dictionary, for it is the latter which conjointly direct the evidential search. The events, the data, the facts that reward the sophisticated exploration may have an identity of their own which evokes their special credence; but nonetheless, that identity is inseparable from the conceptual framework. To alter a theory, even to reject it, is ultimately to alter, even to reject, the fact. A rejected theory is thrust aside not so much because "the" facts belie it as because alternative theories with new conceptions extend the factual interpretation of the available data. Thus the world is no longer flat, nor does the sun revolve about the earth, nor do objects in motion seek their natural position. Yet each of these at some time was the fact of observant men. There are innumerable examples wherein a new conceptual-factual context introduces a different excursion into reality.

No obvious advantage accrues to us in trying to force this treatment of the truth status of theories into traditional philosophical molds. It is better to do as Campbell (1921) and Toulmin (1953) recommend: reserve the language of truth for matters of logic where its use is nearly unequivocal. Theories, rather, should be regarded as "holding" over the range of facts which their hypotheses generate. They are the instruments for deriving experimental hypotheses, the truths of which are attested to by the data. The only danger inherent in this language is the suggestion that the instrumentality should be regarded any the less real because it does not translate directly into the truth functional language which our simple empiricistic conventions dictate. Yet, when we learn to accept the contingent character of all empirical propositions and the inseparability of fact and conceptual framework, we will appreciate the suggestion that strict truth-reductive translations are not appropriate to the language of science.

SCIENTIFIC EXPLANATION

No doubt the retreat of the scientific empiricist from naive realism is a source of amusement to his critics. It is also a source of embarrassment when he hears his confrère adopt the language of fictionalism to describe tasks of theory construction and scientific explanation. This freedom of invention is the heritage of pragmatism, and like pragmatism it too has been interpreted as sheer license happily purchased by the coin of clever people. However, a close reading of Charles Peirce or even of William James (and of contemporary instrumentalists such as Nagel) would reveal that the emphasis upon fiction misrepresents the case for scientific invention. One needs only reflect upon the character of scientific explanation.

In general, events are explained by one of two strategies: by instantiation, or by higher order deductions. In the one case, a particular event is expressed as some particular value of a variable in a general proposition (law); in the other, the law, of which the event is a particular instance, may itself be a hypothesis deducible from within a theory. In neither case does one have the fictionist's freedom to construct just any explanation that aesthetic whim may dictate. Theories, for example, contain laws, theoretical constructs, a logical calculus, and a dictionary. To a large extent the calculus and the theoretical terms are inventions. There may also be a conventional element in the statements of laws and the dictionary. However, in no case are the inventions peremptory. They reflect the factual conceptual traditions of the given science. They also reflect the selective principles of comprehensiveness and simplicity which, at a more subtle level of ontology, are the guides to theoretic evaluation and theoretic convergence.

It is one of the interesting speculations of conventionalists that every theory is salvagable. This is a corollary of fictionalism. But no one, not even Pierre Duhem (cf. N2.6), has thereby argued that every theory is worth saving. The complex hierarchy of many scientific theories makes some particular set of constructions preferable to another. It is well known that Ptolemy, Tycho Brahe, and Copernicus could each provide a model of the solar system, each with a different set of constructs, and each with confirmational success. Yet, the construction eventually selected was the one that fitted most readily into a more comprehensive system. Kepler and Newton assured us what kind of inventions would be eligible for scientific license. And the issue of the freedom of invention was thereby closed.

When we turn to the idea of a hierarchy of explanation, we especially realize there is a guidance implicit within scientific invention. One seeks not only an explanation of a particular set of events but also a theoretical construction that itself is derivable from within some still more basic science. Chemical explanations, for example, were conceived in terms wholly unique to the phenomenology of chemistry itself. But the advantages and the guidance of atomic constructions are now all too apparent. Geneticists could have continued to think in terms of the gross characteristics of genotypes, but the molecular models of biochemistry offered explanations of the duplicative powers of the genes. And psychology can continue to build hypothetico-deductive models in learning theory, knowing (perhaps unconsciously) that issues of alternative theories will be resolved by developments in neurophysiology.

Perhaps nowhere in science are the issues of reductionism and of the hierarchy of explanation more debated than they are in psychology. The gap between psychology and any lower order discipline is wider than that between any other set of hierarchical cousins. One can feel comfortable in reducing thermodynamics to statistical mechanics, or genetics to bio-chemistry, or even meteorology to thermodynamics. It is "natural" to seek their respective reductive explanations. But it is a long way indeed from behavior and the constructs of learning and personality theory to the microstructure of physiology. No one pretends to fit motivational or rein-forcement theory into the family of hypotheses deducible within an extant neurophysiology.

Nevertheless, one suspects that disclaimers against reductionism and against the hierarchical scope of explanation are passing predilections. The psychologist must implement explanations of behavior by chains of in-ference mediating between observables. If he is theoretical at all, he must make constructual conjectures; their locale can only be the organism itself. One does not claim, therefore, that psychologists should be physiologists. But lest the psychologist think he need only contrive heuristic gimmicks, he should be reminded that it will be the lower order science that will eventually dictate the veridical selection from among alternative construc-tions. As between stimulus and response there is the mediating process. One can model that process in any way he chooses, but there is a sense in which there is an "actual" microstructure. It is that set of descriptions which will be deducible within a mature next-order discipline. It is in the hier-archical context of explanation that one can indeed make claim for onto-logical convergence.

NOTES

NOTE 2.1

As a philosopher of science, Poincaré (1905, 1913, 1914) has gained renown for his exposition of the conventionalistic implications of positivism. Since direct verification of theories is not possible, the status of theories must be couched in terms of their success and convenience in accounting for the data. The "hy-pothesis" of science is an invention. It predicates how we are to look at things; that is, how we are to represent events and how we are to construct the world that underlies appearances.

Because of the contingent status of science, conventionalists have at times been accused of being rather flippantly arbitrary about serious matters. But a reading of Poincaré's popular philosophical works reveals that he was considerably more cautious and conservative than the reader is likely to assume on first acquaintance with the off-hand relativism that seems to characterize his treatment of time and space. "It is not nature which imposes them [the frames of time and space] upon us, it is we who impose them upon nature because we find them convenient" (1913, p. 13). This seems to set the tenor of his work. And it is supplemented by the fact that he stresses intuition and not logic or observation as the source of mathematical and scientific invention. Yet Poincaré was critical of any treatment of conventionalism which would lead to a radical nominalism. He contends against his contemporary LeRoy who argues that conventionally "the scientist creates the fact." Certainly there are limitations to observation, and certainly we are unable either to perceive or to comprehend total pictures, but this is no reason to conclude that what we do comprehend and conventionally construct is either an unreal or a distorted picture of the world.

Language is conventional, it is also the source of invention; for

. . . without this language most of the intimate analogies of things would have remained forever unknown to us; and we should forever have been ignorant of the internal harmony of the world, which is, we shall see, the only true objective reality (1913, p. 13).

Then speaking directly to LeRoy, Poincaré writes:

Some people have exaggerated the role of convention in science; they have gone so far as to say that law, that scientific fact itself, was created by the scientist. This is going much too far in the direction of nominalism. No, scientific laws are not artificial creations; we have no reason to regard them as accidental, though it be impossible to prove they are not. Does the harmony the human intelligence thinks it discovers in nature exist outside of this intelligence? No, beyond doubt a reality completely independent of the mind which conceives it, sees it or feels it would for us be forever inaccessible. But what we call objective reality is in the last analysis what is common to many thinking beings and could be common to all; this common part, we shall see, can only be the harmony expressed by mathematical laws (1913, p. 14).

Moreover Poincaré distinguishes between the conventions of mathematical representations and the postulates of science itself. One does not ask of a geometry whether it is true.

The geometrical axioms are therefore neither synthetic a priori intuitions nor experimental facts. They are conventions. Our choice among all possible conventions is *guided* by experimental facts; but it remains *free*, and is limited only by the necessity of avoiding every contradiction . . . What, then, are we to think of the question: Is Euclidean geometry true? It has no meaning. We might as well ask if the metric system is true and if the old weights and measures are false; if Cartesian co-ordinates are true and polar co-ordinates false. One geometry cannot be more true than another; it can only be more convenient (1905, p. 50).

On the other hand, physical postulates, such as the law of inertia, are descriptions of ideal states of affairs. They may serve as useful conventions for making calculations, but they are in a sense subject to empirical check. In other words, it is conceivable that a state of affairs might obtain which would entail our rejecting the postulate. This is a useful distinction, but the example of geometric representation of space is perhaps ill chosen. Astronomical data at present are thought relevant to determining whether our space is Euclidean or Riemannian. Poincaré does wish to assert, however, that the truth of Euclidean propositions, as such, in no way is contingent upon the properties of our own space.

NOTE 2.2

In the philosophy of science, discussions of theoretical entities often take atomic physics as their reference. It is here that the bombardment of particles culminates in the cloud chamber photographs whose gross detail supports our impression of a world composed of fragile billiard balls. But from the tracks made by the minute condensations of water vapor to the inferred structure of the atom is a tortuous inferential path.

Another example of theoretical inference, simpler in detail yet of equal subtlety, is that involving crystalline structure. The pattern of inference is ingenious and is perhaps worthy of more attention than expositors in the philosophy of science have given it.

Until the early part of this century, crystallography was, for the most part, a descriptive science. Considerable knowledge had been gained from classifying different types of crystals, observing their properties, and even formulating lattice networks in which to describe the structure of the crystal. Little attention had been given to the internal structure of crystals other than to assume that homogenous sets of molecules, or atoms, which seek a minimal state of potential energy tend to arrange themselves in regular assemblies so as to minimize their volume of occupancy. This was a matter of speculation. Was there any means of inferring the dimensions of the intracrystalline structure itself?

In 1912 Max von Laue proposed an experiment in which a crystal was to be treated as a diffraction grating on the basis of its molecular structure. Although the purpose of the experiment was to detect the wave properties of x rays rather than crystalline structure as such, the subsequent contribution to crystal analysis was a notable one. The actual argument is a simple one to grasp. If it is assumed that the molecules of zincblende, say, are arranged regularly along sets of planes, then the sets of molecules in the strata of planes should serve to diffract light as a diffraction grating does. First, consider diffraction effects. When any physical wave front (air, water, light) meets a barrier with a relatively small aperture, the wave front squeezes through, as it were, only to fan out as a diffraction front as it emerges. An essential condition is that the aperture be small relative to the wave length (the space between successive wave crests). Now, if we have series of such apertures or slits, such as is the case in a diffraction grating, light passing through those slits is diffracted according to the spacing of the slits (usually 15,000 to 30,000 slits per inch of grating surface) and the wave length of the incident light. Light of different wave lengths is differentially diffracted. Consequently, the grating diffracts sunlight just as a prism does. If we mount the grating in a reflecting spectroscope, as in Figure 2.1, we note that a source of light from S hits the grating G at an angle of incidence equal to i, and an adjustable focal target F determines an angle of diffraction θ. By adjusting F we find the image of S diminishes and decreases in brightness as a function of this angle θ. The reason for this is that the wave front from S strikes A on G before it does B. In

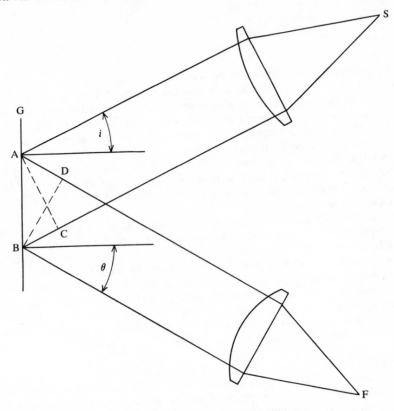

Figure 2.1 Spectroscopic analysis of diffraction effects

fact the distance BC measures the extent of *retardation*. The wave front emerges from A before it does from B, and its diffracted retardation is equal to AD. One gets the brightest image at F if the sum (or difference) of the retardation effects is such that the successive wave fronts from G reinforce one another (i.e., superimpose trough upon trough and crest upon crest). This relationship can be expressed by the equation

$$AD - BC = b \, (\sin \theta - \sin i),$$

where optimal images are obtained at values of θ such that $AD - BC$ is equal to some whole number times the wave length. The details of this sketch are not difficult; what is important for the subsequent argument is the fact that if one knows the wave length of the incident light and the angles i and θ he can determine b, *the distance between slits on the grating.*

Turning now to an analysis of crystalline structure, let us visualize the particles of a crystal arranged equidistantly along a plane A, as in Figure 2.2. Each particle serves as a reflector such that it radiates light in all directions. However, it is only along the wave front P′C that the crests reinforce one another. As in a mirror, the angle of reflection r equals the angle of incidence i.

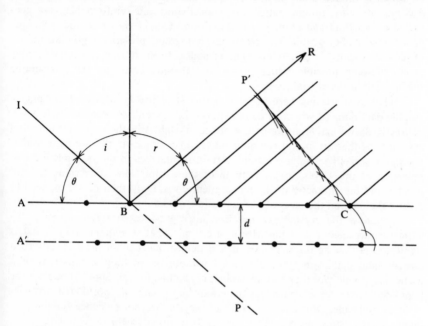

Figure 2.2 Scattering of waves for the analysis of crystalline structure.

Suppose now we consider another array of particles on plane A′. Although the new set of radiating crests from the plane A′ is not shown, they will not reinforce those from the plane A unless the following relationship holds:

$$n\lambda = 2d \sin \theta,$$

that is to say, unless some multiple of the wave length is equal to twice the product of the sine of the glancing angle θ and the distance d between lattice planes. This amounts to saying that $n\lambda$ is a quantity representing the magnitude of retardation of incident light as between adjacent lattice planes. The image in the direction of R is optimal only when n is some whole number.

Let us now consider the problem of inferring the structure of the crystal. We would like to determine the distance d between lattice planes when λ is known and when θ is chosen such that the image from the several planes reflected is optimal in the direction R. This is easily determined by

$$d = \frac{n\lambda}{2 \sin \theta}.$$

If the incident light is adjusted such than an optimal image is obtained at its primary reflection R, then $n = 1$ and the calculation of d is straightforward.

This is a simplified picture of what actually occurs. First, it only shows the wave front advancing in the plane of the page. Second, troughs of reinforcement occur on more than a single front. Hence, in the second, third, and higher orders of reflection, one finds the effects of the usual diffraction patterns. And third, in order to obtain the actual data one must pass an x ray through a crystal which is rotated upon its own axis. As different planes and glancing angles θ come into play, unique patterns of cancellation and reinforcement are generated on a cylindrical photographic emulsion. This is known as the technique of a rotation photograph. The resulting photograph presents a gridlike matrix of darkened spots, i.e., of reinforcement nodes. From it, one can infer the distances between possible lattice planes and thereby construct the interatomic spacing within the crystal itself.

What is interesting here is the fact that structure is inferred from photographic data none of which actually pictures the crystalline structure itself. Only indirectly do we arrive at the nature of the crystal. And then only by initiating assumptions that are not at the moment testable. For example, we assume that x rays are wavelike. We also assume certain regularities in the transmission and reflection of the waves, to say nothing of the assumptions concerning the apparatus and the character of the x rays themselves. Only then do we proceed to deduce the data on the basis of our crystalline model.

Doubtless the crystallographer has other good reasons for assuming the latticelike arrangement of particles in a crystal. That is another story. What is significant is that he infers details of a structure that cannot itself be observed directly, and that cannot be constructed without his making assumptions of a particular atomic world and of an explicit crystalline model. Should one note the laminated character of mica, he may well appreciate the postulated arrangement of molecules. But flakes of the mica crystal are not evidence for the particular model being tested. Much less real, it would seem, is that large-scale recording of a somewhat regular distribution of dark spots on a white background which the rotation photograph displays.

NOTE 2.3

In the preface to his *Quantum Mechanics,* P. A. M. Dirac writes:

> The classical tradition has been to consider the world to be an association of observable objects (particles, fluids, fields, etc.) moving about according to definite laws of force, so that one could form a mental picture in space and time of the whole scheme. This led to a physics whose aim was to make assumptions about the mechanism and forces connecting these observable objects, to account for their behavior in the simplest possible way. It has become increasingly evident in recent years, however, that nature works on a different plan. Her fundamental laws do not govern the world as it appears in one mental picture in any very direct way, but instead they control a substratum of which we cannot form a mental picture without introducing irrelevancies. The formulation of these laws requires the use of the mathematics of transformations. The important

things in the world appear as the invariants (or more generally the nearly invariants, or quantities with simple transformation properties) of these transformations. . . . The new theories, if one looks apart from their mathematical setting, are built up from physical concepts . . . which cannot even be explained adequately in words at all (1947, p. vii).

In this and other passages, Dirac is not arguing for a mere conventionalistic representation of the physical world. There is ontological significance to the fact that as we enter the world of microparticles, of photons and quantum effects, it is no longer possible to draw pictures or to visualize objects. Rather one must look for the invariant properties of mathematical expressions. What the language tells us is that underlying reality is remotely and subtly related to the world of objects with which we are familiar.

He also writes, "In order to give absolute meaning to size, such as is required for any theory of the ultimate structure of matter, we have to assume *that there is a limit to the fineness of our powers of observation and the smallness of the accompanying disturbance—a limit which is inherent in the nature of things and can never be surpassed by improved technique or increased skill on the part of the observer*" (1947, p. 3). Thus there is a point at which any conception of a material world that would postulate palpable properties of objects behind the barrier of observation is not just contradictory within the theory, it is both logically inconceivable and unreal.

NOTE 2.4

The literature on the "existence" of hypothetical entities is extensive. We shall return to it later in the discussions concerning hypothetical constructs and intervening variables. However, in an important sense, the issue is more demanding in physics than in psychology. The physicist's examination of microstructures necessarily results in his reaching limits and barriers of observation. He cannot "illuminate" objects whose dimensions are of the order of the wave length of light. Such objects diffract the light, creating a penumbra of locale known to us as the uncertainty effects. Moreover, any effort to enhance our resolution of the object by using sources of illumination with shorter wave lengths increases the impact that such sources have on the submicroscopic structures being studied. Thus, there comes into play the complementary set of uncertainties under which simultaneous accuracies cannot be obtained for both position and momentum of a particle. (This, of course, is to say nothing of the technological limitations upon our even carrying out the "thought experiments" proposed by people like Bohr, Heisenberg, and Einstein.) Questions of existence, therefore, are more pressing to the physicist than to other scientists. He cannot produce palpable evidences in the way that other people can. Since the submicroscopic entities are necessarily inferred, the question arises whether such entities can be considered real at all. The temptation is great to consider them convenient fictions, with a different status than that we attribute to objects that are the direct reductions of sense data.

The ontological predicament with respect to submicroscopic entities has been discussed by Nagel (1961), Bergmann (1961), Hanson (1958, 1963),

Feyerabend (1958, 1962, 1963). Ontological predicaments must, however, succumb to linguistic analysis. What is an existence statement? What is "evidence for"? Are we asking for anything more than a classification of the logical status of hypothetical physical entities? For a nontechnical presentation of the issues from the point of view of linguistic analysis, see B. Mayo (1954). For a defense of realism built upon linguistic analysis see G. Maxwell (1962a,b) and J. J. C. Smart (1956, 1963).

Physicists themselves (e.g., Bohr, Heisenberg, Born) have been outstanding proponents of pragmatic instrumentalism. In an important book, *The Structure of Science* (1961) Ernest Nagel sees the issue as essentially a terminological one.

NOTE 2.5

In recent years an alternative psychophysical law has been refined and emphasized by S. S. Stevens (1951). Rather than the Fechnerian logarithmic function, $S = k \log R$, he obtains a power function by varying the operational context of judgment. Thus, instead of requiring subjects to discriminate as between physical stimuli, Stevens requests that they make direct estimations of sensations as such. For example, a subject is given a reference stimulus and instructed to assign some arbitrary number of units to it, and then he is given a variable stimulus and is asked to adjust it until it is $\frac{1}{2}, \frac{1}{3}, \frac{1}{4}, \ldots$ units of the standard. Note that the units are not assigned physical weights; the scale is presumed to be strictly psychological. If the experimenter then plots the logarithm of judgment against the logarithm of stimulus intensity, he finds that the median judgments tend to plot on a straight line with slope n. The slope then determines the exponent for the appropriate psychophysical law:

$$S = k R^n$$

where S and R represent the values of sensation and stimulus intensity, respectively.

On examination the difference between the power and the logarithmic laws poses some interesting philosophical questions. Is one law correct, and the other incorrect? Is one just a better approximation to a true psychophysical relation than the other? Or, are there really two laws? And even perhaps more important, do the direct estimation procedures really get at subjective judgments in contrast to the response-oriented discriminations of the classical procedures?

These are interesting questions, and only peremptory responses can be given here. Doubtless the role of experimental instructions plays a part in these differences of laws. With respect to magnitude estimation, Stevens shows that direct estimation and classical discriminable difference techniques give different results. But with respect to the fractionation technique mentioned above and the classical technique for giving the plot of j.n.d.'s, it can be shown in some cases that the power and logarithmic measures are essentially equivalent. The difference is conventional. It depends upon whether one prefers to take ΔS, the increment of sensational difference as a constant over the range of all physical intensities, or whether one wants to take the ratio $\Delta S/S$ as the constant. According to one's preference, he will obtain a logarithmic or a power law. In the one case, the constancy of ΔS means the equivalence of discriminable sensational differences over the range of physical stimuli. In the second case, the constancy relates to comparisons of sensation alone, not to stimulus intensities. Treisman (1962) has argued that the direct estimation (or "private data") hypothesis is not at all uniquely different from the traditional discrimination procedures. No operational test exists for choosing among the procedures. There is no reason to believe that direct estimation techniques come any nearer to quantifying the private data of consciousness than Fechnerian techniques.

Criticism of direct estimation from another quarter is discussed by Attneave (1962). Following up a suggestion by Garner (1954), he proposes that direct estimates utilize some numerical scale which, though undefined by the experimenter, is itself a psychophysical function. The magnitudes of numbers themselves are discriminable on a logarithmic scale, although in pure number theory the magnitude of the move from one number to its successor is the same throughout the set of all integers. When one takes into account judgment of the number continuum as itself a psychophysical function, then "the discrepancy between 'equal-interval' and 'direct magnitude' scales might disappear" (Attneave, 1962, p. 624).

The purpose of this digression is to show that putatively different laws may differ only with respect to their conventions. To this extent it is clear that ontological issues are not at stake. As Stevens and others argue, direct estimation techniques may possess certain advantages for scaling; but such pragmatic considerations should not be taken as a basis for arguing that we are dealing with essentially different realities in the two psychophysical procedures.

NOTE 2.6

Pierre Duhem (1906), in a classical discussion, argues against the conclusiveness of experimental tests of hypotheses. He is especially critical of the notion of the "crucial experiment." No test can resolve theoretical controversies, first, because specific hypotheses cannot be isolated from the presumptive fabric of the total theory and, second, because any given hypothesis of the theory can be modified so as to alter the theory's testable consequences. Thus he writes:

> In sum, the physicist can never subject an isolated hypothesis to experimental test, but only a whole group of hypotheses; when the experiment is in disagreement with his predictions, what he learns is that at least one of the hypotheses constituting this group is unacceptable and ought to be modified; but the experiment does not designate which one should be changed (1914, p. 187).

He then proceeds to argue against the Newtonian inductive method of deducing integrative principles of theory from observations and established laws. Theoretical synthesis rests on the creative fruits of hunch and intuition, and not on logic. With respect to Ampère's preference for Newtonian inductivism, Duhem writes:

Very far from its being the case that Ampère's electrodynamic theory was *entirely deduced from experiment,* experiment played a very feeble role in its formation: it was merely the occasion which awakened the intuition of this physicist of genius and his intuition did the rest (1914, p. 199).

But if theories are freely modifiable, and intuition and ingenuity alone determine what conceptions the scientist is to introduce into his theoretical framework, how is one to judge which of the hypotheses ought to be abandoned? Duhem says "good sense" ought to be the judge. Unfortunately, discussions of good sense are likely to be no more incisive than those of intuition. As to the eventual choice among alternatives, all that Duhem can offer is faith that in the end good sense will prevail. "The day arrives when good sense comes out so clearly in favor of one of the two sides that the other side gives up the struggle even though pure logic would not forbid its continuation" (p. 218). One suspects that Duhem's own good sense led him to prefer formal simplicity.

In the writer's opinion, good sense for the conventionalists must eventually rest in preferences for hypotheses supporting theoretic convergence.

CHAPTER 3

The Language
of Psychology

IT IS COMMON PRACTICE to title works in the philosophy of science as the language of this or that science. The analyst claims that all philosophical analysis is about language and therefore all analytic works should be so acknowledged. Unfortunately, this shifts attention from what it is we are trying to say to the language itself. By our attempting to show that philosophical puzzlement stems from linguistic muddles, we sometimes forget that there is a world of experience about which, we presume, there is something to say. Aside from syntactical conventions, we are concerned with problems of meaning. We feel on fairly safe ground when our expressions have explicit extension, when they point to recognizable "facts" and relations. We feel less sure when our expressions have intentions but no explicit set of defining events (cf. N3.1). Nevertheless, we encounter both types of expression in science, and presumably both have claim to anchorage in the indisputable data of experience.

In the language of psychology both types of expressions find their place. We initially speak of the data language, the observation language, the factual language. This is the language of the observables, of the dependent and independent variables as stated in formal expressions of empirical relationships. But we may also speak of the language of mediating processes and of mediating variables. Here factual reference becomes somewhat more remote. And for the empiricist, the lack of an immediate empirical reference for the mediating variable presents an occasion for some philosophical reflection. Even more remote are the languages of inference, constructs, and theory. They involve matters requiring special attention. Discussion of these languages will be deferred until later chapters. Here only the language appropriate to the variables of description and connection is considered.

FACTUAL LANGUAGE

What is a fact? This is one of the most disarming of questions. At first glance it calls for a straightforward answer. "Facts are facts! Waste no time over the obvious, when there are really significant problems for the empiricist to contend with." It is as if we were to say that facts, like sense data, are the givens. The facts are given and the facts decide. But immediately it may occur to us that there is a difference between sense data, sense impressions, or whatever we would call the raw data of awareness, and the facts that are constructed of these raw data. Furthermore, we are a bit cautious about embracing the naive inductive method of our Baconian inference. According to Bacon we proceed from the enumeration and collation of similar facts to generalizations, laws, and other universal-like statements. Yet, we are immediately reminded that observation requires skill. An observer who could claim no other credentials than those of naïveté would see very little that would be of interest to the scientist (cf. N3.2).

Consider the factual language of behaviorism itself. From Watson on, behaviorists have concurred that the basic data of psychology are to be behavior itself. That the basic facts of psychology are to be publicly observed responses was taken so much for granted that few writers were to give more than passing attention to the concept of response itself. Strangely, however, psychologists who could reach significant methodological agreements differed as to the language of fact. Behaviorists generally have agreed that the response language is a molar rather than molecular language; it speaks of complex coordinations and movements of the organism rather than of reflexes and muscle twitches. Yet the terminology adopted by the theoretical behaviorists shows such diversity that we know it is impossible to separate the language of fact from that of a theory.

Recall the cat in the Thorndike puzzle box. It claws, bites, struggles, strikes, and finally escapes. Simple facts it would seem. Yet to Thorndike it was a random trial-and-error sequence of responses supported by an initial, instinctive, response-repertory; whereas to Tolman, such a sequence of events could be seen as a demonstration of persistence and "docility" culminating in the subject's responsive orientation toward its goal-objects (Tolman, 1932). Something in this behavioral situation is identical for the two observers and something is very different. It is as if the data are the same, but the facts differ. Yet even here we must speak as if the data are the unexpressed givens. When these data find expression in the language of fact, cognitive processes have transpired to transform them ontologically from their status of potentiality to one of actuality. One does indeed get a different picture of the data of behavior if he reads Tolman than, say, if he reads Thorndike, Guthrie, Hull, or Skinner. One gets a different picture of the primate's behavior if he reads Köhler, rather, say, than Yerkes or Harlow. And it is not necessarily the case that one is a better observer than another. The observers may differ only as to their theoretical dispositions. The argument over facts may very well turn upon which observer operates from the more defensible set of preconceptions.

The story now becomes the familiar and often trivial one of perceptual and cognitive relativism. It is the story of frames of reference (Sherif), of the new look in perception (Bruner, Goodman), of the cognitive structure (Lewin, Krech, Crutchfield), of psychological phenomenology (Koffka, MacLeod, Snygg, Combs). Explicitly told, it is as old as the Herbartian doctrine of apperception where "apperceiving attention is a combination of imagination, which works from within, and the sensation coming with external impression" (Herbart, 1898; p. 209).

The doctrine is so self-evident nowadays as to be a truism. We perceive according to our inclinations, our beliefs, predispositions, sets—according to our apperceptive mass. One does not arrive on the scene as a naive observer recording facts on a blank tablet wherein such facts are to repose in their own pristine integrity. Rather the data of pre-perception are neutral until configurated under the clutch of the apperceptive mass. Observation is not merely a matter of bringing data into the focus of awareness but rather one of assimilating them into the prevailing conceptual system of the person. Still, what is so obvious to the student of ordinary perception may appear less significant to the student of science. Facts of science are presumed to warrant a privileged status. They are often expected to transcend conceptual frames of reference. Koch, for example, directs his respondents to describe their empirical independent and dependent variables in a "theoretically neutral . . . immediate data language" (1959, p. 679); and a group of expositors of modern learning theory responded to the question, "Is the data language explicit and theoretically neutral?" as a touchstone of scientific sophistication (Estes *et al.,* 1954, p. xviii).

Thus, it is thought that the facts of scientific observation can be quite different from the facts of everyday perception. The rigors of operational procedure, the checks, the precautions against bias, give to them a degree of reliability not found in the "facts" of the untutored observer. It is as if the scientist is tutored to overcome his biases and to safeguard against his preconceptions. Presumably, then, facts are to stand apart from the conceptual frameworks in which the observer operates. Operational procedures may prescribe certain conceptual limits for scientific facts, but then once the operational rules are accepted by conventionalistic agreements, the facts as thus derived should be neutral with respect to theoretical points of view converging on given experimental issues.

Now, one should suspect any such pretentions to factual neutrality as are suggested in the preceding paragraph. Historians and philosophers of science (e.g., Hanson, 1958; Feyerabend, 1962), students of language and knowledge (e.g., Whorf, 1956; Wittgenstein, 1953), as well as students of perception agree that factual statements are conceptually contaminated (cf. N3.3). How a scientist sees the world is no more a matter of veridical observation, *in any absolute sense,* than is the way any culture-bound person sees the world that is unique to his frame of reference. The welter of pre-perceived events may be factually and theoretically neutral, but just how our events-as-experienced are precipitated from this neutral stuff is a complicated constructual matter involving sensitivity, selectivity, and the entire epistemic apparatus of structuring which is prior to the experience itself.

PARADIGM OF LOGICAL ATOMISM

As an initial approach to the clarification of factual statements consider a perceptual rubric based upon the schema of logical atomism. Potential punctate inputs can be treated as statements of atomic facts, either true or false. Perceptual configurations can be treated as molecular propositions that are extensions of the atomic facts, but that achieve a figure-ground pattern in the following way: each atomic fact, i.e., each potential input, is judged true or false according to whether it has some given property. Inputs having the property contribute to the figure, all other inputs, regardless of their properties contribute to the background. Thus any perceptual configuration is a molecular proposition obtained over the census of all inputs taking true or false values.

Doubtless this is a simplified schema of actual perception, but it is relatively easy to think of applications that exemplify this dichotomizing, census-taking model of perceptual construction. Imagine the following apparatus and experiment. At the nodes of a 20 by 20 grid are light sources such that each source emits either a subdued white, blue, or yellow light. Thus any random stimulus pattern would look much like an Ishihara-type card, and a particular stimulus pattern in relatively coarse grain would be achieved by setting up a nonrandom figure in a particular hue against a random background. Suppose further we undertake the following experiment. Three sets of stimulus panels are constructed such that barely detectable single-digit numbers are imposed on a random background. Set one gives a figure in blue, Set two gives a figure in yellow, and Set three gives two different but partially overlapping figures, one in blue, the other in yellow. Assume two groups of subjects, such that members of Group one are trained on the blue-figure panels and are rewarded every time they make a correct response to a brief stimulus exposure, while members of Group two are similarly trained on the yellow-figure cards. The experimental test comes when members of both groups receive the

Set-three cards in which the superimposed figures are presented. Doubtless we should find (on comparison against a relevant control group) that the blue-reward group would tend to perceive the blue figure, whereas the yellow-reward group would tend to see the yellow. This much we can infer from related experiments in the literature (e.g., Schafer and Murphy, 1943). And if we wished to draw a preliminary conclusion, we could say that the conceptual framework of one group was bluish figure and the conceptual framework of the other was yellowish figure, that the conceptual framework emerged as a function of reinforcement, and that the factual apprehensions of both groups were "correct" in their respective conceptual frameworks.

However, there is another conclusion to be drawn. Consider the stimulus world of a given subject, say from Group one. Each 20 by 20 card can be regarded as a true–false extension where a light is coded "true" if it is blue and "false" if not blue. Thus in all there would be 2^{400} possible stimulus configurations. These are the potential inputs. Suppose now the subject sees and names a six. The naming of the six belongs to his factual language. But the six can be relatively small or relatively large; it can be displaced to one or the other margin of the panel; it can be tipped, distorted, broken; etc. The naming of the six simply indicates that the particular configuration belongs to a class of many molecular propositions, each member of which possesses the property of being like a six. The language of fact does not report the *particular* stimulus configuration, i.e., the particular extension of atomic events, but only that the configuration belongs to a particular class of molecular propositions.

It is important to distinguish between a particular molecular proposition with its extension of atomic events, and a factual expression that indicates only that the molecular proposition warrants a specified class membership. The one is semantically anchored to a unique world occurrence, whereas the other only classifies the occurrence according to a set of many possible occurrences all possessing the defining property. One names *the* occurrence as an event in its ontologically given state; the other names a class having no such ontological status. Failure to appreciate this distinction leads to many philosophical perplexities.

When speaking in a factual language, we must, therefore, be careful to distinguish whether we are alluding to molecular events and their atomic extension, or whether we are attributing class membership to these events. Although there are troublesome initial conditions for judging an atomic event to be true or false, once these judgments are made then there remains no conceptual freedom for ascertaining whether molecular propositions are true or false. It was in this sense that logical atomists could take their atomism as ontological bedrock. However, what class a given proposition belongs to is quite another matter. Class membership depends on definitions wherein the conceptual framework is all-important. As Wittgenstein has said, what is or is not to be judged a cow is for the public to decide. It is not at all a matter of ontology.

In the foregoing sense, then, a fact is a general proposition determined by the conceptual predispositions of the factual classifier. We must distinguish the raw data of pre-perception from their factual reification through conceptual conventions. The raw data are neutral, so to speak, but they are unexpressed. Facts cannot be neutral for they reflect our classificatory penchants.

When we consider the concept of response the issues come into vivid relief. The raw data underlying our factual representations of response are the states of the effector elements and they are amenable to truth functional analysis. Responses are integrated over time, as it were, to compose the continuity of the parcel of molar behavior. For example, "turning left," or "running toward the goal," or "entering the cul de sac" are all molar behaviors involving complex sets of molecular responses. But the factual statement of molar behavior is a general proposition. It specifies only that certain observable events must obtain in order for us to classify a particular set of response events as a member of the class of such and such behavior. "Turning left" means only that the animal was seen to enter and disappear past the door to the left alley. It does not specify just what complex of response states should implement the behavior. In fact, many of the response factors may be considered irrelevant, such as position and movement of the head, the side of the alley passed, or even aspects of hesitancy and rate of movement. There are many ways of an animal's turning left but the myriad of possible response states is irrelevant to defining the class of act itself.

Why, we should then ask, just this set of defining properties for the factual class and not another? Why, for example, is not the rate of locomotion significant? In some cases it is judged not to be. And what of vicarious trial and error? And the momentary exploratory episodes? And what of whisker and tail performances? We do not even bother to report so many events because they are conceived as being nonsignificant and irrelevant to the description of the phenomena in question. This much can be taken for granted, but the question remains: What determines the relevant items of response from the irrelevant? What determines the defining properties of behavior? Doubtless the answer is to be found in the conceptual framework which the behaviorist brings to his study of learning.

In maze learning one may conceive of running a maze as a concatenation of discrete behavioral events marked off at various choice points. Therefore, running the maze is a complex affair of many behaviors with sequential connections (e.g., Hull, J. A. Deutsch, 1960). Many facts compose the sequence. One may also conceive of the running of a maze as an almost unitary act in which the minutiae of sequential behaviors are irrelevant as compared with the goal-orientation and goal-pursuing activities of the animal subject. What then, is the unit of behavioral description? It depends upon what one is predisposed to consider as relevant. A contiguity theorist may entertain many behaviors with small time spans, and purposive overtones are likely to be missing in the factual descriptions. A purposive behaviorist may entertain only meaningful units of behavior with a longer time span including a terminal response (e.g., Muenzinger, 1942). For the two people who observe the animal, the raw data are in a sense the same. But the facts differ! Different sets of factual propositions are considered appropriate for describing observation.

ROLE OF THE *A PRIORI*

The thesis expressed here is that, one, a distinction is to be made between the raw data and the facts of experience, and two, factual reification of these data entails a conceptual framework. This is the empiricist counterpart of the Kantian doctrine of apperception. Kant distinguished between *noumenon,* the unknowable thing in itself, and *phenomenon,* that which is known by virtue of the transcendental unity of apperception and the categories of understanding. His great lesson is that the flux of raw data would remain an unperceived flux were it not for prior structuring according to certain categories of understanding which reify events on a space–time frame. It is the nature of a perceived event that it has structure, that it be seen as isolable in the welter of sensory flux. The principle of association would be inoperable were it not that events are impressible in familiar categories of experience, were it not that prior dispositions order events in the associative complexes that we do in fact understand.

Subsequent empiricists have taken exception to Kantian dogmatism about the innate character of *a priori* associative propensities. The classical space–time rubric of Newton has been modified. The conceptual framework is not so indubitable, nor so compelling of all possible experience, as Kant had thought. Nevertheless, the question: "How are synthetic *a priori* judgments possible?" is one of profound significance. Without the *a priori* element no synthetic judgment, that is, no factual propositions, would be possible. To be sure, we have had to modify our conceptions of the *a priori* (Lewis, 1923, 1929). A conceptual framework need not be conceived as something that is built into the mind, unchanging, enduring, and forming the foundations of a common understanding. Rather, it represents the epistemic hypothesis for our classifying complex events into their factual categories. The fact itself is not seen, but unless we can see complex events as instantiations of fact we would not see them as things at all (cf. N3.4).

The *a priori* element of structuring signifies only that a conceptual framework is prior to the experiencing of the fact. The conceptual framework itself may emerge in the interplay of experience and hypothesis. Thorndike, for example, witnessed the cat's scratching, clawing, biting in its puzzle box confinement. It occured to him that the behavior was random. A response occurred in which the catch to the door was released. The cat escaped and the successful response was stamped-in. For the psychologist, a conceptual framework emerged, one of trial and error and reinforcement. And it was this conceptual framework that predisposed the psychologist to define behavior in the way he did, as a set of acts upon the environment. But another conceptual framework includes the goal object, the end state that terminates the behavioral episode that is of conceptual interest to the cognitive psychologist. Clawing, biting, etc., are now seen as means–end hypotheses. They are not seen as mere random sequences of acts but as acts toward some end.

To the naive empiricist it would seem that the facts of latent learning experiments, for example, are the same for any person regardless of his theoretical leanings. Indeed, one hardly contests the reporting of the results of such experiments. However, the facts that one incorporates into his theoretical discussion may be quite different for different analysts; for on the one hand, making a correct response is seen as a reinforced act, and on the other, it is a sign of expectancy (cf. N3.4). The act of classifying response-sets into categories of behavior is a conceptual affair. Initially superficial agreement as to factual propositions may be reached among people of diverse theoretical dispositions, but then a closer scrutiny reveals that the defining properties that the theoreticians choose to emphasize may be quite different. The raw behaviors that they seek to classify in terms of factual propositions may be seen as instances of different classes. And the difference in kind may be at the source of subsequent discrepancies in theoretical accounting.

RESUMÉ OF THE CONCEPTUAL ACCOUNT OF FACTS

Several implications follow from this account of facts. Let us pause to consider each in brief:

(1) Are facts theoretically neutral? One may as well ask, can one express himself verbally without recourse to language. The language of fact cannot be purified of the conceptual framework from which the defining characteristics of class memberships are taken. The raw data of pre-perception may be neutral but then we cannot speak of them. There is no way to report such data in factual propositions (cf. N3.5).

(2) Are facts true or false? The inclination is to treat all facts as true; otherwise they would not be facts. However, the language of truth

does not wholly apply. Putative instantiations of facts may be true or false, and for any given event complex, we can assert whether or not it is a member of the class named by the factual proposition. Still the same event complex may be classified according to different factual propositions, in which case it is seen differently. But the difference is in the set of defining properties. Different emphasis may be incorporated and different sets of irrelevances, such that when the same event complex yields different factual statements, it can be attributed to differences in the conceptual framework in which the factual propositions are stated.

(3) Are crucial tests possible? This familiar question has several ramifications, but in the present context, we would have to insure that the *sine qua non* of a crucial test is that the experimental facts should be theoretically neutral. The defining characteristics for the factual propositions should be independent of conceptual frameworks. But, as maintained here, this is not the case. Facts that are seen to agree in name display at the experimental confrontation an open texture of interpretation. They may possibly be seen as supportive of discrepant hypotheses. Thus the facts of latent learning experiments have never been conclusive. This open texture has always provided an escape clause, as it were, for the avoidance of crucial decisions.

To these implications, the following points may be added:

(4) Determination of facts according to the conceptual framework is neither strictly an empirical nor strictly a logical matter. Rather, it concerns the psychology of scientific invention. It cannot be an empirical matter without our introducing an element of circularity. We would have to assume that the nature of fact is itself to be decided as a matter of fact. Nor is the nature of fact a matter of logic, for logic like factual propositions begins with definitions and rules. To say that the determination of factual propositions is a matter of the psychology of invention is merely to say that factual propositions derive from the conceptual potential for *a priori* structuring.

(5) Emergence of a new conceptual framework results in the modification of factual propositions. This follows from the fact that new ways of conceiving result in new ways of perceiving. This is inevitable, for fact and conceptual framework are inseparable.

(6) Since the growth of a science involves a hierarchy of conceptual frameworks, principles of choice must operate for ascertaining which classifications and which factual propositions provide the preferred catalogues of perception. But conceptual frameworks implicit within theory construction are subject to such noninductive criteria of selection as simplicity, comprehensiveness, reducibility, and correspondence.

OBSERVATION VARIABLES

Let us now look more closely at the implications that the foregoing thesis has for the factual language of psychology. For example, the language of S-R habit elements and the language of cognitive or purposive behaviorism reflect not so much a difference in the raw data of response as a difference in behavioral classification. This being the case, it is not clear that issues which are divisive, e.g., latent learning, are such that they can be settled by experimental design. We come more to the point, however, when we examine the language of observation itself, of the independent and dependent variables. Behaviorists, as a group, have been notoriously lax or inconsistent in their definitions of stimulus and response. Considering their early polarization in the stream of physicalism and logical empiricism, this comes as a bit of a puzzle. One would think that with public verification being elevated to the role of epistemological doctrine, behaviorists should have agreed upon what it was they were to observe. But this was not the case. Nor is it now. We have only to consider some definitional efforts.

Stimulus Variables

Stimuli, environmental conditions generally, and the facts of organismic control exhaust the classes of independent variables. Other things being equal, it is the stimulus variable that is salient. But what is a stimulus? The lack of conceptual agreement is well publicized (e.g., Gibson, 1960). Koch states the situation for both stimulus and response:

> It has become a truism to observe that early behaviorists were systematically ambiguous in their definitions and applications of the concepts "stimulus" and "response." The term "stimulus" was indiscriminately applied to states of affairs ranging from the physical energy change operating on a single receptor to the behavior evoking effect of a complex social situation, while "response" could designate anything from the contraction of a single muscle cell, to the name of a class of end results brought about by a widely varying range of movement sequences (1954, p. 9).

It is not clear that the situation has improved. The following usages are in vogue. Stimuli may be proximal, they may also be distal. As external energy changes they may be the actual elicitors of receptor activities or they may be potential elicitors residing in an object world. They may be specific energies activating the single receptor unit. They may be situations playing upon the entire sensory manifold. They may be only external energies, they may include activity within the organism. Is this sampling, then, a sign of conceptual confusion (Gibson, 1960)? Or is it more a sign of conceptual diversity necessitating different factual classifications? Consider the following:

Distal versus proximal stimuli. This is the well-known distinction of Koffka, 1935; Brunswik, 1944. For the most part Hull, Tolman, Skinner, each in his individual treatments, considers the effective stimulus to be distal. For example, Tolman defines stimuli as "environmental entities which evoke expectations, i.e., sign-gestalt-perceptions, memorizations or inferences; . . ." (1932, p. 451). And for Skinner, " 'stimulus' refers to any part of the environment that is related to some specified operant or respondent according to the laws of the system" (Verplanck, 1954, p. 293). In contrast Hebb prefers what appears to be a definition of proximal stimuli: stimuli "are events which excite the neurone from outside the CNS . . ." (1958, p. 93). And Hayek in the same vein defines stimulus as "an event external to the nervous system which causes (through or without the mediation of special receptor organs) processes in some nerve fibres which by these fibres are conducted from the point at which the stimulus acts to some other point in the nervous system" (1952, p. 8). If there is any doubt as to the locus of the proximal stimulus, Hayek adds that it is "the last known physical event in the chain which leads to the production of the impulse" (1952, p. 8).

Now it should be apparent that the differences in these definitions are indicative of conceptual preference rather than conceptual confusion. Tolman, for example, conceives of stimulus as a goal-object with positive and negative valence as reflected in the expectations of the organism. The conceptual framework is adaptive and cognitive. It requires treating stimuli as meaningful goal objects. Skinner, on the other hand, conceptually suppresses the cognitive element in the event complex and treats stimuli as cue-occasions for response. Cognitive implications of the stimuli are accommodated by his insistence that only events tied to a response (i.e., effective stimuli) can be classed as stimuli. In any event, with these two conceptual frameworks at our disposal, we know in each case what constitutes the empirical evidence of a stimulus. With Hebb and Hayek quite different conceptual frameworks are involved. Both Skinner and Tolman are radical behaviorists in that they eschew any internalization (physiological analysis) of behavioral process. Hebb, on the other hand, thinks in terms of neural processes, the cell assembly and the phase sequence, as mediating behavior. He is committed, therefore, to a stimulus concept that fits into his conceptual system (1949). In similar fashion, Hayek is concerned with the internal processes for classifying various sensory orders. He is a constructualist somewhat in the sense presented in this chapter. Classification is a function of stimulus equivalence, generalization, and transfer. It is a function of apperception and not of some object structure as independent of sensory organization. Therefore, his conceptual system requires a neutralist treatment of the stimulus event. And the best way to assure the neutrality of the stimulus is to define it as a proximal event.

Potential versus actual stimuli.   One can, of course, be eclectic about defining stimulus just as the Hullians seem to be. Stimuli can be either external or internal, potential or actual. Spence (1956), for example, finds that the term "stimulus" performs several different functions. It can designate "independent stimulus variables that the psychologist was said to manipulate" (1956, p. 39). Some stimuli are *intraorganic;* some stimuli are *situational,* e.g., levers, alleyways, card symbols, auditory cues, shocks, etc. Only if some response is connected with the stimulus can it be said to be *effective.* Skinner (1938; cf. Verplanck, 1954) and Tolman (1932, 1959) make stimulus contingent upon its evoking, or being the occasion for, some response. Thus all stimuli are effective stimuli. But Guthrie and Estes insist upon the situational enumeration of stimuli wherein both potential and effective elicitors and cues are included. For Guthrie, stimuli are "the physical changes which are *potential* occasions for the initiation of sense organ activity and consequent afferent activity leading to response" (1959, p. 178). And Estes writes ". . . it should be emphasized at the outset that by *stimulus* and all the variants of the term I refer to environmental conditions describable in physical terms without reference to the behavior of the organism" (1959, p. 455).

Again we may ask, is there conceptual confusion concerning whether stimuli must be actual or merely potential? Or is the choice one of conceptual necessity? For both Skinner and Tolman, but especially for Tolman, a stimulus must be an occasion for response, otherwise what purports to be a stimulus does not at all figure into the behavioral situation. But with Guthrie and Estes the situation is different. Response occurrence is a probability function with respect to stimulus sampling (Estes 1950, 1959; Voeks, 1950). One could not entertain this kind of sampling concept unless within the domain of stimulus elements he included some stimuli which would be noneffective.

Response Variables

Just as one should distinguish between a member of a class and the class itself, so should he distinguish between a molecular response that is an explicit set of effector events and a molar response that is formulated as a factual proposition naming a set of many such molecular responses (all equivalent only in that they share some defining property, such as pressing the lever). Just what the defining property is for the factual proposition is a conceptual matter[1]: In its preoccupations with learning,

---

[1] No consistent distinction is made or maintained between response and behavior. It is tempting to take response as some specific set of effector events and behavior as the classificatory factual proposition—as is done for expository purposes in Chapter 7. However, this is contrary to current usage of the term 'response.' Thus its meaning is left somewhat ambiguous and is clarified only where confusion would be likely.

behaviorism incorporated the reflex arc and the conditioning model into its conceptual framework. Understandably, then, response was limited to the designation of muscular contractions and glandular secretions where specific sequential tracing from stimulus to response was, at least, conceptually possible. When concern with adaptive function rendered the reflex concept inadequate, larger units of response description became necessary but with a concomitant loss in specificity. It was not that the facts supported the molar over the molecular point of view. It was simply that different facts emerge as intrinsic to our moving from reflexology to functionalism. Where behaviorists now take the pains to define response, it is clear that their differences of opinion are dictated by their conceptual preferences and not by discoveries or confusions about real response entities in the world apart.

As it is with stimulus so it is with response. Not only does the conceptual framework determine the definitions of the observation terms, it determines the type of experiment undertaken. The apparatus of operant conditioning was invented and perfected by the Skinnerians, and not by Tolman, for example. And there is more to this historical fact than the possibility that Skinner may have been the more mechanically inventive of the two. But if the psychologist believes that organisms in some sense apprehend the world and are insightful, the response opportunities need be somewhat richer than those provided by simple lever devices. A complex apparatus for measuring pupillary reflex can be a fine piece of equipment but it would not provide data of interest to a psychologist who defines his subject in terms of means-end activities.

A very few examples will suffice to illustrate. Focusing upon the molecular elements of response, Hebb defines behavior as "the publicly observable activity of muscles or glands of external secretion as manifested in movements of parts of the body or in the appearance of tears, sweat, saliva and so forth" (1958, p. 2). No need for the scope of response that would give play to expectation, means-ends, or even consummatory acts. The conceptual system is one of brain function and it dictates a response concept the facts of which can be implemented by specific sets of efferent outputs.

Skinner (1935) and Estes (1950, 1959), on the other hand, refer to response as a class of many sets of events. Their treatments of response are thereby akin to the treatment of a factual proposition as outlined in this chapter. A given response, such as withdrawing from the grid in the presence of light, pecking the target, etc., is a class of many possible event-complexes and names no specific occurrence except generically. Note what Estes writes, ". . . the term response refers not to a physiologically or anatomically defined unit, but to the class of activities, e.g., all behaviors which result in depression of a bar, all behaviors which result in cutting a photocell beam or entering an endbox . . ." (1959, p. 392).

Although Tolman makes no explicit mention of the logical status of his response terms, it is clear that he too is interested in classes of acts and not specific concatenations of response. Thus he writes: "I also felt response could not be defined as a specific muscle contraction but must in some way be defined as a directed, goal-oriented manipulation or 'performance'" (1959, p. 59). And, "responses are for me to be conceived of as 'performances' rather than as specific muscle responses or gland secretions" (1959, p. 147). 'Conceived of,' to be sure, is the proper expression. Tolman's purposive orientation requires that the response variable has sufficient scope to include goals and ends. One has no need for specific response, for means-utilization is both flexible and manifold. Specificity of response would indeed become an encumbrance to the theoretical system, as it would in fact be for any system that makes reinforcement contingent on acts as complex as pressing a bar or taking one path over some other path.

Venn Maps of Stimulus and Response

To summarize, recourse can be made to simple Venn diagrams. We can think of the Venn domain as the universe of all possible raw data stimulus points, or, on the other hand, of all possible raw data response points. Then any class of stimuli as represented by a factual proposition can be represented as a class within the domain; *mutatis mutandi,* for response. Now consider the case wherein two conceptual frameworks are brought to focus upon the same domain of raw data response points. According to the present thesis, the relevant language of response may be different for the two conceptual systems and the two response classes, for their more or less coincident behavioral episodes will not be the same. Suppose a cognitive behaviorist and a reinforcement behaviorist are concerned with behavior at the choice point of a simple T maze. Then the response classifications might be represented by Figure 3.1. Let R_r designate relevant response for the reinforcement behaviorist, such as turning right or turning left. Let R_c designate relevant response for the cognitive behaviorist. Note that R_r is wholly contained in R_c. That is to say, every response ("turning left" or "turning right") in the classification schema of R_r is a response in the classification schema of R_c. Assuming R_c is the response class for the cognitive theorist, then some points are considered responses in his conceptual system which are not considered so in the system of the reinforcement theorist. For example, these might be the vicarious trial and error motions which are significant to the cognitive theorists but are not so to the reinforcement theorist.[2] Continuing in the same

---

[2] This is not to suggest that reinforcement theorists need necessarily ignore VTE, but initially the extension of response classes to incorporate VTE was undertaken by purposive behaviorists (Muenzinger, 1938; Tolman, 1939).

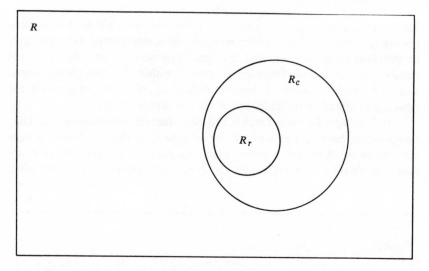

Figure 3.1 Response classes for two different conceptual systems.

vein, a possible schema of stimulus classification is found in Figure 3.2. Here the classes of stimuli S_e and S_h are defined from different conceptual systems. The stimulus classes that are of interest are

$\{S_e\}$, the stimulus class for E,

$\{S_h\}$, the stimulus class for H,

$\{S_e \sim S_h\}$, the raw data points included in E's stimulus world but not included in H's,

$\{\sim S_e S_h\}$, the raw data points not included in E's stimulus world, but included in H's,

$\{S_e S_h\}$,   the raw data points which are included in the stimulus world of both E and H.

As an application of this schema let E stand for Estes and H stand for Hebb. Then $\{S_e S_h\}$ is the class of stimuli where both Hebb and Estes concur; for example, stimulus objects to which the subject attends and responds. Next $\{S_e \sim S_h\}$ is the class of unactualized, potential stimuli, i.e., objects in the stimulus world which for one or another reason do not elicit significant receptor activity. And $\{\sim S_e S_h\}$ may be the class composed of internal afferent events and, for that matter, might also contain the spontaneous unelicited firing of the sensory neurones.

One can, of course, construct other schemata to represent other conceptual differences of opinion. But unless the class compositions of the factual propositions coincide exactly, there will be inconsistencies and conflicts as concerns comparisons of the factual language. As noted, the classical conditionist may see many events as response which do not at all find their way into the response vocabulary of a purposive behaviorist.

Such a predicament is quite understandable and need not be troublesome providing opposing theoreticians recognize that one factual language may be different from another, and that the hypothesis of one theory is not testable by the factual language generated within the conceptual framework of another theory. Linguistic difficulties seem to arise when the ontological status of the language of fact is misinterpreted.

It has already been emphasized that factual propositions, as class designations, have referents of a different type than that of simple existential assertions. Although a named class can have a finite number of members, and thereby its name names the concrete aggregate, we do not often

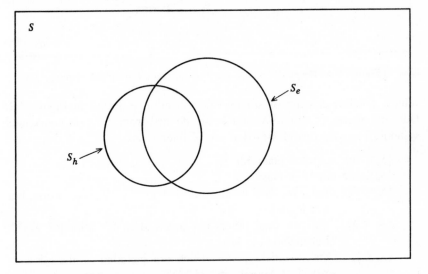

Figure 3.2 Stimulus classes for two different conceptual systems.

correctly apply the name to designate the aggregate. Rather we use the name as if it names a thing and not the selected aggregate. Suppose we say, "Subject S turned right." This is the fact. From this, we can infer that the actual response occurrence, as an explicit event sequence, was such that, by virtue of the applied defining properties, it could be assigned to the given class. By using the term "turning right" we point to no specific act or event. We only assert that whatever the specific and unique act, it had the defining property "turning right." Thus to assign a property over a set of variables is to construct a class.

Consider once again Figure 3.2. Every point within the domain represents a molecular proposition whose truth is an extension of its atomic elements. Each point, therefore, is ontologically basic—its represents a possible occurrence or state of the stimulus world, such that if the possible occurrence does take place it takes place as a recognizable event in the universe. What has been here called the event is a point in the domain or universe. It is the existent, it is neutral, and it is not a fact! The status of fact arises only when apperception allows us to assign a given property to the specific event. What properties we assign to the event are not alone determined by the event, for the property emerges only as it functions in a conceptual framework.

The Venn diagram should not be taken too seriously as a model for the distinctions that have been made. For one thing, the mere need to speak of raw data means that we deprive them of their neutral status. And merely to call such events points in the phenomenal flux is surely to give them an identity which it is hard to describe except in factual terms. These difficulties cannot be avoided. Nevertheless, granting certain conventions for isolating events in the domain of possible experience, then constructions and classifications will be relative to conceptual schemata. We can, for example, agree as to the molecular elements of raw response. But whether a response sequence is one of reflex brevity, or one of means-end expanse, or one which is always terminated by a reinforcement episode, is not a definitional matter that can be decided by one's looking to the domain of possible experience with an open and unbiased mind.

MEDIATING VARIABLES

There would be more homogeneity to the themes of this chapter were we to confine our attention to observables and the language of fact. Mediating variables fall into a different category. Since they serve to mediate between the independent stimulus variables and the dependent response variables they do not appear to reside within the precincts of the observation language. There is, however, a sense in which we use mediating variables as part of the observation language. We refer to internal states as if they are writ large on the surface of observable events. For example, we deprive an animal of food so as to reduce it to eighty percent of its ad lib weight. The animal is active, it looks hungry; "Looking hungry" is part of the observation language. However, the state of hunger itself may not be among the set of observable events. We may insist that hunger is some internal state of the organism; tissue deficit, biochemical disbalance, or some other unspecified state. In that case, the data of observation can only serve as the grounds for inference for the hypothetical internal state.

How much of the mediating variable is inference? How much is construct? This is the significant question. When Woodworth (1929) made room for mediating organismic variables in the stimulus–response schema, he did so in recognition that organisms were not simple processors, such as one might expect of tropismic or reflex organisms. Behavioral laws are not so simple. The statement of the external stimulus conditions yields insufficient information for the making of response predictions. The past history of the organism, drive, permanent and momentary disbalances in organic function, attitudinal structure, these and many more conceptual processes intervene as the executives for the response mechanisms. Some of these mediators were tied to the side of manipulatable independent variables. Thus their locus falls more within the stimulus complex, as for example, need and deprivation. Some of the mediators were tied more to the unmanipulatable dependent variables. Such factors as momentary oscillations and unknown rhythms of the organic systems were located in the response complex. Initially though, all mediators were inferred from response. Why, for example, under these stimulus conditions does just *this* response occur and not some other? It is the behavior that signifies the mediator.

As Hull and Tolman undertook their systematic developments of behaviorism, the issues of the status of mediators became more refined. The emphasis was to be upon public observation, otherwise the hard won advantages of empiricism would be lost. Hypotheses and conjectures can be useful if they lead to discoveries and to the opening of new factual vistas. But if hypotheses merely serve some weak explanatory function with little possibility either of fitting into the body of established science or of achieving existential status, then like all progeny of metaphysics they are distractive, and they are dispensable. Under the circumstances, it is safest to stay within the boundaries of the observation language. In such a case mediators are not to be internalized. They are to be logical constructions constituting a more explicit statement of the behavioral setting.

Mediators as Constructs

Consider need, for example. As a construct, we ignore any aspect of its hypothetical residence in the internal milieu. What the need statement signifies is that certain environmental conditions, such as history of food intake (hunger) or history of sustained disapproval (sense of failure), are antecedent to given response options. Statement of need supplements to a substantial extent the fund of independent variables. We can, of course, concentrate on response rather than stimulus setting. What we then construct is a kind of dispositional term whose meaning is explicated in terms of test-conditionals. The subject displays certain kinds of behavioral dispositions (demands, expectations, fears, etc.) if under a given set of stimulus conditions a specified response or set of responses occurs. In either case, however, we are concerned with logical constructs. Regardless of whether the mediating variable is a construction from the complex of independent variables or from the complex of dependent variables, no existential status is attributed to the mediator aside from the aggregate of constitutive events reported in the observation language.

Mediators as Inferred Entities

Now a physiologist, for example, may not be satisfied with such empiricistic conservatism.[3] The complex S-R connections lead him to place the mediating variables within the organism itself. States, mechanisms, entities are inferred which when incorporated into the model of the behavioral system permit the deduction of response hypotheses. A motivational state is not explicitly definable in terms of the independent variables. Need is more than a maintenance schedule, demand is more than response under a given set of stimuli and behavioral options. Somewhere within the organism, it is hypothesized, there are structures for which the evidence is now only indirect and incomplete.

The question as to what mediating variables are, or should be, has evoked considerable discussion in the psychological literature. MacCorquodale and Meehl (1948) were the first to clarify the distinction for psychologists. Intervening variables as treated by Tolman, by Skinner, and to large extent, by Hull are logical constructions; hypothetical constructs as conceived, say, by Hebb (1949) and Duffy (1962) are hypotheses concerning entities for which the evidence is both indirect and incomplete. Contrary to what some writers (Bergmann, 1951; Kendler, 1952) have intimated, the question appears to the present writer to be a significant one. But its significance rests in the assessment of the role that mediating variables are to play in our choosing among alternative theories. The question and the issues shall come up again in subsequent discussions.

MENTAL LANGUAGE

Before closing the door upon the language of psychology, we should consider the question of mental states, raw-feels and other data of consciousness. After all, there was a time when the mental language, and the shared physical language, was *the* language of psychology. Now the contemporary behaviorist is inclined to accept the verdict of Watson, " 'States of consciousness' like the so-called phenomena of spiritualism are not objectively verifiable, and for that reason can never be the data for science" (1929, p. 1). The muddles over consciousness have been a bar to scientific progress.

Such has been the judgment of learning and response oriented psy-

---

[3] It would seem that "conservatism" is the correct word here. Why people adopting this conservative attitude have been called "radical empiricists" (e.g., Skinner) rather than "conservative empiricists" is, for etymology, one of the curiosities of semantic irrelevancy.

chologists. There is no need for consciousness and mind as private, mentalistic referents. Still consciousness and the introspectable contents of "mind" keep cropping up. Our language is so traditionally steeped in mind stuffs and in qualities and dimensions of consciousness that it is difficult for the behaviorist to carry off his operational reductions of such terms as meaning, thinking, cognition, perception without having the old ways of thinking obtrude. As a result textbook writers allude deferentially to the historical efforts of the introspectionists, take Watson's brash but poignant judgment as the text for a discussion on methodology, and then proceed to use the language of their ancestors, larded as it is at the sinews with the overtones of consciousness and introspectable feelings.

Yet it is not alone out of carelessness that the vocabulary of mentalism will not be suppressed. Clinicians and personologists are no longer unique in their need for speaking of levels of awareness. With the successful probing of the subcortical centers of the central nervous system, neurophysiologists have given new heart to the dead issues of psychophysical parallelism. "Activation" and "awareness" need not be part of the psychological language, as the behaviorists were careful to point out; yet when a group of neurophysiologists convened to discuss this important work in subcortical structure and function, the title of the proceedings became *Brain Mechanisms and Consciousness* (Delafresnaye, 1954).

So, what of the mental language? Is there something to say for the mental domain? If so, does the mental language say it? These are the significant questions.

Doubtless there is something to refer to. 'Raw-feels,' 'sense-data,' 'sense-contents,' whatever term we use to refer to the stuff of consciousness, that stuff seems indubitable. It is not clear that the behaviorist or the physicalist has ever denied consciousness as such. Watson, we may think, comes close when he writes, "The behaviorist finds no evidence for 'mental existence' or 'mental processes' of any kind." But this presents a puzzle. For what is evidence but the stuff of consciousness? What would constitute evidence of mental content and mental process? It is like asking, what is the evidence of evidence. We may ask, what is the evidence that some putative structure is real, but it is quite a different matter to ask what is the evidence of that evidence we use.

There seems to be no justifiable argument for denying consciousness —for ignoring consciousness and its raw data perhaps, but not for its outright denial. That being the case, is there a reliable mental language? Can we develop a mental language as precise and publicly teachable as the physical language, without our begging some kind of privilege? The one is a public language, the other is private. The objects of reference, the particulars of the physical language, are publicly observed objects. One has recourse to the court of public approval as to whether a term in the language is used properly. This is not the case, however, for the private language. The particular content of consciousness, the "thing" that is referred to, is private. There is no public access to the data referent. Such are the linguistic implications of the egocentric predicament, of solipsism, of subjectivism, of that whole panoply of variations on the privacy of the primal data.

One difficulty of a mental language, then, is its lack of reference to data in a public domain. Only if the data are public can the semantic requirements for ostensive definitions be fulfilled. Another difficulty, and equally disturbing, is one alluded to by Wittgenstein (1953). I cannot be sure, even in the private domain, that I have learned to use the mental language correctly. The ostensive use of terms derives from our associating words with objects. Correct usage then is contingent upon my seeing whether the object possesses the defining properties I associate with the word. For example, the object in my pocket is a member of the class "eraser." I can say the object is an eraser, because it can be compared with other existent objects possessing the defining property. But can I claim the same for the private data language where the objects to be classified and named are the raw data of consciousness? Suppose I am experiencing a red sense-datum. What ostensive check is there upon my having used "red" in my private data language correctly? Proceeding as above, I would have to refer my red sense-datum to a class of many such data, i.e., to call up other members of the class. But it is the character of such data that they are transient, occupying, as it were, the momentary span of consciousness. Recall will not help me here; for even had I vivid imagery, I could not recall any past experience, be sure it was the one I had intentions of recalling, and still retain the present sense-datum there in the focal vortex of the sensorium. Thus, not only does a mental language lack public criteria of correct usage, we are not even sure that it is amenable to treatment under any conceivable set of private criteria.

Here end for the time being our misgivings over the mental language (cf. Chapter 7). Still we continue to use mentalist terms; and like Feigl (1950, 1958) and the neurophysiologists (Delasfresnaye, 1954), we continue to recognize the provisional dichotomy of the mental and the physical. However, whether there is a true mental language, or whether what purports to be a mental language contributes anything to the description of psychological events which is not translatable into the dispositional language of physicalism, is a matter for analysis. In the present book, the context for this analysis is established in the subsequent discussions on reductionism. The thesis to be maintained is that terms in the presumptive mental language are contaminated by behavioral reference. In the writer's opinion, no psychologically feasible method (i.e., an experiential method precluding intuition and recourse to postulation) exists for learning a strictly mental language. Nor is it clear of what use it would be, if we did in fact have one.

NOTES

NOTE 3.1

"Intension" and "extension" are here used in their customary philosophical senses. The *intension* of a term or phrase is the set of defining properties such that if any event exhibits those properties it then belongs to the class of objects named by the term or phrase. The *extension* of the term or phrase is the denumeration or identification of all such objects as one intended by the term or phrase. Intension refers to the matter of defining the class, whereas extension refers to the discriminative acts of populating the class.

Analogs are *connotation* and *denotation; sense* and *meaning.* For short discussions of shades of meaning see Stebbing (1948), Black (1949), and Pap (1949).

NOTE 3.2

Further clarification is required concerning raw data. In general these are the neutral inputs as concerns the raw material of perception and observation. But where should we locate them? In the world, as Russell does with his "sensibilia"? or as J. S. Mill does with his "permanent possibilities of sensation"? Or in the receptor system where we can give them a coding as input? Because of its amenability to treatment in the paradigms of logical atomism, the latter alternative is preferred. This, however, introduces a difficulty. Set, conditions of the receptor, and other phasic states affect the sensitivity of the receptor. Thus raw data are subject to dispositional factors of the organism just as are perceptual events, and, therefore, they cannot be theoretically neutral.

This is an unfortunate predicament and one that is difficult to avoid. To place raw data in the physical world as independent of any receptor activity is an indefensible metaphysical gambit. Yet to place raw data in the receptor activity is to destroy their neutrality. It would seem that the "counsel of despair" is to regard them as relatively neutral. That is, raw data are coded as sensory input under "optimal" conditions of observation . . . from which we infer that for every punctate input there is a source of physical energy sufficient to elicit firing of the receptor.

We do, of course, infer a world external to ourselves. It is on this basis that we assume a certain neutral stuff, or a thing in itself, or a real, which we use as the backdrop for our perceptual pluralism. Since this world-as-stimulus-potential is presumptively one of physical stimulus energies, we may think of the world as potentially elicitive of complex sets of punctate receptor response, in which the set for a given observer takes its unique space–time coordinates. Thus each such set of punctate receptor elicitations represents a space–time perspective. But then one might ask: how can these sets be neutral? For, each observer carries with him a unique space–time perspective. True, but the neutrality rests in the fact that the perspective affords a vantage and an aspect of the object and not a vantage or an aspect of the perceiving organism. The raw data space–time perspective is not contingent upon the attitudes, momentary sets, and other dispositional conditions of the organism.

The substance of such a doctrine can be found in the phenomenalism of Mach (1897) and Russell (1917). It is interesting to speculate what implications there are here for any substantive world. Since objects are systems of stimulus energies they cannot particularly be anywhere, until detector systems located at specific space–time positions process the information contained in the energy inputs. It is not simply a case of *esse est percipi*, but of how any system of ambient energies could crystallize into a world of objects without the presence of detectors with unique space–time perspectives.

NOTE 3.3

1. Note these two quotations of Goethe:
> "Were the eye not attuned to the Sun
> The Sun could never be seen by it."
> (quoted by Hanson, 1958, p. 4)

and,

> "All that is factual is already theory."
> (quoted by Klüver in his introduction to Hayek, 1952)

Thus we run the gamut of factual relativity, from naive phenomenalism to what Feyerabend (1962) calls the *pragmatic theory of observation*. The theme has become a truism, yet people continue to speak as if facts stand apart ontologically, as if they have an eternal validity, or as if the ingredients of those facts (e.g., sense data) possess that enduring status.

In the text it has been argued that the raw material of experience out of which factual classifications are made as repositories of perceptual knowledge is itself not subject to factual description. Feyerabend has made a somewhat similar distinction as the basis of his lucid exposition of a pragmatic theory of observation—in the writer's mind, as explicit and perceptive an account of factual relativism as can be found in recent literature. He writes:

> . . . the fact that a statement belongs to the observational domain has no bearing on its meaning . . . Whatever restrictions of interpretation we accept are determined by the language we use, or by the theories or general points of view whose development has led to the formulation of this language (1962, p. 39).

If one insists upon ontological bedrock for observation, all we can say is that observation is caused, and that specifically it is caused by the behaviors or acts of observation:

> An observation sentence is distinguished from other sentences of a theory, not, as was the case of earlier positivism, by its *content*, but by the *cause* of its production, or by the fact that its production conforms to certain

behavioral patterns. This being the case the fact that a certain sentence belongs to the observation language does not allow us to infer anything about its content, more especially, it does not allow us to make any inference concerning the *kind* of entities described in it (1962, p. 36).

Our instrumental and operational tactics in science should make for ready appreciation of the pragmatic aspect of observation.

> Taken by themselves, the indications of instruments do not mean anything unless we possess a *theory* which teaches us what situations we are to expect in the world, and which guarantees there exists a reliable correlation between indications of the instrument and such a particular situation. If a certain theory is replaced by a different theory with a different ontology, then we may have to revise the interpretation of *all* our measurements, however self-evident such a particular interpretation may have become in the course of time. . . (1962, p. 37).

And speaking of the meaning of observation, Feyerabend writes:

> Nobody would dream of demanding that the meanings of observation statements *as obtained with the help of measuring instruments* remain invariant with respect to the change and progress of knowledge. Yet, precisely this is done when the measuring instrument is a human being, and the indication is the behavior of this human being or the sensations he has, at a particular time (1962, p. 37).

(Behaviorists should take note, for results are, with but rare exceptions, reported as if the facts of response have existential status independent of the observational behavior of the experimenter. That this observational behavior is dictated by the experimenter's conceptual framework has been a major theme throughout this chapter).

Feyerabend draws two significant conclusions from his analysis of observation. One, he rejects the idea of *reductionism,* in which the facts and theoretical constructions of one science can be reduced to those of another. Two, he is critical of the idea of *meaning invariance,* i.e., the idea that facts once agreed to are invariant so far as concerns all subsequently developing theoretical perspectives. In rejecting meaning invariance, Feyerabend finds he must also reject the idea of reducing one science to another.

2.   Hanson (1958) approaches the problem of perception and factual construction somewhat more informally. He notes that scientist and nonscientists alike may receive the same data, but as individuals they see different things. "There is more to seeing than meets the eyeball." Physical states of two different observers, for example, may be very nearly alike, but what is seen can be quite different. The findings of perceptual studies of ambiguous figures, shifting perspectives, and impoverished cues all indicate that different things are seen for what proximally are identical stimuli.

Furthermore, one cannot separate interpretation of visual data from the apprehending of a thing seen; "theories and interpretations are there in the seeing from the outset." Hanson is critically sympathetic to the Wittgensteinian notion that language is instrumental in structuring fact. "Knowledge of the world is not a montage of sticks, stones, colour patches, and noises but a system of propositions" (1958, p. 26). Expressing some reservations on Wittgenstein's doctrine of picturing (*Tractatus*), he interprets the formal structure of science as placing limitations on factual perspectives. Thus in supporting the Copenhagen interpretation of quantum physics, he feels that so long as the formal structure of microphysics is as it is, there is no alternative but to accept uncertainty (Heisenberg), complementarity (Bohr), and unvisualizability (Dirac), as unavoidable aspects of our factual presentation.

The debates between the contemporary determinists and the votaries of the Copenhagen interpretation cannot be gone into here, but mention should be made that, as one of the former, Feyerabend (1957, 1961, 1962) believes that overemphasis upon the intrenched and inflexible character of language results in pessimism. Bohr was an obdurate spokesman for his Copenhagen point of view on grounds that the observational problems of quantum mechanics were not to be overcome. (Bohr writes ". . . it is decisive to recognize that, *however far the phenomena transcend the scope of the classical physical explanation, the account of all evidence must be expressed in classical terms*" (1949, p. 209).) Thus the uncertainty principle places an inescapable limitation upon observation and upon further penetrative speculations concerning hidden variables. Feyerabend's critical discussion of quantum measurement problems can be found in Körner (1957) and in Feigl and Maxwell (1961). Hanson also speaks to the issues in the latter volume. Also see Feyerabend (1958) and Hanson (1958, 1962).

3.   In a series of articles Katsoff (1947, 1949, 1953) makes some of the same points on behalf of an interpretative theory of observation. Responding to the question: "If facts are known what is it that is known?" Katsoff answers that the fact is a proposition whereby supportive perception is the interpretation of sense data in the context of an existential hypothesis. The hypothesis constitutes the interpretative framework. "Every scientific observation involves a set of categories *a priori*" (1947, p. 688).

Katsoff's argument yields the following conclusions:

(a) Sense data, as such, are not facts (a rejection of naive empiricism and radical positivism).
(b) Facts result only as the interpretation of sense data (therefore, rationalism is insufficient).
(c) Every scientific observation presupposes a set of categories (the requirement of the *a priori*).
(d) A differentiation is to be made between the sense data events (the *ding an sich*) and the facts. Factual propositions are expressive of interpretative perception, never of the sense data.

Katsoff cautions against an inflexible factual language, on the one hand, and uncritical relativism, on the other. For example, he takes to task Snygg and Combs for their statement: "A fact, we find, is not *something*, an independent thing that we can memorize and depend upon and know that it will always be true. It is true only in its own frame of reference, which means that it is false in others" (Snygg and Combs, 1949, p. 4).

It is the last clause that is clearly exceptionable. A fact in a foreign frame of reference, so to speak, is not false, it is simply meaningless. To endow factual propositions with general testability from alternative frameworks is to lose sight of the fact that such propositions are meaningful and capable of validation only in their own framework.

NOTE 3.4

Kant made it clear to subsequent generations of scientists and philosophers that the conception of a naively impressible perceiver is inadequate. His analysis of the basic spatio–temporal framework and categories of perceptual construction was to the point. Even though his perceptual idealism was rejected on the grounds of its presuming enduring epistemic propensities of the mind (non-Euclidean geometries and theories of relativity put an end to these aspects of Kantian *a priori*), the *a priori* foundations of knowledge were clearly recognized by pragmatists, positivists, empiricists, and mere epistemologists. Defenses of the *a priori* presuppositions of knowledge subsequent to Kant can be put into the following categories:

(1) *Intuitional a priorism.* Essentially the argument of Kant. As noted, it had to be rejected because of radical innovations in mathematics and physics.

(2) *Psychological a priorism.* Here restricted to the generic principles and schemata of associationism. If ideas are to be associated by similarity, contiguity, and contrast, then principles of the relevant classifications and associations must be incorporated into the processing mechanism prior to any experience. Otherwise initial experience could not be processed, no associative configurations and classes could emerge.

(3) *Epistemological a priorism.* All *a priorism* referred to in this note has epistemological significance. Here we are concerned as to how the *a priori* functions in the matter of existential enquiry.

Feyerabend and to some extent Hanson, as reported in Note 3.2, would be designated as defending epistemological *a priorism,* as could be Katsoff. However, the most explicit statements (in terms of *a priorism* itself) have been made by Lewis (1923, 1929), Pap (1946, 1949), and Schlick (1930).

Lewis' pragmatic conception of the *a priori* has been very influential in contemporary philosophy of science. Rejecting the absolute intuition and categories of Kant, Lewis still finds an imperative for *a priori* presuppositions so far as the empirical sciences are concerned. Empirical knowledge without the *a priori* schemata of our "definitive concepts" would be impossible. "We cannot even interrogate experience without a network of categories and definitive concepts." Thus he writes:

> A name itself must represent *some* uniformity in experience or it names nothing. What does not repeat itself or recur in intelligible fashion is not a thing. When the definitive uniformity is a clue to other uniformities, we have a successful definition. Other definitions cannot be said to be false, they are merely useless. In scientific classification the search is, thus, for *things worth naming.* But the naming, classifying, defining activity is essentially prior to investigation. We cannot interrogate experience in gen-

eral. Until our meaning is definite and our classification correspondingly exact, experience cannot conceivably answer our questions (1923; 1949, p. 289).

Laws are *a priori*. They define our concepts and the categories by which we classify our facts. Thus:

> In the case of an empirical law, a mere generalization from experience, if the particular experience does not fit it, so much the worse for the 'law.' But in the case of the categorical principle, if experience does not fit it, then so much the worse for the experience (1929, p. 224).

As Pap (1946) points out in his discussion of Lewis, the categorical, or *a priori*, propositions are true in intension. They include the set of defining properties essential to the classification of the facts. But the actual search of events and classification is a matter of the extension of an *a priori* proposition. One knows the extension of the proposition only *a posteriori*. But note that what is a fact to be classified can only be a fact in a classificatory schema.

Pap himself has undertaken a defense of the *a priori* in science. He draws upon Dewey, Lenzen, and Cassirer as well as upon Lewis and finds himself in substantial agreement as to the prerequisite of *a priori* classificatory schemata. However, he gives somewhat greater attention to the empirical origins of these *a priori* categories. Defining concepts arise by our noting similarities among events, by our relying, it would appear, on some kind of intuitive credence. But once formulated, empirical laws function analytically in the following way. Suppose an event is perceived as conformal to the defining concept. Then it is appropriately classified, as it were. The event is known. But suppose it is nonconformal in some respect. How will it be seen? If no available defining concept and class is available, it will be seen against the backdrop of some available class as being, in some sense, incomplete, aberrant, or refractory. For example, suppose the defining concept is the law of reinforcement. The class of learned responses then may include this law *a priori* as among its defining principles. But now suppose some behavior has many symptoms of a learned response yet is not wholly amenable to classification as reinforced response (e.g., as in some latent learning experiments). In such cases, the definitive concept must either serve to exclude the deviant event or it must undergo some modification itself in order to admit the deviant event. But so long as the category remains unchanged, it can only function to exclude the deviant event.

This argument crops up again in discussions of conventionalism and instrumentalism as pertains to law. What it clearly points out is that a question as to whether a given phenomenon is or is not a member of a given class (e.g., whether a behavior is a learned behavior or not) is not a question that can be easily settled by experiment. It is often a question of analysis.

(4) *Linguistic a priorism.* Not to be rigorously distinguished from epistemological empiricism so long as the state of knowledge is formulated in purely linguistic terms. Wittgenstein (1953) utilizes this type of *a priorism* when he emphasizes the conceptually limiting (or should we say "expansive") influence that language has on seeing and on picturing. And Stebbing (1933), in agreement with Lewis, prefers to formulate the conceptual framework in terms of linguistic instruments. She writes:

What use can we make of a priori propositions? Fortunately, I can reply very briefly. We do not use a priori propositions in order to obtain true generalizations concerning matters of fact. Such a procedure would be impossible. I accept Wittgenstein's statement: "In life it is never a mathematical proposition we need, but we use mathematical propositions only in order to infer from propositions which do not belong to mathematics to other propositions which equally do not belong to mathematics." The same may be said with regard to logical principles. As for conventions and definitions—we use them in order to enable us to arrange what we know in an orderly system (1933, p. 197).

Stebbing does not admit an empirical principle for the a priori; she is not interested, as Pap is, in the etiology or the psychological origins of the a priori. However, the difficulty for Pap is that the problem of psychological origins of the a priori involves him in an infinite empirical regress. That is why intuitive credibility on limited experience is taken by him as supportive of the empirical foundations of the a priori.

(5) Physiological a priorism. In some respects, one of the most obvious treatments of the a priori requirements for experience. Just as Brain (1951) speaks of physiological idealism, so might we speak of physiological a priorism. Without some innate properties and structures of the nervous system, no experience, no perceptual construction (not even that ultimately derived from learning) would be possible. This was a thesis defended by early nativists (e.g., Hering, Müller) with respect to spatial constructions. Physiologically, these nativists were Kantians. And following them, empiricists such as Lotze, Helmholtz, and Wundt never fully succeeded in freeing themselves of a priori principles. Even though the doctrine of local signs (Lotze) rejected the notion that spatial characteristics were given implicitly within the perceptual data, it had to allow innate propensities of the mind for processing the data to cognizable spatial impressions and ideas. Doubtless in such terms, the doctrine of the a priori becomes all but trivial. Yet it serves to emphasize that the tabula rasa models of early empiricism are naive.

The Gestalt psychologists have been at the forefront of physiological a priorism. Their field models of brain process, the doctrine of isomorphism, and ultimately the principles of perceptual organization all suggest the notion of the a priori foundations of experience. There is, however, an important precautionary note. Kantian a priorism is disavowed by the Gestaltists; the principles of prior organization belong to physical theory and not to the inherent propensities of the knowing mind. Koffka, for example, writes:

> In our case the formulation that structure is innate but processes are not, adds very definitely to the understanding of the nature-nurture dichotomy. For it makes it explicit that each process depends upon a set of conditions, of which the innate structure is one, the factual stimuli are another, and the laws of organization a third . . . But as we have emphasized, the laws of organization fall entirely outside the scope of our dichotomy. The laws of electrical potential, of surface tension, of maximum and minimum energy, hold for any system and are quite independent of the particular system considered, much as the nature of those systems will determine the actual processes which follow from the universal laws. To call these laws innate is therefore nonsensical; for innate can only mean: dependent upon the particular nature of the system as it is on account of its biological origin (1935, p. 549).

Perhaps so, but even should the Gestalt theory prove satisfactory, the reason that just this set of physical laws prove applicable and not another is to be found in the structural development of the brain as coded in the genetic material. The whole point of signaling out the autochthonous factors of perception was to propose that certain unique laws of perceptual organizations (proximity, similarity, closure, Prägnanz) are explainable in terms of genetically determined structures. Allusion to the laws of physics notwithstanding, the Gestalt psychologists have seldom been successful in disavowing their Kantian heritage.

Speculations along this line are also found in Hayek's interesting but neglected book, *The Sensory Order* (1952). His major thesis, a kind of contingent phenomenalism, is that sensory perception is an act of classification in which the input is processed "isomorphally," as it were, by any number of classes of sensory processes which impart to the phenomenal event the properties it has. The specific class linkages can either be learned or species acquired—the ontogenetic and phylogenetic aspects of "linkage" acquisition.

However, no sensory input is perceived except that it can be isomorphally accepted by the classes of sensory order. No object or phenomenal constructions are possible except in terms of the prior apparatus of classification. Moreover, these are not classes with the ontological status of Platonic reals; the properties and qualities of sensory order are not of the objects themselves but are abstractive attributions of the nervous system. Thus, his central thesis is:

. . . we do not first have sensations which are then preserved by memory, but it is as a result of physiological memory that the physiological impulses are converted into sensations. The connections between physiological elements are thus the primary phenomenon which creates the mental phenomena (1952, p. 53).

An impulse-complex within the nervous system will be processed and thereby perceptually reified only if the impulse elicits the activity of the classifying complex. Since many such impulses may activate the class complex, any given input loses its uniqueness in the process of perceptual reification. In other words, perceptual reification means that the phenomenon emerges as an abstractive reality.

The neurological speculations of Hayek's thesis, its implications for both philosophy and psychology, are too extensive to go into here. But apropos of *a priorism*, the following comments can be made:

(1) Perception is impossible without prior categories or classificatory assemblies for the processing of input.
(2) All perception is abstractive in the sense that it attributes properties which are class defining and thus are meaningless as unique descriptions.
(3) The classificatory structures or assemblies are either species determined or are learned, but in either case, they are prior to any experience.

Hayek offers us an analysis of perception that is the antithesis of that of certain existentialists (e.g., Marcel). According to them all classification is corruptive of the particular experience. Only particulars are real. As soon as an event is classified and surrenders its individuality to categories of shared properties, it is no longer an event. Hayek's model of sensory processing, on the other hand, adamantly asserts that without the "abstractive" classes there would be no phenomena at all.

NOTE 3.5

There are contexts in physics where facts cannot at all be separate from their conceptual framework. A counterpart to the argument for the neutrality of facts is that a given fact should be one thing and not another. For example, an electron should be a particle, or it should be a wave. It should have sufficient integrity not to pretend to both. But according to the principle of complementarity, it is indeed both. Contingent upon the experimental set up, it is seen as a particle or it is seen as a wave. And all together, it must be seen as both. If a beam of electrons is directed through a slit, the usual diffraction pattern is observed which is characteristic of wavelike phenomena. Now, if the intensity of the beam is reduced so that only an occasional electron is emitted at the source, punctate scintillations occur at the screen according to a probability law that is isomorphic to the intensities of a diffraction pattern. However, the punctate scintillation must be seen as a particle striking the screen and not as a wave phenomenon.

But, you may counter, the electron is not seen at all. It is a kind of construction. True, but the light patterns on the screen *are* seen. And they can be seen both as signifying a wave interception and as signifying a particle interception. Moreover, they must be seen as both, each manner of seeing according to its respective conceptual frame. This is essential to completing the picture quantum physics has of its microphenomena.

CHAPTER 4

Theories and Models

NAÏVETÉ has been used in much of the foregoing discussion as a back-drop against which various themes of the empiricistic argument have been developed. We have addressed ourselves to the following questions: As observers do we apprehend facts as they occur in their pristine naive factualness? or are they apperceived from within some conceptual framework? Is the mind, the brain, a naive recorder of events with all the properties of an impressionable blank tablet? or does it possess certain inborn, or even developmentally acquired, propensities to organize experience in certain characteristic ways? The answer to such questions nowadays seems obvious. Perception involves conceptual frameworks. One cannot divorce the questing after fact and the search for empirical hypothesis from matters of theory. The significance of theory here is two-fold: one, theory prescribes the conceptual framework for our isolating and classifying facts; and two, it is the source of hypothesis by which we direct our fact-getting, fact-creating activities. Thus in certain important respects theory takes precedence over matters of acquiring data.

This has not always been so. Empiricists such as Francis Bacon and John Stuart Mill were eager to exploit the methods of experiment and induction almost to the exclusion of theory and system building. Nature with all its presumed regularities, its laws, its uniformities was there to be interpreted, at least for those who would use the correct empirical methods. Bacon's *Novum Organum* (like Mill's *System of Logic*) was in large part a book on method in the sciences—one of the first, in fact. Nature was "to be interpreted rather than anticipated," by which Bacon meant the observer was to free himself of preconceptions and anthropomorphisms that would prejudge all of experience. His faith in tools and inductive method was such that he believed all observers, regardless of native ability, could, with sufficiently simple and explicit methods, be equally effective in their inductive efforts. Good method was to prevail

over giftedness and inventiveness. Man's innate propensities, his predilections, his language, his traditions, conspire to deceive him. But, with
good inductive regimen, he could come to apprehend the formal aspects of
nature, those regularities which Bacon assumed for natural phenomena
(cf. N4.1).

But even as Bacon himself intimated, he was "more one to sound
the bugle than to marshal the troops." His own speculations about heat
were unfruitful and he is distinguished more for his ignorance and rejection of his scientific contemporaries than for any appreciation of the
theoretical turn that science must take.

Doubtless there is something refreshing in the absolute reliance that
the naive empiricist places upon experience. We find it in Bacon in his
attacks upon the pretensions of rationalism. We find it again in J. S. Mill
who, in a work ostensibly on logic (*A System of Logic*), was to reaffirm the tenets of naive empiricism against the intrusions of rationalism
and deductivism. Mill's famous methods of experimental inquiry (like
the Baconian method of positive and negative instances) were based on
a quaintly restricted conception of science: nature is uniform, it is lawful, and above all it is causally interrelated so that the propositions,
the language, we use to describe nature is a causal language. This being
the emphasis, there is no occasion to speak of theories. There are hierarchies of laws, to be sure. Thus, at the pinnacle of "the ultimate laws
of causation" would stand those of Newton. Below these are the derived
laws, such as those of Kepler, which, in accordance with the unique
factual coexistencies (sun and planets) of the system, are derivable from
the more inclusive laws. This has the touch of reducibility which we find
to be characteristic of formal theories. But ultimate laws are not theories.
They are not invented, they are not arrived at as an inductive gambit
of some kind; rather, according to Mill, they are to be *discovered* as other
laws are discovered—by the application of methods of experimental inquiry. Mill presents a pure empiricism built upon the presuppositions
of uniformity and lawfulness; but the presuppositions are invested in the
object world, and not in the mind of its perceiving subject. For the
radical empiricist such presuppositions are both important and hazardous.
They involve him in the circularity of inductive support. He must evaluate his presuppositions by the very methods the presuppositions were made
to support.

Be that as it may, Mill's empiricism was inviolate; he held consistently that all hypothesis is fundamentally empirical, that material causation, without any metaphysical implications of efficient causation, is alone
supported by experience, and that "experience cannot offer the smallest
grounds for the necessity of a proposition." The source of all law is empirical generalization.

Mill's empiricism has been found wanting for several reasons; for the circularity of his inductive methods, for his inductivist accounts of logic and the foundations of geometry, and (especially for us) for his treatment of hypothesis in scientific method. It is not that Mill ignored the role of hypothesis; in fact he found it indispensable. Rather, he intimated that all hypothesis was to be of an empirical nature, both as to content and as to origin. One needs hypotheses if he is to apply any of the respected methods of inquiry; he needs hypotheses if he is to derive by ratiocination verifiable consequences of the laws such hypotheses express. However, these hypotheses have a different origin from those which we may incorporate into formal theories. They, themselves, are suggested by experience rather than by the deductive requirements of some formal system. As such, their truth is to be directly affirmed or denied. It is the initial hypothesis itself which is verified and not the propositions derived therefrom. It is this treatment of hypothesis which contemporary empiricists have qualified or denied (cf. N4.2).

HYPOTHETICO-DEDUCTIVE METHOD

In a sense Mill and the inductive empiricists pay lip service to the so-called hypothetico-deductive method of inference. But what they propose is not the same as the method of contemporary theoretical inference. The source of hypothesis was for them a kind of intuitive induction in which experience itself prompts the hypothesis to be tested. The empirical consequences of the hypothesis are more or less direct. One cannot really affirm the consequences of the hypothesis and deny the hypothesis itself. According to the hypothetico-deductive method of contemporary logical empiricism, the situation is quite different. The hypothesis may be constituted of a set of postulates. Then by virtue of rules of inference and correspondence rules one derives hypotheses or propositions the truth of which is an empirical matter. Linguistically, the postulates are statements in the theoretical language. Transformation rules supplement the logical manipulations, such that propositions amenable to interpretation in the observation language are thereby derivable. The postulates themselves may, or, as is quite usual, may not have direct interpretations (translations) in the observation language. "What then," we may ask, "is the truth status of such postulates, of the presumptive hypotheses of the system?" Can we say that they are true or false as Mill would claim for his own hypotheses?

Obviously not. The truth status of an hypothesis that serves as the antecedent in the logical schema of material implication remains indeterminate irrespective of the outcome of an experiment testing the consequent of the hypothesis. The truth of the consequent of the implication is necessary for the truth of the antecedent, but it is not sufficient. Thus every test of a hypothesis is provisional and tentative, in that a hypothesis is tentatively true providing it is not disconfirmed. Yet we are reluctant to claim truth status for the hypothesis other than to attribute to it a *plausibility* residing in its being sufficient to generate derived hypotheses that are not disconfirmed. If we are able to make a clear distinction between presumptive hypotheses which belong to a theory and derived hypotheses which belong to the data language of experiment, then it should be clear that the epistemological status of the two types of hypotheses is quite different. Hence our questions concerning the truth status of theories, of theoretical entities, of crucial experiments, of the ontological necessity of models, and so on.

These questions will come to occupy our attention, but first, a comment on the hypothetico-deductive method in the context of empirical testing. Almost from its inception, experimental methodology, based as it is upon sampling and statistical inference, has acknowledged greater confidence in procedures for rejecting hypotheses than in those for accepting them. John Arbuthnot (1710) gave us what apparently was our first essay in hypothetico-deductive testing (cf. N4.3), but it is Karl Popper, in our own lifetime, who has most keenly analyzed the hypothetico-deductive method as a strategy of disconfirmation (1959). Let us assume a theory T constituted by a body of presumptive hypotheses $P_1, P_2, \ldots, P_n$. By virtue of transformation rules, certain derived hypotheses are obtainable which then by means of correspondence rules are either partially or wholly translatable into observation statements. The derived hypothesis is the experimental hypothesis and is that which is subject to evaluation by our verification or falsification procedures.

We have seen earlier that certain types of propositions (hypotheses) are relatively easy to confirm—for example, existential propositions. Thus, if our hypothesis states what a given subject will do, such as choosing an alternative X over an alternative Y, then a simple observation will attest to the truth or falsity of the hypothesis. But if the hypothesis is a general statement, say an empirical law, then confirmatory evidence from finite sampling is insufficient to establish the truth of the hypothesis. Thus a more conclusive result is obtained with disconfirmatory results, for the falsification of a general hypothesis is not subject to sampling doubts. Appropriately then, we find that the predominant strategy of experimental test is that of the null hypothesis; namely there is no difference between the universe sampled and the value of the corresponding parameter as deduced from some theory (often set up as the foil). If we then can reject the null hypothesis, our results and decision are relatively conclusive; but if we cannot reject the experimental (null) hypothesis, then by virtue of the decision policy of traditional significance tests we must accept the hypothesis. In that case our decision to accept is exposed to double jeopardy. One, it may be subject to sampling errors in which the "confirmatory" results prompt our accepting an hypothesis which may be false. This is a statistical problem, and though an important one, it does not concern us here. But two, a confirmatory experiment resulting in acceptance of the hypothesis, even should it be warranted statistically, only gets us as far as the truth status of the derived hypothesis. So far as the presumptive hypotheses of the theory are concerned, support reaches no further than the pragmatically tacit agreement that hypotheses which generate true results are useful, and, in some sense, justifiable.

Hence the strategy of so-called "deductivism" as against "inductivism." Presumptive hypotheses are justified so long as they lead to confirmed results. If alternative theories, with different sets of presumptive hypotheses, arise to generate the same set of confirmed experimental hypotheses, then the data, as such, are irrelevant to the assessment of the different presumptive hypotheses. The matter of choosing among theories, each leading to the same experimental results, rests on factors such as simplicity of structure, parsimony, comprehensiveness, and reductiveness which, themselves, are not part of the purely empirical activity of science. Looking at deductivism from the vantage of confirmation, then, it would appear that experiment serves to determine whether the given theoretician, with his creative penchant for presumptive hypothesis, should continue along his given direction rather than along another. Experiment tells him when something is amiss, when modifications in the set of postulates are called for, when he should restrict the range of the theory's application. This would be the case in event of negative results. Experiment also tells him when he can continue in the solace that his theory is a "sufficient" generator of interesting hypotheses.

Now this might appear to be a cavalier treatment of the seriousness with which the theoretical scientist takes his work. As a rule, he is not content with the suggestion that a good theory may be little more than a sufficient myth. But to get at this, he must look to the character of his provisional hypothesis rather than alone to the results of an experiment.

If deductivism, or the hypothetico-deductive method, is inconclusive as concerns positive assertions about evidential support of its presumptive hypotheses, it proves inconclusive also in the region of decision wherein presumably lies its strength. Namely, this is the region of disconfirmation. According to Popper, falsification and the criterion of falsifiability are to be defended on the grounds that they are more conclusive than verification and the criterion of verifiability. Doubtless the argument holds for general propositions and at least equally for existential propositions of the form, "the subject will perform the action X and not the action Y on trial K"; that is, an experimental disconfirmation is conclusive if we are concerned with the experimental hypothesis as such. But in the hypothetico-deductive test of the theory and its presumptive hypotheses, the situation is different. We know that experimental confirmation of the derived hypothesis is necessary for the truth of the theory. However, a theory is not a simple proposition. It is a body of presumptive hypotheses $(P_1, P_2,..., P_n)$ such that the falsity of the theory only means that one or more of its conjoint presumptive hypotheses is false. But which hypothesis (or hypotheses) is false, which needs to be modified, augmented, or withdrawn, is not a question that can be answered by the given experiment. As Pierre Duhem (1906) has argued, a theory contains both explicit and implicit assumptions; a disconfirmatory experiment means only that there is error somewhere in the presumptive structure of the theory. In time the theory may undergo modification, such as Hull's theory (1943, 1952) underwent with respect to its treatment of the results of latent learning and exploratory behavior. But the modification is not one made explicitly determinate by the outcome of the initial disconfirmatory experiment. The revision of hypotheses is teased out as the theory itself was teased out, by invention, by trial and error, by anything but the dictates of a logic of discovery (cf. N4.4).

The foregoing is not to argue that the inconclusiveness of experiment in the deductivist schema disqualifies in any substantial way hypothetico-deductive methodology as an instrument of inference and scientific construction. Quite the contrary, formalized theories being what they are, there is no alternative to this methodology. But one should be cautious about overemphasizing the empirics of the experimentalism, both in the constructual and the confirmatory aspects of a theoretical science. It has been sufficient here to point out that the truth status of the postulates and other presumptive hypotheses of a theory is not unequivocally determined by experimental facts. The postulates themselves need not have any direct interpretability in the observation language. Nor need they be a matter of conjecture arrived at by means of an intuitive induction embedded, as it purports to be, in experience.

It is this latter point that distinguishes contemporary hypothetico-deductive method from the deductivism of Mill. There is neither a logic nor an empiric of scientific discovery. Postulates are inventions. Conceived as they may be, as analogy, as inductive hunch, as abstractions to sets of ideal objects, or as uninterpreted variables in abstract calculi, there is no rule, no algorithm, for scientific invention. The Bacon–Mill reliance on intuitive induction wherein the hypothesis has been extrapolated from the complex of experience will not do as an article of systematic investigation.

Much has been made of the absence of any logic of discovery. Both Bacon and Mill would let good methods of inquiry do much of the work of discovery. But both had relatively naive conceptions of science. Neither conceived of a presumptive hypothesis being made independently of facts except as that postulated entity was assumed to be part of a causal complex. The situation in the nearly formalized theories of science is quite different. Initially the presumptive hypothesis may be so abstract or so idealized in its empirical reference that no conceivable defense of the hypothesis can be found on the basis of direct experience. In physics, the kinetic theory of gases assumes dimensionless and perfectly elastic particles of which there is no empirical counterpart. The laws of motion of Newton are purely presumptive, since no demonstration of the laws is possible except in that they lead to verified empirical consequences. In learning theories such as those of Guthrie and Estes, one-trial stimulus–response bonding is assumed although the simple S–R units are for the most part idealizations. But what is more distressing to the pure empiricist is the fact that the structure of the theory may contain postulates that have no ready interpretation at all in the observational language. We are then left with abstract calculi bridging the inferential gulf between antecedent empirical states and derived experimental hypotheses. There may be some argument, as I think there is, for rendering presumptive hypotheses less abstract and more reductive, as it were. But the hypothesis, the invention, determines the search for data as much as data suggest the presumptive hypotheses (cf. N4.5).

In summary, then, deductivism and the hypothetico-deductive method lead us to three somewhat obvious but important conclusions. One, experimental tests are always inconclusive and tentative—they do not confirm the truth of the presumptive hypotheses of a theory, but only attest that such hypotheses could be true. Two, the given experiment, if disconfirmatory, does not indicate precisely what presumptive hypothesis is in error. And three, the source of inventiveness of hypothesis rests in the theoretician. As yet, no device is known for manufacturing scientific discovery, nor does it look as if there ever will be (cf. N4.6).

STRUCTURE OF THEORIES

'Theory' like 'hypothesis' is a term that belongs to the common language, its meanings running from description to explanation, from the abstract to concrete hypotheticals. With the work of N. R. Campbell (1920), however, the term 'theory' in the language of science has come to designate "connected sets of propositions" which serve as the formal basis for the prediction and explanation of phenomena (cf. N4.7). Generally, we are thought to have explained something whenever we can show that it is an instance of a familiar principle. Thus a law may serve as the major premise of a syllogism, or as the material implication in the *modus ponens*. The event in question now being inferred as an instance of the law is then said to be explained by the law. Instantiation of a law, to be sure, presents one level of explanation, but it should be clarified that a lawful explanation is not the same as a theoretic explanation, nor is a law the same as a theory.

Theories, of course, make use of laws, but they are distinguishable from laws, as such, in certain obvious ways. First, a theory embodies propositions, principles, and syntactical structure such that its corpus is sufficient for deriving experimental hypotheses in the form of empirical laws. Thus an experiment suggested by the theory seeks the instantiation of a law. Second, a theory involves presumptive hypotheses (i.e., theoretical constructs), which are not completely interpretable in terms of the observation language. They are the instruments for mediating theoretical inference, and are not subject to verification in the same way existential statements are. Third, a theory pulls together some set of laws. It performs the function of synthesis such that more than one law is inferable from its set of assumptions.

Now these properties of theories are very loosely specified. Theories can vary in their formal refinements, say from the nebulous meteorological speculations on the origin of air mass systems to an axiomatized mechanics, from theories of personality to an axiomatized theory of learning based upon stochastic processes. Yet regardless of their specificity and regardless of their pretensions, all theories aspire to fulfill their purpose as systems of inference—as unequivocal, consistent, and, of course, useful systems for deriving confirmable hypotheses.

One must note initially that formalization of the theory is desirable. This hardly needs saying in the physical sciences. But in the descriptive sciences, i.e., those of macrophenomena such as personology, ethology, etc., the point requires emphasis. Explicit statements of the postulates and correspondence rules of the theory are necessary for ascertaining whether a hypothesis does indeed follow from the presumptive bases of the theory. A postulate or a set of presumptive hypotheses which are ambiguous or which contain contradictions and inconsistencies can result in the derivation of contradictory experimental hypotheses (cf. N4.8).

Consider, for example, classical psychoanalytic theory. The basic concepts of the theory are a mixture of behavioral categories, presumptive hypotheses and interpretive facts. This is as it should be. The difficulty arises in our not spelling out either the classes of response or the logical implications of the postulates with precision sufficient to generate unequivocal hypotheses. Rationalization, compensation, ambivalence, reaction formation: these, to play the pun, are mechanisms that defend against any unequivocal test of the theory. In a sense these mechanisms are behavioral hypotheses. But they are imprecisely specified; they may ramify in such a way that both behavior A and some other behavior belonging to the class not-A are derivable from the same set of postulates. For example, both parental rejection of the child and parental over-protection can be derived from a set of postulates including factors of the id and superego. Thus the theory, as it stands in its loose formulation, may be incapable of disconfirmation (cf. Kaplan, 1961). One or another postulate may perhaps result in an unequivocal inference but together they may combine to generate any hypothesis you please. One visualizes a damping factor operating or an irony-variable, so to speak, such that from some total set of postulates, if behavior A, then one subset of postulates, if behavior B, then another subset of postulates. Together they achieve the irony factor: namely, that if some other behavior than the one predicted occurs, that deviant behavior is perfectly understandable in terms of an appropriately selected subset of postulates. Even Hull's theory, with its laudable aspirations to hypothetico-deductive formalism, has been criticized for being too loosely structured to permit precise and unambiguous deductions of testable theorems (cf. N4.9).

It hardly need be said that in the fields of psychology, theory is both multifarious and inchoate. Doubtless there is some inverse relation between the multiplicity of theories and their state of formal systemization. If one reads books on the theories of learning, the theories of personality, the theories of perception, etc., he finds compilations of relatively crude sets of propositions which are a mixture of speculation and gross generalization but which offer very little in the way of precise theorems deducible from an explicit set of assumptions. On the other end of the scale of hypothetico-deductive refinement is Euclidean geometry, whose axioms and postulates and derived theorems have proved useful in mapping terrestrial space. One, however, does not plead excepting the social or life sciences from the paradigms of scientific method. All theory, as here visualized, is to serve the purpose of generating precise hypotheses within the framework of the hypothetico-deductive method. The formal analysis of such theory is called for regardless of the state of a science. Without its formal structure, what may pass for a theory in a given science is little more than a masquerade.

FORMAL STRUCTURE OF THEORY

One of the earliest of formalized theories in the history of science was that of classical mechanics. From a set of definitions and the laws of motion and gravitation, Newton was able to deduce the laws of planetary motion, the orbit of the moon, the patterns of the tides, and nearly every other phenomena of mechanical significance. By operating in this same framework of classical mechanics and by adding certain postulates about gas particles, perfectly elastic collisions, and random motion of the particles, Boltzmann and Maxwell were able to derive the classical laws of gases, thus extending the system to the range of phenomena covered in thermodynamics. By operating from within the same framework and by adopting the postulate of the constant speed of light and the Lorentz transformation, Einstein was able to derive the adjusted values of variables in a relativistic mechanics. This is an impressive array of intellectual achievements. The formal structure, in principle, is the same for all of the theories involved; and it is the same for all theories in psychology and psychoneurology which serve the function of generating experimental hypotheses.

In his classic work in the philosophy of science, N. R. Campbell (1920) writes: "A theory is a connected set of propositions which are divided into two groups. One group consists of statements about some collection of ideas which are characteristic of the theory; the other group consists of statements of the relation between these ideas and some other ideas of a different nature. The first group will be termed collectively the 'hypothesis' of the theory; the second group the 'dictionary' " (1920, p. 122). To these two groups Campbell added the set of propositions which would constitute the model of the theory. And then later a painstaking analysis by Braithwaite (1953) led to his making an important distinction between the calculus of a theory and its model. Thus, following Campbell and Braithwaite, the aspects of a formalized theory are

(1) *The presumptive hypotheses of the theory:* These constitute the postulates and axioms of the system; sometimes explicitly stated as such, sometimes stated as hypothetical constructs with provisional and instrumental status. A significant feature of the postulates is that their evidential support is usually indirect. There may be barriers of inaccessibility precluding direct evidential support of the hypothetical term; there may be no conceivable evidence in direct support of the term; or "interpretation" of the term may be the progressive gaining of evidential support through subsequent experimentation. In this rest the problems and critique of the theoretical terms. But as a theory is initially contrived, the concern of the theoretician is not so much with the truth of the presumptive hypotheses as it is with the empirical truth of the derived theorems. Only after he has empirical support of the theorems of his theory does he become concerned with the "status" of those hypotheses.

(2) *The syntax and calculus of the system:* Every theory requires a language in which it can be expressed. This is to be taken for granted. A significant feature about this language is the set of transformation rules by which values of one class of variables can be transformed into the values of another class of variables. Thus the calculus of a theory is represented by a set of equations or logical formula specifying operations to be performed on certain variables in the formal (theoretical) language of the theory. Thus for example we might find a theory utilizing a probability calculus or an infinitesimal calculus for continuous variables. As the

calculus stands, it is empty of content. That is, questions of interpretation do not belong to the calculus itself. The only requirement is that it be consistent and otherwise logically rigorous.

(3) *The dictionary of the theory:* Theorems derivable within the calculus of the theory will contain nonlogical, as well as, logical terms. Such nonlogical terms are empirically definable by means of the dictionary of the theory. That is, the terms are translatable into, or are true by virtue of, statements in the observation language. Thus the dictionary is that which ties experimental hypotheses in the theoretical language to their observational implications. Moreover, the dictionary provides the rules by which we assess the truth status of the derived theorems within the empirical context of verification. Terms such as "correspondence rules" (Carnap) and "epistemic correlations" (Northrop and Margenau) have also been used to designate the function of this dictionary.

(4) *A model of a theory:* The first article 'a' in this heading is called for (and not 'the') for two reasons. One, there is conceivably more than one model of a theory or a calculus; and two, it is a question for debate as to whether a model is indispensable to the formation and interpretation of a calculus. A model of a theory is some set of propositions, nonequivalent to the propositions of a calculus, which can be said to interpret that calculus. As a rule, models are of the nature of some material or theoretical analogue; but they need not be. The language of models also includes those "models" that are purely abstract. Families of equations may, for example, constitute a "mathematical model" which in its respective applications functions as an analogue as between two sciences, and which is given different interpretations by virtue of different dictionaries. As we shall see, the question whether models are necessary may be gratuitous. Models, analogues, and scientific metaphors play an all but indispensable role in theoretical invention.

Postulates, calculus, dictionary, and model: these constitute the ingredients of a theoretical system. Axiomatization of the theory does not add anything to the theory as such, it merely provides the metascientific language for a logically rigorous derivation of theorems within the applied calculus. Given some calculus then the calculus and its application can be axiomatized in such a way that all statements within the theory will be logically consistent.

Let us now consider an application of the foregoing schema. Attempts to develop postulate sets within psychology (e.g., Hull, 1943, 1953; Voeks, 1950; MacCorquodale and Meehl, 1953) are too complex and at the same time too crude for our initial purposes. Therefore, let us turn to an extremely simple world of behavior calling for simple theory.

Consider the world and behavior of dice, in which members of the species may or may not be alike. They live in a world, so to speak, having the following ecology. Any one or several of the dice are placed in a cup, shaken, and rolled. The "behavior" of the given die is simply its outcome as designated by the number of spots on the face-up side. We are not concerned with how the dice are picked up, shaken, and thrown; these factors are ignored just as in human behavior we may ignore such background detail as the fact that there is oxygen to be breathed and there is light to make stimulus cues effectively visible. The behavioral data are simply the outcomes as obtained singly or combinatorially for a given trial or for a sequence of trials. There are a number of questions that are of empirical interest. Do the two dice differ? Does one class of outcomes occur more frequently than another? Given certain data, can we make any inferences concerning the character of the dice thrown? In other words, we seek and perhaps expect to find certain regularities. And we can reasonably expect to develop laws and a theory concerning such behavior.

Let us now propose a theory based upon the traditional probability calculus. First, we proceed in purely formal terms, without regard, for the time being, for a complete set of definitions or a dictionary. There are various ways of doing this but let us adopt in abbreviated form a set of postulates and axioms after the fashion of Kolmogorov (1933). First, we define a sample space, such that any possible behavior (outcome) is mapped within the space. Furthermore, subsets of these outcomes can be taken so as to establish an event space over the same domain. Then, by virtue of relatively simple operations within the language of set theory, we can formulate the following set of axioms.

We will call the probability of the event E, $P(E)$; and the probability of E conditionally upon a sampling procedure, $P(E|H)$. Now, without further specification as to the nature of $P(E)$

A1. $P(E) \geq 0$
A2. $P(S) \leq 1$, where S is the domain of all possible events.

From this it follows that

$$0 \leq P(E) \leq 1,$$

since the definition of an event E can include any, all, or none of the outcomes in the sample space.

A3. $P(E_1 + E_2 + \cdots + E_i + \cdots + E_n) = \sum_{1}^{n} P(E_i)$ if the set $\{E_i\}$
      is composed of mutually exclusive classes (i.e., for any two members of the set E_i and E_j, $P(E_i E_j) = 0$).

From these axioms can be derived some basic theorems for the probability calculus.

T1. $P(E) + P(\sim E) = 1$

T2. $P(E \sim E) = 0$, where $\{E \cap \sim E\}$, from which this probability derives, is the null set.

T3. $P(E_1 \cup E_2) = P(E_1) + P(E_2) - P(E_1 E_2)$

What is popularly known as the multiplication theorem in elementary probability theory is not precisely a theorem but arises by way of defining independence with respect to conjoint sets. Thus we may add

A4. $P(E_1 E_2) = P(E_1)\, P(E_2 \mid E_1) = P(E_2)\, P(E_1 \mid E_2)$

As a precautionary note, $P(E)$ is the probability of E without specification as to the domain to be sampled. If sampling conditions are to be imposed upon the sampling domain, this is indicated by the conditional $P(E|C)$ where C is some event, hypothesis, or other factor relevant to a sampling procedure. From this axiom, we can define *independence* as follows.

D1. E_1 and E_2 are independent if $P(E_1 \mid E_2) = P(E_1)$.

In addition, E_1 and E_2 are mutually exclusive if their conjoint set is null. Thus,

D2. E_1 and E_2 are *mutually exclusive* if $P(E_1 E_2) = 0$.

Two other theorems can be deduced from the axioms to complete our probability theory. Letting $p = P(E)$ and $q = P(\sim E)$, we have $(p + q) = 1$ which can be expanded according to the binomial expansion. Thus

T4. $(p + q)^n$

$$= p^n + np^{n-1} q + \cdots + \frac{n!}{r!\,(n-r)!} p^r q^{n-r} + \cdots + q^n = 1.$$

Furthermore, if we assume two probability domains, one of events and the other of sampling domains themselves, we can apply A4 to derive the simplest form of Bayes' theorem. Suppose E is the event, and H is the domain sampled in which H itself belongs to a specifiable probability space. Then substituting in A4 we obtain

$$P(H \mid E) = \frac{P(EH)}{P(E)}$$

$$= \frac{P(H)\, P(E \mid H)}{P(H)\, P(E \mid H) + P(\sim H)\, P(E \mid \sim H)}.$$

The formal theory is complete. But as a theory of behavior of the dice, it must have a dictionary. In fact, as exemplary of our formal schema of a theory, this theory of dice behavior should have a set of postulates, a calculus, a dictionary, and possibly a model. Let us see.

First, the axioms and definitions serve as the postulates of the theory. Some terms are undefined, such as 'occurrence.' Some terms are only formally defined (i.e., by implicit definitions), such as '$P(E)$' itself. At this point, we need not concern ourselves as to whether or not a given die has some property specified by $P(E)$. Second, the corpus of the theory serves as a calculus. Rules of arithmetic are, of course, subsumed, and actual calculations may be expedited by some elementary conventions of combinatorial analysis. Third, and this is the significantly pragmatic feature, a dictionary is derived by translating terms in the theorems into terms in the behavioral language. Then, by the conventions of this dictionary, we can ascertain whether a theorem which is true by virtue of the calculus alone is also true by virtue of true statements in the observation language. And fourth, any random device simulating the behavior of the dice might serve as a model (e.g., a lottery). However, the whole of our probability calculus has served as a model for many behaviors and could as well be designated the formal model of our theory.

We are ready now to apply the theory to the behavior of our dice. What hypotheses might we test? What would be analogous to testing a theoretical construct within the theory? As a presumptive hypothesis concerning the dice let us assume that implicit within the "structure" of each die there is a hypothetical factor which we will call its "random propensity." No structural details are given for this propensity, but it must be so stated in the theoretical language that observable consequences can be derived from it.[1] Some such consequence we designate an empirical hypothesis with respect to $P(E)$. How we derive this hypothesis is actually immaterial. But let us assume some rational of homogeneous structure of a perfect cube such as to give the hypothesis: $P(E_j) = \frac{1}{6}$, where E_j is one of six equally inclusive classes which partition the total event space.

How can we test this hypothesis? It should be obvious that we cannot do so with the observation of a single outcome. Either the event will belong to the class E_j or it will not; and, as some probability theorists have never tired of telling us, singular occurrences are not amenable to quantification or to interpretation in the language of probability. We can, of course, take a sequence of many singular occurrences. This, in fact, is what we do. By the aid of a dictionary it is possible to establish a correspondence between the language of set theory with its sample points and the language of occurrences and events in the behavioral language. An expression of the form $P(E)$ is translatable by the dictionary into a relative frequency of those occurrences having the property of the defining event with respect to the total number of all occurrences. Then according to our procedures for testing hypotheses we confirm or disconfirm our hypothesis on the basis of some prescribed decision policy. What that deci-

---

[1] See K. Popper (1957) for a propensity interpretation of probability.

sion policy is, is for the present immaterial. What we conclude upon our decision is whether or not our theoretical construct is plausible.

There are, of course, other hypotheses we might test. For example, we might test the hypothesis that one die has a greater propensity for one face than for another. We might test the hypothesis that two dice behave independently and randomly, as indeed they are assumed to do for their consort in the game of craps (simple combinatorial analysis is required in the calculus). One could test hypotheses for even–odd preferences (using the binomial theorem). Or, perhaps more interestingly, one might assume that an individual die has moods in which the mood phases themselves are describable as a random variable. Assuming two moods, H and $\sim H$, and the probability distribution of each, and assuming that any given sampling of behavior is obtained under the same mood, then Bayes' theorem could be utilized for testing hypotheses about which mood is assumed to prevail at the time of sampling. Details of such tests need not be spelled out, although it would be a simple matter to do so. It is apparent from our theory that experimental hypotheses can be deduced against which actual behavioral tests can be made. What is interesting is the fact that we endow our behavioral objects with properties and dispositions not directly observable. Experimental hypothesis as elucidated within the formal framework of the theory gives us what vision we have of the theoretical constructs. Such vision is, of course, greatly restricted. If we would see the construct in some existential detail, presuming there is such detail, then we would have to probe the structure of the theory itself so as to implement a dictionary for the theoretical term under surveillance.

Aside from the system of axioms, the one theoretical construct upon which our theory rests is that of $P(E)$. Various terms and phrases have been used to describe it, e.g., 'propensities', 'dispositions', 'randomness', or just plain 'probability'. These uses have dispositional implications, such that if $P(E) = k$ then certain behaviors are expected. Indeed, we could define $P(E)$ in such a way that we would say $P(E) = k$ if, and only if, the relative frequency of E to all events out of n trials is exactly k. We would then have an explicit reduction of $P(E)$. That, however, is not quite how we used the theoretical construct in our theory. For one thing $P(E)$ could be equal to some real number, k, where $0 \leq k \leq 1$, and the actual relative frequency of E in n trials be some number other than k. That is to say, we expect sampling error. The relative frequency of E in actual experiment could very well be $k + \epsilon$, where ϵ is reasonably small, we would still accept that experimental result as support of our behavioral hypothesis generated by $P(E)$. For another thing, there is an objection here to defining $P(E)$ as an explicit reduction to a finite set of trials in the history of the die. That is not what we mean when we set up the hypothesis $P(E)$, for the hypothesis is prior to any trials. It is an expectation, as it were, not a result. Finally, one can be quite unclear about the meaning of $P(E)$, as such, except that for every purportedly meaningful theorem of the theory there is a translation into the behavioral language. Thus $P(E)$ could be nothing more than a pragmatic gimmick.

Although our example here is somewhat trivial, it demonstrates quite clearly the quandaries that might arise about the meaning of our theoretical terms. All that we require of our postulates is that they have testable consequences. Should they have such consequences and should the experimental hypotheses stating these consequences be confirmed, then we more or less cautiously conclude that the postulates, the theoretical constructs, are plausible.

Still, we are inclined to look for more than a cautious predication of plausibility. What is it that is plausible? Does $P(E)$ have some kind of existential status? Is it a fiction? Is it pure invention? Is it a convention? Is it an inferential crutch? From such questions one can glean four different theses as concerns the nature of theoretical constructs.

(1) The theoretical construct is a real entity. By this is meant that it is directly translatable into the observation language. Its name may designate a real object, however hidden that object may be from initial observation.

(2) The theoretical construct is a logical construction. By this is meant that it is translatable into the observational language in which the translation indicates a set of logical operations performed on a finite set of particulars. There is no thing, as such, to which the theoretical term refers—only a set of things entering into certain completely specified logical operations.

(3) The theoretical construct is a convention. As such, it has no existential status. It can be a fictional entity, a contrivance, an abstraction without exemplification. It could even turn out to be descriptive of something that is real. As a convention, however, it is a device, a component of a deductive system without existential pretensions.

(4) The theoretical construct may be an incompletely specified postulate of real entities. As such it is translatable into an incomplete set of observational consequences. These specified observational consequences are the minimal set of conditions necessary to the truth of the construct. However, the construct has an open texture. In the surplus or as yet unspecified properties inherent in the construct, we find room to include the possibility of additional consequences. Thus the construct has a potential for ramification which it would not have if it were a convention or an explicitly definable logical construct.

For psychology the place to debate the nature of theoretical constructs is in the context of reductionism (Chapters 6 and 7). However, a few points should be noted. Alternative (1) above can be easily dismissed. If the theoretical construct is a hypothesis about some potential (as yet unconfirmed) real, then it serves merely as a place holder for eventual exemplification. One might say that under alternative (4), the surplus meaning view, we aspire to eventual reification of the construct. We act as if alternative (1) indicates the ontological status toward which theoretical terms move. But we cannot hold such terms as designating real states, for the evidences (even the indirect evidences) are as yet incomplete. There have been cases in the history of science where theoretical constructs that were initially hunches led eventually to their own reification under observational refinement (e.g., the case of genetic determiners, or of some types of viruses). To the extent we hope to achieve the progressive transformation of theoretical constructs from their status under (4) to their status under (1), we are interested in transforming all science into descriptive science (a position held by Mach).

The best place to examine the conventional character of theoretical constructs is in the section on models which follows. This leaves alternative (2). It will be argued in Chapter 7 that explicit definition of theoretical constructs removes such constructs from the domain of legitimate theory. An "explicit definition" is given for the purported theoretical construct if we can substitute for that term an explicit set of observational terms combined by means of a completely specified set of logical operations. Thus should one choose, he could define $P(E)$ explicitly as the logical operation of relative frequency (i.e., $P_f(E) = (\Sigma X/N)$ where $X = 0,1$ according to observation) over a finite number, N, of trials. But then, from the point of view of theory, the theoretical construct would be a tautology derived from its own extension over the set of observations. In effect: if H then $P_f(E)$; but since $H = P_f(E)$, then if $P_f(E)$ then $P_f(E)$. That is to say, such theoretical terms (logical constructs) may be useful in the observation language (e.g., in the refinement of law, as argued in Chapter 7); but they can only serve in a trivial way as instruments of inference. This is the argument of intervening variables as against hypothetical constructs (cf. N4.10) and the issues can be summarized briefly as follows: If the theoretical term is to be given an explicit definition in the observation language and is to enter into the interpreted calculus of the theory, then the only hypotheses deducible from it in the language of the dictionary will be the logical consequences of its own set of observation statements. On the basis of a theory whose only postulates are intervening variables one will not get interesting hypotheses. Only by combining the intervening variable with other theoretical constructs that are not so extensionally limited, or by opening the texture of the intervening variable's own extension, as, for example, by analogy, will the theory generate experimental hypotheses that are not trivially evident within the presuppositions of the theory (cf. N4.11).

MODELS

As philosophers of science have reached considerable agreement concerning the formal nature of theory and the ideal of hypothetico-deductive methodology, they have turned their attention increasingly to the problems of models and theories. The essential question is: Does a theory that incorporates an abstract calculus as the skeleton of its formal structure require an interpretation of that calculus in a language different from the calculus itself? Is a model indispensable to the utilization of a calculus within the theory? It would appear that the answer to both of these questions is "No, models are not indispensable." However, the debate that has occurred has stemmed, one, from a lack of agreement concerning the nature of a model, and two, from a mixing of logical problems in scientific inference with psychological problems of scientific inventiveness.

That the answer to our question appears to be "No" follows, by example from an analysis of the simple theory of dice behavior given in the preceding section. The calculus of probability as formally stated is purely abstract. The probability variable $P(E)$ is undefined except within the abstract system of real numbers. The theorems of the formal system are uninterpreted as they stand in the initial calculus. Utilization of the calculus in the theory of the dice occurs by means of our constructing a dictionary by which the theorem can be translated into our expectations concerning the frequencies of observable events. Or, with respect to state variables, certain operational conventions may be adopted for assigning values to P within the range allowed by the relevant axioms of the calculus. But the calculus can be used without our conceiving any model for the variables of the calculus. Although, conceivably, one might make an *a priori* assignment to P on the basis of the classical procedures of enumerating equally likely classes of outcomes, this is merely a convention (i.e., an arbitrary procedure, not at all entailed by the logic of the calculus) for assigning one value rather than another to the parameter P. Moreover, the calculus is indifferent, as it were, to our dictionaries. No model is required for the point-by-point elaboration of its theorems. The usefulness of the calculus is decidable on grounds of its serving as the basis of inferring verifiable hypotheses. Decidable, yes, but perhaps not alone decidable on such grounds. And that is where the utility of models enters the picture.

First, however, we must backtrack and pick up the argument with the discussion concerning the meaning of 'model' as it is used in the philosophy of science. Likely we are all prepared to accept the distinction between the model and thing modeled. That much is apparent. However, some models are much like the thing modeled, whereas other models are quite unlike the thing modeled in that they either are fictional or are logically abstract. Beginning with replicas at one extreme, we ascend the scale of abstraction from scale representations to conventions and on to abstract calculi themselves. When does a model cease to be a model? At the one extreme, that of the replica, the model converges on the object of theory itself; it may become a "true" description of that object. At the other extreme, the abstract treatment of a model may turn it into a calculus itself, so that the point of differentiation between a calculus and a model seems to be lost. This latter point is the source of some confusion in the argument for the indispensability of models.

Types of Models

For the present discussion a distinction is made between *formal* models and *structural* models.[2] Questions of the realism of models are in the background but it is apparent that so far as formal models are concerned, the language of realism, if used at all, will have esoteric overtones not to be found in the realism of palpable structures. The logician tends to define a *formal* model as that by which any set of valid sentences of a theory are satisfied or represented by another set of entities which are the realization of the theory (Tarski, 1941; Suppes, 1957). As it stands this definition is somewhat remote from the actual models that scientists deal with. Two features, however, serve to bring out its specific applicabilities. One, there is a set of valid sentences of the theory in a language that is partly theoretical and partly observational (at the dictionary ties). Two, there is also a set of entities, such as those of set theory, in which the formal relations of the theory can be realized. It is the model that interprets the calculus, and the fact that one realization or model of the valid theorems of a theory can be achieved does not preclude the possibility of alternative realizations. The logician has one thing in mind when he seeks a model of a theory. For him a theory is a system. He wants to know if he can build a model for the theory such that every theorem of the model is isomorphic to a theorem in the theory. He seeks complete representation of one system, the theory, by another system, the model.

As remote as some discussions of logical models may be from the subject of concrete models, their relevance should not escape the theoretical scientist. For if he takes his own models seriously and holds out for them on the grounds of say their simplicity or their microreductive potential, he must be sure that his model, as rigorously expressed, does in fact satisfy the requirements of isomorphic representation.

[2] This is a simplification for expository purposes only. There is a fairly large literature in which problems of classifying models are touched upon. See for example, Hesse (1953, 1961, 1963); Gregory (1953); Hutten (1954); Apostel (1960); Suppes (1960); Lachman (1960); Beament (1960); Black (1962); Kaplan (1964); Rosenbleuth and Wiener (1945); Braithwaite (1962).

There is, however, a more obtrusive feature of formal models. This is the fact that the set of entities of the model need have no specific interpretability in the observation language. That is to say, theoretical terms in the theory when represented in the model may have no meaning other than that which they possess by virtue of their being parts of the abstract system. One notes, for example, that a model of the probability calculus may be purely abstract, as indeed it is in its axiomatization. And in some mathematical learning models, no effort is made to interpret in empirical or even familiar construct language the algebraic form of the models (Bush and Mosteller, 1955; Luce, 1959). The structure of the model is logical structure made explicit by a careful statement of the theory. Aside from its representation of valid experimental hypotheses, it stands aloof, as it were, from such mundane intermediating processes as might concern the neurophysiologist.

Presumably any rigorous theory can be axiomatized. It can be given a formal model which may or may not be anchored to statements in the observation language at various stages of some process function. Mediating process is, of course, not precluded from the formal model. However, the insistence that formal models are only concerned with representing valid theorems of a theory seems to license the theoretician to adopt any logical conventions he may find to be useful. Consequently, he may ignore mediating process where, so far as a traditional learning theory is concerned, the reduction of mediating variables is purely speculative. At least so far as the neuropsychologist is concerned, this may have certain heuristic disadvantages. The question of inventiveness becomes foremost; and it is by no means clear that a theoretician who is concerned primarily with rigorous formalization can continue to create and embellish upon scientifically interesting theories (Restle, 1959).

By *structural* models, I mean those models whose entities in some sense are more palpable than those we find in formal models. Two initial comments are in order. First, the fact that a model may possess palpable structure does not preclude its being axiomatized and formalized within a representative abstract model. Second, the meaning of structure is by no means preempted by its reference to palpable objects. Geometry and Boolean algebra possess structure, so to speak. It is the business of the logician to show just what structure various calculi have. Still this does not obviate the fact that some models are interpretable in other than abstract terms. A structural model, therefore, is taken to be one such that not only is it a realization of a theory, but the realization is such that some of its nonlogical terms are interpretable in an existential medium *different from that of the thing modeled.* By "existential medium" I mean some uniquely classified domain of predicates in the observation language. Thus for any abstract calculus of a structural model, if the model is well represented by that calculus, there are some variables whose values are determined by operational conventions. In the language of palpability, a structural model is something we can build, visualize, construct, put on paper, etc. Even though unconstructed in fact, the ultimate realization of such models entails a familiar space–time context. The problem of analogy, of course, remains open. One might have a mechanical analogue, say, of muscle action; it would be a structural model of the muscle but with limited analogy (cf. N4.12).

Most models in psychological theory, I think it is safe to say, are of a structural type. A formal model requires systematic axiomatization and successful efforts along this line are quite rare (Bush and Mosteller, 1955; Estes and Suppes, 1959; Luce, 1959; Fitch and Barry, 1950). In this context what one notes is not so much whether the theoretician has achieved a fully representative formalization in his abstract model but whether or not he wishes to remain aloof from giving an interpretation of the nonlogical variables of the system. It is interesting too that formal models have been achieved primarily (though not exclusively) in the area of statistical learning theory. Stochastic models and the probability calculus are particularly amenable to formalization. However, they need not be purely formal. There have been many efforts to build structural models that effect the random processes and behaviors describable in probabilistic language. For example, in the area of neurophysiological theory, we find structural models for random functions presented by Marshall and Talbot, 1942; Osgood and Heyer, 1951; Eccles, 1953; Pitts and McCulloch, 1947; Hebb, 1949; Milner, 1957; Rosenblatt, 1958.

Cybernetic models. The subject of cybernetics, even as it is applied to psychology, is far too extensive to give it more than passing attention. Still, its emphasis upon functional units, feedback, and schematic functionalistic diagrams renders it especially relevant to the model-making enterprises of the behavioral scientist. The details of cybernetics belong to the communications engineer. We shall not be concerned with these. However, the method and analysis of the new discipline are quite relevant to problems of both modeling and scientific inference.

Norbert Wiener, who along with his colleagues is credited with inducing the birth and with christening the new science, defines cybernetics simply as "the entire field of control and communication theory, whether in the machine or in the animal" (1948, p. 19). This is a broad definition but the approach of the new science was at the time quite unique. Relying heavily on the principle of feedback, cyberneticists were able to lay down complex schemes of function which were descriptive both of physical and biological systems of communications and control. So far as the physical systems were concerned, the components implementing a system could be clearly identified and classified. In biology, however, only partial information was available; but by virtue of impressive analogy, cybernetics served as means both of description and hypothesis concerning certain biological processes.

The schematics of cybernetics are simply an elaboration on the old black-box principle. If no simple laws are ascertainable as between input and output or as between stimulus and response, and if interposed between the observables there are mediating complications, then it is convenient to introduce the black-box analogue. Thus Woodworth, in his remarkably successful textbook (1922), interjected the organism, O, between stimulus and response as a catchall processing center for all those factors that make S–R psychology a more complicated discipline than pure reflexology (cf. N4.13). As such, however, the black-box is a mere substitute for the enclosed brackets of ignorance. Certain functional relations may be implemented by the black-box but details as to mechanics, process, and structure are missing. Thus, the brain has suffered both the eminence and the indignity of being a black-box. Early ablation studies undertook the partition of the big black-box into smaller black-boxes, leaving mechanics and process untouched but adding a little to our knowledge of function and structure.

It should be noted, however, that black-box schemata are not quite the same as those of cybernetics. Black-boxes are, in logical terms, place holders; they are the guarded lacunae to be filled in by future generations. Cybernetics schemata, on the other hand, are structural and functional hypotheses which model the internal details of the boxes. In fact, the black-box itself must be partitioned according to the cybernetics hypothesis. The case here is trenchantly presented in a paper by Mario Bunge (1963). According to him, "a general black-box theory" enables one to describe mathematical functions as between input and output for crudely classified systems; but it does not give interesting results so far as scientific (i.e., theoretical) inference is concerned. Black-box theory is a kind of crude phenomenology; it states gross functional relations without elucidating any system for deducing hypotheses about those relations.

As compared with black-boxes, then, the distinguishing feature about the cybernetics model is that it partitions a behavioral system into meaningful functional units, the meaning of each unit being some explicit hypothesis as to how that function is achieved. Thus, for example, a system may require a memory unit. With the specification of the unit, one can prescribe certain mechanisms or hardware sufficient to effect the kind of storage the system seems to have. Furthermore, the application of cybernetics exemplifies a pragmatic rather than ontological approach to modeling. Although cyberneticists such as McCulloch and Pitts may be interested in constructing models of the nervous system with an optimal amount of positive analogy, the preliminary work entails constructing alternative systems that will achieve the types of function under study. A memory system, for example, can be implemented by IBM cards, magnetic tapes, magnetic drums, mercury cells, program panels, etc.; but when modeling the memory of the nervous system certain of these schemata can obviously be eliminated. Our anatomical knowledge of the nervous system might favor reverberatory circuitry, or permanent impress either on the circuitry or cellular structure itself (Gaito and Zavala, 1964) (cf. N4.14).

Generally then the difference between black-box modeling and cybernetics is one of functional detail. But that difference is a significant one. Where black-box analysis simply indicates the presence of a mediating process or unspecified structure, cybernetics makes a functional analysis of mediating components such as to propose various structures sufficient to effect such functions. As Gregory has pointed out (1961), black-box schemata, at their very highest degree of refinement, are blue prints from which a mere technician might produce a structure of given black-box components; but such schemata have no explanatory power. They contain no hypotheses as to how the components work. A cybernetics model, on the other hand, being concerned with the structures and functional details of the components and even with the design of components, serves as an explanatory basis of control systems. Gregory continues in a Cambridge tradition largely instigated by Kenneth Craik (cf. N4.15); namely, the structural and functional properties of systems are inseparable, and though there may be major differences between metallic and colloidal components, the analogy in function between inorganic and organic systems is sufficient for us to utilize cybernetics as the basis for at least lower level explanation. Gregory finds that both functional analogues and the language of physical control systems (e.g., criteria of efficiency) are useful in generating hypotheses concerning organic behavioral systems.

Perhaps the most poignant feature of his argument is to be found in a critique of ablation studies. There are several points to this critique which are worth noting. First, ablation studies are designed essentially for making black-box identifications. Impairment of behavior after ablation leads to isolating some component of neural tissue as being apparently indispensable to normal functioning of the organism. However, the level of explanation is quite primitive—like indicating the removal of some tube in a television set as the cause of certain aberrations of the picture. Second, disturbance of a system occasioned by ablation may have indirect effects not traceable by tissue removal alone. For example, if the system is not a simple telephonic network, mass removal of a cell complex may affect functioning of some cells which under normal circumstances are more or less independent of the ablated cells. In general, understanding of the functioning of complex redundancy systems, such as the central nervous system appears to be, is not likely to be achieved by means of ablation intrusions. And third, and perhaps most important, neurophysiology needs theoretical models to define and specify what it is we are to look for in the way of structural detail. Without hypotheses the search is restricted to crude classification of anatomical detail. Cybernetics hypotheses as to memory function, attentional scansion, recognition, and perceptual invariance suggest the possibility of neural networks and systemic interactions that very likely would remain obscure without that theoretical guidance. Here Gregory touches upon a now familiar adage: theory guides discovery, and not vice versa (cf. N4.16).

Truth status of models.   We have seen earlier that the terms 'true' and 'false' can be applied to theorems of a theory but not to the theory itself. Is the situation any different for models? According to empiricistic conventions (and the thesis of extensionality) truth values can be assigned to propositions which reduce to statements of observable states of affairs. A model would then be a true model if all of its assertions were true. But models are models of things. If we take the "thing" to be a theory, then the model of it could only be true if every nonlogical assertion in the model were true by virtue of its being a correct empirical assertion. In that case the theory and its isomorphic model would become a true description of the phenomena which are the subject matter of the science. Should we choose to call the thing modeled "the phenomena of the given science," then the model itself may be a theory of the data. And if every nonlogical assertion of the model is true, then just as above, the model again becomes a true description of the thing modeled—so the argument would appear to go (cf. N4.17).

Now there are three features of the discussions of models which militate against so restricted a treatment as is given in the preceding paragraph. One, in the open discussion of models, we have to include relatively abstract systems of postulates, axioms, and transformation rules, as well as the potentially concrete artifacts we usually think of as being appropriately named by 'model'. Two, in light of alternative models for the same theory, such models may possess a conventional character in which the truth status of nonlogical terms is indeterminate. And three, it may not be our intention that a model be a replica of the thing modeled. We may intend only that it be an entity with sufficient positive analogy that we can understand and predict the phenomena to which that model is applied. This touches upon the metaphorical aspects of models. Let us briefly consider each of these points.

A set of statements which describes the terms, operations, and range of application of some calculus may serve as the model of a theory. This would include for the most part what a logician construes as the model of a system. The essential feature of such a model is that it be isomorphic with the thing modeled. That is to say, that for every statement in the theory there is a statement in the model such that every theorem in the theory is derivable within the model.[3] As an example, we might again take some model utilizing the probability calculus in its logical structure. Since the nonlogical terms of the calculus remain uninterpreted within the model itself, it would be quite irrelevant then to ask whether such terms were subject to truth analysis. In the astronomy of antiquity one might indeed have used the geometric models of the epicycle and eccentrics for generating theorems of planetary position without visualizing as matters of fact any of the myriad of motions which the geometric entities suggest. The only motion that is describable or representable so far as factual access is concerned may be that of the apparent planetary positions; thus, only hypotheses about such positions are subject to verification. In stochastic learning theories, θ, the parameter sometimes designated as the rate of learning, may be just such an abstract entity. As such it designates no object, but its place in the formal model results ultimately in statements which by means of a dictionary can be tied to experiment. Is θ true? To be sure, since θ is a parameter, one estimate of θ might be better than another in that it generates truer hypotheses about behavior. Still it makes little sense to state that the confirmed hypothesis makes θ true, not even if the statement in the model which is isomorphic to the true hypothesis necessitates θ being some specific value. Or to put it another way, the only recourse we have to making θ true is to show that the true hypothesis can be generated by the model incorporating θ, and *only by that model*. Such a condition would be realized only if all models were true descriptions of things in the sense of N4.17.

The second point follows on the first. If models are conventions and mere instruments of prediction, then no part of the model, no nonlogical term, carries with it existential pretensions—or if you choose, it carries with it *only* existential *pretensions*. There is no intention of making the models a true and exhaustive description of phenomena (cf. N4.18).

The third point asserts that it may not be our intention that a model be a replica of the thing modeled. In that case it would be irrelevant to ask of the model if it is true. Rather at most we should say of a model that it is more or less true. That is, it is true to the extent of its positive analogy, it is false to the extent of its negative analogy. But by being more or less true, it is neither. The language of truth or falsity is applicable only as a manner of speaking. What makes a model a metaphor (Black, 1962) is that it possesses some negative analogy. It is like the thing modeled, but not exactly. Some aspects of the model are thought inapplicable; they are either suppressed or idealized. Thus a gas can be thought of as a volume of perfectly elastic particles behaving much like,

---

[3] Pains are not taken here to bring in the fine distinctions between set theoretic, algebraic, and other abstract models; or between isomorphic and homomorphic relations. The reader is referred to Apostel (1960) for a general discussion and to Suppes (1957), Chapter 7, for a more technical discussion of these matters.

but not quite like, billiard balls. The negative analogy that tells the lie rests in the fact that particles of some finite mass have internal structure that contaminates the ideal of perfect momentum exchange. The psychology of tension systems and psychic energy is, of course, loaded with negative analogy. The model of the psychoanalytic energy system with its pipes, reservoirs, and overflow spouts (Hendrick, 1934) is hardly to be taken seriously at all. Yet energy systems, principles of least effort (e.g., Zipf, 1949) and other paraphernalia of mechanics seem to be such useful expository devices that we succumb to the enchantment of the metaphor and begin to reify what initially serves as a crutch for establishing certain crude descriptive categories.

The point is well stated by Hinde (1960) in an article titled "The Energy Model of Motivation." He reviews motivation models of Tinbergen, McDougall, Lorenz, Freud, and J. S. Brown, only to find that motivational energies do not systematically exploit the analogy to physical energy systems. 'Energizing' appears to be an appropriate term for describing behavior onset and activation; analogy comes to us so easily. Still even for those who seek physiological foundations of motivation (e.g., Tinbergen and McDougall), the energy manifestations of behavioral onset are only roughly analogous to energy transformations in physics. First of all, there is a confusion between behavioral and physical energy systems. One can speak of behavioral energies in a metaphorical sense, but he cannot make point for point identifications wherein the repositories of behavioral energy are also repositories of physical energy and where both satisfy conservation principles. A precise dictionary for translating the behavioral energy language into the physical energy language does not as yet exist. Secondly, one cannot use physical energy analogy (other than as expository metaphor) and *not* embrace a reductionist view of theoretical constructs. Physical energy is a very real thing, as close to ontological basics as we are likely to get. There is an element of insincerity in our holding to closed or open physical energy systems while playfully inserting "as if" constructs to mediate behavior. Hinde holds that MacCorquodale and Meehl are correct in their calling for neurophysiological reduction of hypothetical constructs. Thirdly, the analogues of energy storage and dissipation can be quite misleading when applied to behavioral science. The concept of energy level is inapplicable to behavioral analysis; where some behaviors conserve energy, others seek actively to dissipate it. A system that needs stimulation and energy dissipation more than it needs equilibrium or conservation (e.g., Heron, 1957) is hard to match against simple physical systems. The moral is, of course, that analogy, i.e., negative analogy, can be quite misleading if the person takes a model as a replica of the phenomenal system.

Let me now reiterate the foregoing argument. A model is to be judged by its positive analogy. To the extent there is negative analogy then some hypotheses as derived from the model are not true for the thing modeled. Models, therefore, are potentiaily misleading and corruptive. But lest one takes this as the salient lesson of modeling, he should hasten to note that models are also effective heuristic instruments. In terms of the conceptual framework, models enter into our apprehension and interpretation of facts. We bring positive analogy to focus upon the phenomenal flux. Both our classification and our understanding of phenomena are contingent upon analogy, upon what Pepper (1948) calls the "root metaphors" and what Black (1962) calls "conceptual archetypes."

Are models indispensable?   "Yes!" say Campbell (1920), Hesse (1963), and Suppes (1962). "No!" say Duhem (1914) and Braithwaite (1953). "Helpful!" say Black (1962) and Nagel (1961). Even when these people agree, they come to their answers for different reasons. Let us briefly inspect their arguments. Consider the no's first. Duhem (1914) argues that all theories are essentially conventional so far as concerns their theoretical terms (cf. N9.19). Any effort to interpret these terms either existentially or as material analogues smacks of unwarranted metaphysics. Models will be misleading in that they suggest hypotheses not testable within the body of experimental theorems of the theory. Rigor in scientific thinking is achieved by attending to the derivation of testable hypotheses and not by postulating palpable entities presumed to be like those found in our concrete experience. He does not, however, disdain analogy. "The history of physics shows us that the search for analogies between two distinct categories of phenomena has perhaps been the surest and most fruitful method of all the procedures put in play in the construction of physical theories" (1914, p. 95). But analogies should not be confused with models.

> Analogies consist in bringing together two abstract systems; either one of them already known serves to help us guess the form of the other not yet known, or both being formulated, they clarify each other. There is nothing here that can astonish the most rigorous logician, but there is nothing either which recalls the procedures dear to ample but shallow minds, nothing which substitutes the use of imagination for the use of reason, nothing which rejects the logically conducted understanding of abstract notions and general judgments in order to replace it with a vision of concrete collections (1914, p. 97).

Braithwaite (1953, 1962), with his characteristic rigor in argument, gives a somewhat similar answer.[4] Both the theory and the model of the theory are interpretations of the same calculus. For the theory, the

---

[4] If one savors an irony here of the ample, empirically minded Englishman beating the rationalist Frenchman at his own game, he should not be too hasty. Symbolic algebras (such as the Huntington calculus which Braithwaite uses) belong to the spirit of the ample mind with its penchant for extensive classification.

derived formula, the laws, and empirical hypotheses are epistemologically prior to the theoretical terms, whereas for the model the theoretical terms are epistemologically prior. One cannot, therefore, claim that models are indispensable either to an interpretation of a calculus or to the development of a theory. Under some circumstances the positive analogy of a model can be heuristically fruitful but the factor of negative analogy can be as detrimental as the positive analogy can be productive. "The price of the employment of models is eternal vigilance" (1953, p. 93). It is, however, important to emphasize that a theory and its calculus can be uninterpreted so far as concerns the theoretical terms. The essential character of such terms is that they be open-textured and amenable to such modification as will enhance the explanatory and predictive possibilities of the theory.

One would think that an affirmative answer to the question posed in this section would indicate a point of view which is discrepant in some fundamental way from that of Duhem and Braithwaite. This, however, does not seem to be the case. If anything, what is at stake is the role that analogy and the reliance on palpable analogues plays in the psychology of invention. Suppes (1962), for example, renders models indispensable to theory by virtue of his making any systematic corpus of mathematical propositions or calculus a possible model of a theory. Any clear statement of the deductive system in the metascientific language of logic should satisfy the set-theoretic requirements of a model. Fundamental distinctions between mathematical models and formalized theories are not required. Therefore, a model, whether mathematical or physical, is essential to the theory. Moreover, a good physical theory will be well formalized and thus amenable to the axiomatization of so-called mathematical models.

In a series of publications, Hesse (1953, 1961, 1963) has argued for the indispensability of models on the grounds that without them extension of a theory would be impossible. The essential feature for the growth of any theory and for its extension is the positive analogy implicit within its model. Still what looks like a call for the kinds of models Duhem disdains turns into a qualified retreat. For by models, Hesse means to include such formal models as we claim for any systematic body of uninterpreted equations. The positive analogy rests in the fact that an interpretation of a theoretical construct in one science suggests an analogous interpretation of the nonlogical terms of the calculus when that calculus is applied to another science. But here the model can actually be the formal body of mathematical equations that are interpretable both in the fundamental science and in the analogue. Thus, for example, both the theory of heat and the theory of electrostatics utilize the same mathematical equations with, of course, their respectively different dictionaries. One theory with its interpreted calculus serves as the model for the other, the positive analogy being implemented through interpretation of those terms in the calculus which are common to the theory and its model. When Hesse argues for the logical necessity of models, she is not merely exploiting the role models play in the psychology of invention. She asserts that deductive structure is the *sine qua non* of a theory. Selection of an appropriate calculus is a matter of analogy. One calculus, with its formal components and interpretation in one theory, is selected over another calculus because of an analogy which makes it congenial to interpretation in the other science. In general, Hesse argues from the vantage of heuristics. New hypotheses, insights, and theoretical inventions come to us by virtue of the logic of analogy as implicit within the creative process.

Campbell's yes to the indispensability of models remains one of the most defensible answers to the question. Writing of analogy rather than models, as such, he argues not that analogues are heuristic devices or are mere instruments of invention but that they are essential to explicating the meaning of the theory itself. Anyone can invent a theory, i.e., a formal calculus by which he can deduce an established law. However, a theory without an analogy is meaningless (cf. N4.20). It may be true that a theory without analogy would lack heuristic potential but this is not the point. (We could as well argue that as often as not a person may be misled by what materializes in the model as negative analogy.) What is more significant is the fact that a theory would have no epistemological anchorage, no reference, no semantical overtones of any kind, if in fact it were uninterpretable by grace of an analogy. The analogy of a theory is epistemologically prior to the hypotheses and constructs of the theory itself. Thus not only are laws explained within the deductive framework of the theory but the analogy, by means of this priority, serves to explain why events should conform to the laws of the theory (e.g., see Sellars, 1961).

It would appear from these and other accounts of models (e.g., Black, 1962; Hutten, 1951, 1954; Nagel, 1961) that there are no fundamental differences of opinion concerning the need for a logical calculus of some kind in the development and application of a theory. Moreover, it also seems obvious that the purely formal part of a theory need not be interpreted; it need not be modeled in the physicalistic senses of modeling. For example, certain mathematical models in psychology and economics (Braithwaite, 1962) and some formal models in microphysics (Dirac, 1947) cannot be interpreted as a logical blueprint for any empirical process. Still what makes models real to people and what removes them from the domain of abstract contrivances ("for calculational purposes only") are their heuristic and semantic functions. Whether models are explicitly interpretable and convergent upon real descriptions or whether they remain abstract calculi is relatively unimportant so long as they perform the function of explicating the meaning of a theory. This they do by virtue of their analogy.

Semantic functions of models.   We should now examine more closely the semantic functions of a model and its analogy. If both formal and phenomenological analogy are allowed then the semantic functions that a model performs will be different according to whether a model is structural and phenomenological or whether it is primarily formal. Consider first the case of structural models. There is little difficulty in stating what one means by their fulfilling a semantic function. The theory and its model indicate to us that certain laws of physics, behavior, etc., are derivable by a set of postulates, theoretical constructs, or explicit mechanisms epistemologically more basic than the understanding of simple lawful descriptions. It is not just that our analogy suggests that this set of phenomena is like another set of phenomena by virtue of some similarity but that the analogy imparts an understanding of one set of phenomena on the basis of an understanding of another set of phenomena. Assume some abstract model M for a science and its theory T_1. Assume another science and theory T_2 also utilizing most of M. The application of M to T_1 is epistemologically prior to its application by analogy to T_2. What is the source now of that analogy? One cannot say that it is due to the fact that T_2 and T_1 have the same inherent logical structure, for as empiricists have persistently pointed out (e.g., Hume, *Treatise;* Duhem, 1914; Toulmin, 1953) logical relations are not properties intrinsic to physical objects. The source of the analogy is very likely perceptual. One sees positive analogy as between the phenomena of one science, for which T_1 holds, and the phenomena of the other science, for which T_2 holds. Because of the analogy, M (the language of formal inference and the postulates it includes) which is useful in deriving theorems within T_1 is also thought to be useful in deriving valid theorems in T_2. When one observes waves in a liquid medium, and then observes elementary beat phenomena in an acoustics laboratory, he does not see the fundamental wave equations as properties of the two sets of phenomena. Rather the phenomenological analogy is the source of his using the model as a common language for representing two different domains of experience. In bombarding gold leaf with a stream of particles and observing the effects, Rutherford could literally see the structure of the gold leaf as a set of minimally occupied orbital systems each analogous to a solar system. The model of celestial mechanics could therefore serve as the theoretical language for diverse physical systems.

Another example is to be found in the application of the model of information theory. Mechanical communication systems are so rich with analogy that when Shannon (1949) and others perfected a formal model for the analysis of communication channels, practically every other science of input-output systems, whether physical or biological, rushed to borrow the language and the schema of bits, negative entropy, noise, redundancy, etc. (cf. N4.21).

The first point, then, is that the analogy of models may derive primarily from the analogy of perception. Since two or more sets of phenomena may be perceived as having positive analogy they are also understood as having common structure wherein a given model, or a set of analogous models, serves as the language for expressing the nature of the structure.

Now one may also discover analogy by means of noticing the similarity in the formal models as postulates for sets of diverse phenomena. Say for a theory T_1 a model M_1 is developed. This may be the formalization of its postulates and equations. For T_2 a formal model M_2 may be developed. And now, and perhaps not until now, it is noticed that M_2 resembles M_1. Thus an analogy as between T_1 and T_2 and as between the phenomenological domains of each theory is discovered but the discovery is posterior to the recognition of analogy in the models. It is not easy to find examples in which the analogy between models materializes upon recognition of similarities between the formal systems of laws, as such. Newton's law of gravitation, Coulomb's law of magnetic attraction, and the law of the intensity of electromagnetic radiation revealed their homology before the latter two at least were incorporated by Maxwell into a unified field of theory (cf. N4.22).

Now it does not appear that the distinction between analogy by phenomenological similarity and analogy by formal similarity contributes anything, as such, to the imperatives for models. It does, however, serve to bring out what Hutten (1951, 1954) has called the semantic function of models. In the case of phenomenological analogy, the language of the model is common to the sciences that are bridged by the analogy. The meaning of the model is then transported from the science from which it was derived to the science for which the model is constructed. In the case of formal analogy, the language of formal models is found to be appropriate for the derivation of diverse sets of laws. The meaning of the formal model is amplified through its successful applications to phenomenological domains which would, except for that analogy, remain unrelated or more or less encapsulated within their respectively autonomous theories.

Much of the argument over the indispensability of models, as we have seen, stems from the failure to make the clear-cut distinction between formal and structural models. Without formal models, we might argue there could be no theories. This seems to be straightforward. But often the argument for models as the indispensable heuristic ingredient of theories is based on the assumption that such models are to be regarded as structural models, with at least some components of the model being either actually or prospectively interpretable in the observation language. This is a much less impressive argument, since formal systems as such are also open to invention and modification and can be suggestive of new hypotheses at the frontiers of experiment. Nevertheless a strong case can be made for the need for structural models, if not for their absolute indispensability in the sciences whose theories have been characteristically microreductive (and what sciences haven't been?). The proper place to examine the details of the argument is in the chapters on reductionism; the substance of the argument, however, can be briefly outlined.

A theory should not only serve the function of deriving its laws within the system of its postulates and calculus but also, where possible, it should evolve toward explicating the nature of its postulates. Or to put it another way, if empirical laws are to be derivable as the logical consequences of postulates, then it is legitimate to ask why one set of postulates is preferred over some other. There are several criteria that we may wish to impose here in defending our choice, e.g., simplicity, familiarity, comprehensiveness, heuristic richness, etc., but the foremost of criteria would be empirical confirmability wherever there might be some prospect that "sufficient" postulates could be formulated in the empirical language. In a word it is proposed that we keep in mind Russell's maxim: "Wherever possible substitute logical constructions for hypothetical entities." This does not mean that hypothetical constructs are never to be introduced. Indeed, it is these constructs that remove theory from the domain of pure description. But wherever a hypothetical construct serves as a logical mediator, and *where conceivably there is also a physical mediator,* then Russell's maxim would require us to seek the interpretation of the hypothetical construct in observational terms. Thus, as is to be argued in the chapters on reductionism, a stimulus-mediator-response psychology is conducive to the explication of the theoretical language. The criterion of microreduction is essential to behavioral theory. And although formalization of the model of a theory is essential to logical rigor, our aim, it is proposed, should be eventually to interpret the nonlogical entities of the theory in observational terms.

LAWS

An addendum should be appended concerning the nature of law. As treated herein, laws when derived from within a theory are theorems of the formal theory. They are general propositions from which we infer, predict, or explain a given pattern of events. Not all laws, of course, fall within the corpus of theorems of a theory. In fact, considering the large number of propositions asserting lawful regularities, very few laws are explainable or deducible from within a theory. Moreover, the term 'law' even in science is ambiguous. The Newtonian laws of motion are postulates of a formal system; they are ideal descriptive generalizations only remotely applicable to any set of objects of physical systems. From them we can, of course, infer physical laws descriptive of observable events; but they themselves are idealizations whose truth is not something attested to by a given object or a set of objects in motion. We should, therefore, distinguish between lawlike statements that are postulates of theory and are, therefore, part of its theoretical hypothesis and lawlike statements that are theorems of the theory and are, therefore, part of the experimental hypothesis. Only the latter class of statements concerns us here. For the most part, laws are generalizations of relations and conformal patterns from which we may infer individual events, providing the individual events fulfill the conditions of the law's applications.

This last proviso seems, however, to be a qualification that deprives laws of any apodictic character. We should like to think that laws are enduring generalizations. At least if events are not to be looked upon as conformal cosmic imperatives, they should be considered valid statements of empirical regularities. Thus it would seem that it is the nature of a law to be true. However, nowadays these residues of Platonic realism have all but vanished. Laws have become the instruments of classification and inference. They have become "inference tickets" by which we categorize physical process and inferentially exploit our experience. But as to the truth or falsity of laws? Well, that language does not apply.

This is a thesis that has been popular with positivistic philosophers. One finds explicit statements of this instrumentalistic treatment of law in Campbell (1920a, b), Schlick (1938), Ramsey (1931), Ryle (1949), and Toulmin (1953). A law is not true or false in the way an existential proposition can be true or false. A law is a useful statement of properties and relations common to some given set of events. Just what the set of events is, just what is the range of events over which the law applies, is for us to decide. Thus according to Toulmin (1953), we are to ask not whether a law is true or false or probable but rather what is the range of its application. Statements about the range of a law's application can be true or false, but not the statement of the law itself.

There is, of course, much that is significant and insightful in this positivistic thesis. It is descriptive of our actual utilization and refinement of laws. The Boyle–Charles law of gases holds over the middle range of temperature and pressure but not otherwise. The Weber–Fechner law does not hold for extremes in stimulus intensity. And for all laws, their application is restricted to certain *ceteris paribus* conditions. Indeed, the applicability of a law is assured by our readiness to adopt provisos that will exclude all cases that falsify the law. Still this seems like a trivial way to keep laws inviolate. It is in some way reminiscent of

Victor Borge's uncle who invented a cure before he found the disease. One makes a law and then proceeds to discover the facts for which it serves, or rather he preserves its integrity by restricting its use.

Another point should be brought up before comment is made. That is the fact that a law, as an unrestricted universal statement, cannot be subject to verification in a world of finite sampling. All members of a finite set can be known to have some property. But this verification by enumeration is not possible for the infinite set to which lawlike statements apply. Ramsey and Schlick responded to this predicament by withdrawing lawlike statements from the catalogue of propositions. Such statements are pseudo-propositions which we utilize inferentially. That is all.

One can, I think, utilize laws in a slightly different way that would bring both of the foregoing arguments into focus. Laws, in a sense, are borrowed generalizations that carry with them an assumption of applicability. If pressed to demonstrate, we establish the truth of the law on the basis of a finite sampling of events. Thus the law will be true for just these events. Then by analogy, intuition, or any other crutch to inference, we utilize the restricted generalization for classifying some additional set of events, possibly some set of future events. We now apply the law to the extended set of events. If the law holds, then it is a true generalization of this now extended range of instances. If the law does not hold, it has been disconfirmed. That is to say, it is a false generalization for the extended range of hypothesized instances. In this sense of application, laws are hypotheses that are subject to confirmation or disconfirmation for the extended but still finite set of events.

Finally, a reminder that laws are not theories. We can give what are apparently satisfactory explanations of events by showing that they are instantiations of a law. Still, the law is not a theory. A theory logically binds laws together under the heritage of a common set of postulates and definitions. Thus the theorems of the theory compose the family of the derivable laws. And it is deducibility of a law within the theory that constitutes the formal requirement of scientific explanation.

NOTES

NOTE 4.1

In many respects, Bacon's inductivism was a prophylactic empiricism. It stressed protection from the diseases of the idols of false knowledge and it stressed prevention of misconceptions based upon anthropomorphism, metaphysical (rather than physical) causation, and premature generalization. As to the latter of these pitfalls, Bacon's admonition anticipates the counsel of some of today's anti-theoreticians:

> . . . if ever men are roused by my admonitions to betake themselves seriously to experiment and bid farewell to sophisticated doctrines, then indeed through the premature hurry of the understanding to leap or fly to universals and principles of things, great danger may be apprehended from philosophers of this kind, against which evil we ought even now to prepare. (*Novum Organum*, I, 64)

His enumeration of the idols that mislead is well known:

(1) *Idols of the tribe:* inborn penchants, aspects of human nature that predispose one to illusion and false perception.

(2) *Idols of the cave:* autistic confusion due to man's isolating himself from the checks of public discourse.

(3) *Idols of the forum:* misconceptions deriving from the exigencies of public discourse and the vocabulary and language thereby imposed.

(4) *Idols of the theatre:* conceptual restriction and corruption as dictated by prevailing schools, philosophies, sciences, and superstitions.

Nowadays we might list these as the sources of our conceptual frameworks. In light of the stress that has been placed upon our conceptual predispositions, one wonders what would remain of knowledge if all the Baconian idols were destroyed. According to Bacon, what would remain would be an experimentally purified perception revealing physical causality. But according to the point of view expressed in the preceding chapter, even physical causality and pure mechanics requires some apprenticeship at the altars of the idols of the forum and theatre.

NOTE 4.2

It is quite easy to misconstrue what Mill has to say in this context. Speaking against Whewell's intuitionist philosophy of science, Mill writes in the *System of Logic:*

> It is true that for these simply descriptive operations, as well as for the erroneous inductive one, a conception of the mind was required. The conception of an ellipse must have presented itself to Kepler's mind before he could identify the planetary orbits with it. According to Dr. Whewell the conception was something added to the facts. He expresses himself as if Kepler had put something into the facts by his mode of conceiving them. But Kepler did no such thing. The ellipse was in the facts before Kepler recognized it, just as the island was an island before it has been sailed round. Kepler did not *put* what he had conceived into the facts, but *saw* it in them. A conception implies and corresponds to something conceived; and though the conception itself is not in the facts but in our mind, yet if it is to convey any knowledge relating to them, it must be a conception *of* something which really is in the facts, some property which they actually possess, and which they would manifest to our senses if our senses were able to take cognizance of it . . .

I do not conceive that the part which conceptions have in the operation of studying facts has ever been overlooked or undervalued. No one ever disputed that in order to reason about anything we must have a conception of it, or that, when we include a multitude of things under a general expression, there is implied in the expression a conception of something common to those things. But it by no means follows that the conception is necessarily pre-existent, or constructed by the mind of its own materials. (Book III, Chapter II)

Then turning to "the proper use of scientific hypotheses," Mill writes:

An hypothesis is any supposition we make (either without actual evidence, or on evidence avowedly insufficient) in order to endeavor to deduce from it conclusions in accordance with facts which are known to be real, under the idea that, if the conclusions to which the hypothesis leads are known truths, the hypothesis itself either must be, or at least is likely to be, true. . . . We want to be assured that the law we have hypothetically assumed is a true one, and its leading deductively to true results will afford this assurance, provided the case be such that a false law cannot lead to a true result, provided no law except the very one which we have assumed can lead deductively to the same conclusions which that leads to. . . . It appears, then, to be a condition of the most genuinely scientific hypothesis that it be not destined always to remain an hypothesis but be of such a nature as to be either proved or disproved by comparison with observed facts. (Book III, Chapter XIV)

These excerpts, suggestive as they are of hypothetico-deductive methodology, differ in two important counts from contemporary treatments of hypothesis testing. One, Mill makes it clear that the hypotheses themselves are factual in character; they exemplify the rubric of causal analysis. But according to contemporary empiricism, a useful scientific hypothesis may have no immediate observational consequences. Only through correspondence rules applied to key propositions at the end of a deductive chain do facts come to bear upon credence of the hypothesis. And two, Mill speaks of the truth and the verification of hypotheses as if the truth of a consequent in a material implication affirms the antecedent. If hypotheses are to be treated as tools of inference to factual propositions, then Mill has committed an error in logic. However, when pressed to pin the error on Mill, we find that he retreats from adopting hypothetical modes of speaking as the basis of deductive inference. Rather such modes are descriptive of phenomena and causal connections themselves, and it would appear, subject to verification.

NOTE 4.3

John Arbuthnot, physician to Queen Anne, occasional contributor to the Royal Society, composer, and crony of Swift and Pope, argued in behalf of divine providence on the grounds of testing alternative hypotheses concerning random or chance events. In his short paper, "An Argument for Divine Providence, Taken from the Constant Regularity Observed in the Births of Both Sexes" (1710), he argues rather circuitously that the inequality of sexes cannot be attributed to chance. He used a simple heads–tails type model and shows that it would be highly improbable that one would obtain exactly as many male births as female in any given year. Incidental to his actual test, he then argues that a disbalance in the sexes must be part of the plan of "provident Nature" since:

> . . . we must observe that the external accidents to which Males are subject (who must seek their Food with danger) do make great havoc of them and his loss exceeds far that of the other sex, occasioned by Disease incident to it, as Experience convinces us. To repair that Loss provident Nature, by the Disposal of the wise Creator brings forth more Males than Females; and that in almost a constant proportion.

Then in order to dismiss the hypothesis of chance, Arbuthnot assumed the probability of a male birth to be one-half. Checking London birth records from 1629 to 1710, he then finds for each of the 82 years that the number of male births exceeds the number of female births. Applying the appropriate probability, $(\frac{1}{2})^{82}$, he finds the chance of such event ("by a Table of Logarithms") to be $1/(4.836 \times 10^{23})$.

On the basis of what is later to become the principle of Cournot and D'Alembert, namely that if an event is sufficiently improbable, we can say with apodictic confidence that it will not, or cannot, happen, he then concludes male births predominate over female births:

> From hence it follows, that Polygamy is contrary to the Law of Nature and Justice and to the Propagation of the Human Race; for where Males and Females are in equal number, if one Man takes Twenty Wives, Nineteen Men must live in Celibacy, which is repugnant to the Design of Nature; nor is it probable that Twenty Women will be so well impregnated by one Man as by Twenty" (1710, p. 189).

This probabilistic argument in the hypothetico-deductive mode became attractive to several early writers concerning certain astronomical distributions. Reverend Michell applied it early (circa 1767) to the hypothesis of a random distribution of double stars. And Laplace and DeMorgan each independently calculated the probability (≈ 0.00000012) that the inclinations of the planetary orbits should be confined to the small limits that obtain on the assumption that such inclinations could be treated as random assignments. On the grounds of the smallness of this probability, both writers rejected randomness "in favor of some disposing cause" (cf. Boole, 1854, p. 364). This mode of testing in favor of disposing causes is still with us. It is adopted by Neyman and Scott (1956) in their tests of chance mechanisms operating in the scatter of the galaxies. It is also characteristic of the argument adopted by LeCömte du Nouy (1947) in his own quaint calculations in behalf of divine providence.

NOTE 4.4

In one of the early expositions of the method of deductivism for the psychological audience, Hull states: *"Whereas argument reaches belief in its theorems because of antecedent belief in its postulates, scientific theory reaches belief in its postulates to a considerable extent through direct or observational evidence of the soundness of its theorems"* (1943, p. 9). The bridge to belief unfortunately is spelled out only in rather elusive terms of probability. Belief obviously cannot be a case of conclusive verification, for as Mill had pointed out in his treatment of deductivism, a hypothesis would be verified as true if, and only if, it and no other hypothesis could derive the experimental result. Hull intimates that truth status of the theory is a probability function of its true (by verification) theorems—each new verification increasing the probability "that the next theorem derived from these postulates in conjunction with a different set of antecedent conditions will also agree with relevant empirical determinations." There are serious difficulties in using probability here in the way Hull does; at least, his language would have to be qualified. Be that as it may, we support our belief in the postulates of our theory by means of empirical test. Acknowledging that disagreement between theorem and experimental result signifies that one or more postulates are in error, he goes on to say:

> When the breakdown of a generalization occurs in this way, an event of frequent occurrence in new fields, the postulates involved are revised if possible so as to conform [sic] to the known facts. Following this, deductions as to the outcomes of situations involving still other combinations of principles are made; these in their turn are checked against observations; and so on as long as disagreements continue to occur. Thus the determination of scientific principles is in considerable part a matter of symbolic trial-and-error (1943, p. 12).

Hull's use here of the language of conformity as between postulate and fact, along with his adopting a probabilistic support of belief, would seem to indicate that postulates ultimately would have factual reference and, one would surmise, should in principle be subject to direct test.

NOTE 4.5

The problem of what logical systems can or cannot do is a highly technical branch of logic. The consensus seems to be that machines cannot be designed such that they can in principle solve all questions meaningful within their syntax. Whether machines as we now know them can simulate all human activities of reason and discovery is a question of some debate. However, it is clear that machines cannot exceed the limits put upon the logic of discovery by Gödel's theorem of the essential incompleteness of the logical system.

Nevertheless, when we retreat from the ethereal region of computers and science fiction, there is little question concerning the inventive proclivities of creative people. Incubation, insight, intuition, and, alas, accident are the clues to invention, not logic. Hadamard (1945) and Beveridge (1950) offer interesting accounts of the "irrational" aspects of inventiveness in the fields of mathematics and science. Einstein (1933) and Poincaré (1914) give interesting accounts of the intuitive aspects of creativity in their own work. And Russell adds his bit to the theme of the subconscious in his brief essay, "How I Write" (1956).

NOTE 4.6

The issue is debated by Hanson and Feyerabend (Feigl and Maxwell, 1961) though both parties would appear to agree that a logic of invention is impossible. Hanson takes as his historical example the works of Kepler. Kepler recorded his own inventive travails with painstaking detail. Though he engaged in systematic trial-and-error exploration of hypotheses concerning the planetary orbits, it was clear that neither logic nor intuition prescribed principles that would assure him of eventual success. Strangely, Kepler toyed with the hypothesis of orbital ellipses relatively early in his travails, only to discover its successful application at a later time.

In his *The Concept of the Positron*, Hanson (1963) gives an account of the interplay of invention, theory, and discovery in the story of antimatter. This work is further elaboration upon the themes presented in the earlier *Patterns of Discovery* (1958).

It is customary in discussions of logical design and simulation to ask if we cannot design a machine that will invent hypotheses. No trouble at all. Machines can be creative as random generators of hypotheses. They can also learn inductively (e.g., George, 1959, 1960; Scriven, 1960; Ashby, 1963). However, no one has been able to design logical circuitry to assure us that whatever theorem is proposed in a language the machine understands, the machine can proceed to find a proof as to whether the theorem is true or not by virtue of a reliable algorithm (Church, 1936). Although this issue is tangential to inventiveness it does seem to indicate that even a machine would require some unprogrammed intuition in order to resolve all questions that can be meaningfully asked of it.

NOTE 4.7

The account of theory given in the text borrows heavily from Campbell's classic *Physics, the Elements* (1920), also issued by Dover as *The Foundations of Science* (1957). This book has been very influential in the philosophy of science, especially in the discussions of hypothetico-deductive methodology. The Campbellian point of view is adopted and refined by two recent works of outstanding merit, R. B. Braithwaite's *Scientific Explanation* and E. Nagel's *The Structure of Science*. Campbell also gives a more elementary account of his philosophy of science in *What Is Science?* (1920).

NOTE 4.8

It is not the writer's intention to be critical of personality theory, or to avoid its discussion, other than critically. The study of complex interpersonal behavior is just as amenable to scientific study as say the interaction of bodies in their gravitational fields. The argument is that theories are testable and useful only to the extent they permit straightforward inference and can be assessed by our confirmational procedures. The ontological status of theories, tenuous as it is, can only emerge under a rigorous formalization of the theoretical postulates and the principles of inference. In this respect it would appear that personology is still in its preformal, pretheoretical stages of development.

One notes, of course, that simplified theories of interpersonal behavior are being constructed. Two-person interactions, simple dyadic relations, may not be very interesting or insightful so far as complex social behavior is concerned. But in this case, as in so many in psychology, simplification almost to the point of triviality is the price one must pay for syntactic and semantic precision.

NOTE 4.9

In his last revision of his theory, Hull presents postulates from which theorems are derived without proof. Indeed the proofs would have to be informal; for in spite of some basic equations of $_sH_R$ and $_sE_R$, Hull's language is often phenomenological and basic terms are left undefined. It is apparent then that even in treating the postulates as a deductive system, the theorems can be no more precise than the language in which the postulates are stated. (See for example Montgomery, 1951; Koch, 1954.)

Examining some aspects of Hull's theory from the point of view of the precision and warrantability of its predictions, Cotton concludes, "Without clarification and simplification of the theory, it is believed that most predictions rigorously deduced from the theory would contradict or at least differ in form from Hull's empirical equations" (1955, p. 313). He explicitly shows that Hovland's equation of the relation between amplitude of response and number of reinforced trials (used by Hull in support of his theory) cannot be derived within the system of postulates *as stated* by Hull. Noting Hull's use of other workers' data in support of his own theory, Cotton writes:

> In fact no one has publicly questioned the presumption that the empirical data cited in *Principles of Behavior* is embraced by the theory. Yet this presumption is false. There was, to be sure, a romance between theory and fact, but the wedding did not take place. Hull never quite compared the implications of his theory with the data he discussed (1955, p. 303).

Cotton makes some interesting comments about the "degree of specificity" of the data as stipulated in theoretical predictions. Such data fall into three classes of hypotheses: (1) those expressing only inequalities such as greater than; (2) those expressing the general form, such as linear trends; and (3) those specifying numerical values of parameters. Much of experimental work involving classical learning theories specifies hypotheses merely in terms of inequalities: e.g., as between experimental and control groups. It is obvious, however, that alternative theories may easily yield predictions to the same direction of the inequality. More precise tests and more decisive results can be achieved, if, for example, the alternative theories are sufficiently refined so as to predict particular patterns and trends of the values of the dependent variables.

NOTE 4.10

In the chapters of this section, frequent reference is made to the now classical distinction between intervening variables and hypothetical constructs. The original paper of MacCorquodale and Meehl (1948) has stimulated much discussion both in psychology and the philosophy of science. It makes what presumes to be a significant distinction between theoretical terms which are postulating constructions, i.e., explicit operational terms and theoretical terms postulating as yet unobserved entities and processes. MacCorquodale and Meehl write:

> We suggest that the phrase 'intervening variable' be restricted to the original use implied by Tolman's definition. Such a variable will then be simply a quantity obtained by a specific manipulation of the values of empirical variables; it will involve no hypothesis as to the existence of nonobserved entities or the occurrence of unobserved processes; it will contain, in its complete statement for all purposes of theory and prediction, no words which are not definable either explicitly or by reduction sentences in terms of empirical variables; and the validity of the empirical laws involving only observables will constitute both the necessary and the sufficient conditions for the validity of the laws involving these intervening variables. . . .
>
> As a second linguistic convention, we propose that the term 'hypothetical construct' be used to designate theoretical concepts which do *not* meet the requirements for intervening variables in the strict sense. That is to say, these constructs involve terms which are not wholly reducible to empirical terms; they refer to processes or entities which are not directly observed (although they need not be in principle unobservable); the mathematical expression of them cannot be formed simply by a suitable grouping of terms in an empirical equation; and the truth of the empirical laws involved is a necessary but not a sufficient condition for the truth of these conceptions (1948, pp. 103-104).

Subsequent literature on the subject has been extensive. A partial list of references follow, with grouping according to positions taken as regards the ontological status of theoretical terms:

(A) Emphasis upon theoretical constructs (H.C.'s) with realistic overtones, wherein the postulated entity carries with it the possibility of eventual reification: Cronbach and Meehl (1955); Feigl (1950, 1951); Hebb (1955); Hochberg (1961); Krech (1949, 1950a,b); Meehl and MacCorquodale (1948); Maxwell (1962); Sellars (1956).

(B) Operational reduction, with emphasis upon the intervening variable, although surplus meaning may be claimed for the strictly operational concept: Bergman (1951, 1953); Craig (1956), an article on the logical reducibility of *all* theoretical terms to statements in the observation language; Kendler (1952); Madden (1961); Marx (1951); Spence (1956); Tolman (1936).

(C) Conventionalistic interpretation of theoretical terms, no existential hypothesis implied by such terms: Deutsch (1960); George (1953), emphasis upon model; Kendler (1952); Kessen and Kimble (1952).

(D) Contextualist interpretation of hypothetical terms; close to the conventionalist position, but emphasis upon stating the meaning and ontological status of a construct in the context, and context alone, of the theory of which it is a part: Braithwaite (1953); Carnap (1956); Ginsberg (1954); Hempel (1951, 1958); Jessor (1958); Lindzey (1953); Mayo (1954); Meissner (1958); Smart (1956, 1963); Toulmin (1953).

(E) For critical exposition of aspects of the distinction: Beck (1950); Maze (1954); O'Neil (1953); Rozeboom (1956); Seward (1955).

NOTE 4.11

If by an intervening variable I_r we were to mean a logical construction out of response variables (as in case of expectancy, cf. Hempel, 1958), then any theory in which I_r would be the sole theoretical term could not, by virtue of its status in the calculus, generate more interesting experimental hypotheses than would arise from within the radical atheoretical stimulus–response psychology itself. That is, there is nothing inherent within the intervening variable I_r that would lead to hypotheses which could not be derived from a set of laws eliminating I_r, as it were, by its utilizing only primitive terms in the observation language. Regardless of the aura of empirical respectability with which intervening variables have been endowed by people such as Tolman, Hull, and Spence, it is doubtful that anyone holds to a strict reductive definition of an intervening variable. There is always some presumptive factor beyond the empirical ingredients of pure logical construction. For example, if one were to define habit strength as a function of number of reinforcements, as Hull does, he very likely presumes that it is *any* set of reinforcements satisfying some rather general conditions, e.g., reinforced trials in a T-maze. When he speaks of the value of habit strength, he does not reduce the unique value to just this and no other set of N reinforcement trials. In other words, he takes the N trials to be evidence of a definite level of habit strength, but the level of habit strength is something indicated by a set of trials; it is not *the* set of some particular trials. And that is to say, the intension of the proposition about the level of habit strength is not limited to the specific set of ingredients of a logical construction.

Suppose we define $P(E)$ as a logical construction, i.e., as the relative frequency of E for a particular set of N trials. If N were large, we might in fact prefer the estimate $P(E)$ of p to some other estimate, such as that based upon the analysis of equally likely classes. But note the word "estimate". We assume that $P(E)$ is used in such a way that all propositions derived therefrom are not necessarily statements about just these N trials. In fact, if we use the theory predictively, we are talking of some other set of trials of future sampling and so forth. We assume that $P(E)$, the relative frequency, will hold for future cases and in some way manifest itself in our expectations concerning many future trials. Thus, whenever $P(E)$ occurs in some theorem, we are not at all thinking of the particular set of N trials from which $P(E)$ was constructed. For example, we could apply $P(E) = p$, $P(\sim E) = q$, in the binomial theorem and obtain the probability distribution for all possible outcomes in N Bernoullian trials. Should we consider the probability distributions for the event occurrences of experiments involving ten rolls of the die, we would get the expansion

$$p^{10} + 10p^9q + 45p^8q^2 + \cdots + 10pq^9 + q^{10} = 1.0.$$

The terms p^{10} (i.e., $[P(E)]^{10}$), etc., become meaningfully tied to event classes and expected frequency by means of a dictionary. Here $P(E)$ betokens a dispositional property not exhaustively defined by the original sampling from which its value was first determined. The point is that an explicit definition, without the presumption of its dispositional properties, would be forever bounded by its defining set of events. There is invariably a presumptive factor involved in the use of intervening variables. For that reason much of the controversy over intervening variables and hypothetical constructs is misdirected. The more important distinction seems to be that the surplus or presumptive meaning of hypothetical constructs is embedded in models and their positive analogy, whereas the surplus meaning for intervening variables is left unreified or downright suppressed.

NOTE 4.12

The distinction between structural models and formal models one might think has an analogue in a distinction between the tough-minded and the tougher-minded. Structural models frequently suggest either actual structures of the thing modeled or mechanical analogues. Both the replica and the analogue suggest an actual hardware approach. The use of structural models is tough-minded in the sense that their builders leave no lacuna for irreducible agents of mediation such as intuition, entelechy, self-regard, etc. But a purely formal approach may be tougher-minded still. The reluctance to interpret any variables but those in the theorems that are anchored securely to the observation language reflects an attitude in keeping with the most radical of empiricisms. The data language and formal deductive models: these are admissible. There is no place for structural speculations.

NOTE 4.13

It is of interest to follow Woodworth's adventures in search of O-structure through the many revisions of his famous *Psychology*. In the first edition of the book (1922), his stimulus response schema was S-T- R_1R_2 . . . in which T designates determining tendency. To this mediational state he sometimes added P, a preparatory set. By the second revision in 1935, T, and P were absorbed under O, with O indicating a general adjustment set including situational and goal sets. 'Structure' was beginning to appear in the vocabulary. Philogenetic and ontogenetic differences in brain structure were perfunctorily noted. Specifically, the O factor covered structure, condition of the organism, and activity in progress. By the third revision (1940), a contrast between permanent structure and temporary states was emphasized. The dynamism of motivation was beginning to appear and by the fifth revision (1949, in which Marquis appeared as co-author), greater detail was spelled out for the classes of organismic variables. Structure now meant bodily and anatomical structure as manifest in habits and skill. Suggestions were made as to the relevance of modification in brain structure, although it was noted that such internal states were inferred rather than observed. The language of the temporary states (the "conditions" of earlier editions) now made mention of emotional and motivational states, hunger, drowsiness, etc. Activity in progress refers to those states that are later to succumb to feedback analysis. Thus, the ontogeny of black-boxes. Little by little, light intrudes from the laboratory to illuminate the black-box, if not with the actual biomechanics, at least with functional hypotheses. The tradition of Woodworth continues. Note, for example, texts where explicit use is made of the cybernetic schema.

NOTE 4.14

Problems of special interest to the cyberneticist are learning, categorical perception, generalization, and constancy effects. So far as learning and basic adjustment are concerned, actual "hardware realizations" of cybernetic models have been achieved (Ashby, 1952; Shannon, 1951; W. Grey Walter, 1953; Uttley, 1955). But not all models, utilizing different networks and components as they do, can be equally good models of the nervous system. Analogies are more or less good. However, some models such as Uttley's conditional probability machines (1955, 1956), are interpretable in terms of logical nets which might very well be isomorphic with actual neural nets. Good discussions of the application of cybernetics to psychology can be found in George (1960, 1961).

It is of interest to note that the speculative neural network models of McCulloch and Pitts (1943, 1947) stemmed largely from McCulloch's early efforts to design machines capable of recognizing certain general aspects of a physical stimulus world (Wiener, 1948). The order of attempted discovery here is from one model, the cybernetic one, to another, the neural network. Explorations proceeded from functional to structural analogies.

NOTE 4.15

Kenneth Craik, a student of Bartlett's at the University of Cambridge, combined competencies in philosophy and experimental psychology with unique mechanical inventiveness. His experimental work was largely in the field of what we would now call human factors; but in large part, his reputation rests upon his little book *The Nature of Explanation* (1943).

After rejecting *a priorism* and skepticism, Craik argues that the most fruitful language of analysis and understanding is an out-and-out causal language. Thought processes themselves follow external processes. External processes can be translated into the symbols of thought, the thought then amplified through deductive inference and translated back into empirical hypotheses. The practical implications of the argument rest in Craik's thinking that some isomorphism exists between the structures of mental and physical process. Therefore, he firmly believed that it would always be possible to design a mechanical system that would imitate and predict mental processes. Whether Craik's critique of uncertainty and causality will hold up (he was critical of quantum physicists who rejected the principle of causality) is doubtful; but his contribution to the study of simulative procedures has been considerable. He was a dedicated cyberneticist before that science was christened.

Craik died in a bicycle accident while he was still a young man.

NOTE 4.16

One might wish to argue that refined black-box analysis does indeed offer point-by-point analysis of concatenated processes. Thus ablation studies systematically carried out would provide at least lower level explanations (Pribram, 1954). To be sure; but as Gregory (1961) and Deutsch (1960) have argued, inferences from anatomical studies of this type are only good in simple mechanical systems with point-by-point linkages. The neurological speculations of Hebb (1949), Sholl (1956), Milner (1957), Rosenblatt (1958) rule out specific connections in favor of randomized construction of cell assemblies and redundancy. Obviously ablation studies on systems that are neither homologous nor genetically specific cannot be very informative. One wonders how much of Lashley's failure to establish a generally acceptable theory of cerebral organization is due to his reliance upon ablation studies.

An interesting synthesis of ablation strategies and cybernetic modeling occurs in the work of Karl Pribram. In one work (1954), he enthusiastically calls for intensive ablation studies of the small structures of the forebrain. But in his excellent *Annual Reviews* article of 1960, he assimilates a selected review of recent neurophysiology into an elaborate and detailed cybernetic model. The heuristic value of the cybernetic model is also stressed in Miller, Galanter, and Pribram, *Plans and the Structure of Behavior* (1960).

NOTE 4.17

When does a model cease to be a model and become the thing itself? An interesting question. One might answer: "When all the negative analogy is dissipated." Let us see. Consider a relatively simple type of model. Suppose an engineer were to construct a large suspension bridge. He might first want to construct a large model of it in order to test its behavior under wind conditions, load, stress, etc. Perhaps there is some doubt as to the feasibility of such a structure. But stress factors of metal cannot be modeled on any reduced scale regardless of how faithful the scale reduction. Thus, if one were to eliminate all negative analogy, he must eliminate all those features and properties of the model which are different from the thing modeled. In effect, the engineer must replicate the bridge if he is to be sure that all model-inferences about the actual bridge are to be correct.

Suppose the engineer includes estimates of his model in the actual construction of the bridge. He can be certain, *ceteris paribus,* as to the success of its structure if he can first build a model to the scale of the bridge itself. The question is, of course, whether the model is a model of a bridge, or is *the bridge itself*. If one wishes now to argue that to the "perfectly conservative engineer" the cost of a bridge is always twice the cost of the bridge, then he is free to name the "paradox" and puzzle it out for himself.

NOTE 4.18

It is difficult, though presumably not impossible, for a mathematical-model man to escape the affinities of conventionalism. And empiricistic, nonconventionalist credos are sometimes easier to declare at the beginning of a work in theory than at the end.

For example, in their *Markov Learning Models for Multipersonal Inter-actions,* Suppes and Atkinson declare against conventionalism in their opening statements. Adopting the Estes–Suppes (1959) formalism of statistical learn-ing theory, they contend "that in statistical learning theory we have a theory with the same kind of feel about it that theories in physics have." Theoretical postulates are well formed and predictions are non *ad hoc* and precise. "How-ever beautiful the structure of a theory may be, if it does not yield stable, non-artificial experimental interpretations leading to new empirical predictions, it does not have empirical significance," (page 4). They reject the point of view "that by sufficiently distorting the 'natural' experimental interpretation of con-cepts, they may save any theory from failure." However, by the end of their work, these writers are somewhat less confident. In the face of some refrac-tory experimental results, they stress the need for manageable models:

> In advocating this approach we are taking a methodological position with which some scientists do not agree. Our position is in contrast to one which asserts that a model should be discarded once it is clear that certain of its predictions are in error, but this position postulates a clearer con-nection between learning models and the actual behavior of organisms than we are willing to grant exists. Naturally, it is always better to choose from the available models the one that best fits the data, but in the pres-ent state of psychological knowledge, no single model is clearly superior to all others in every facet of analysis (1960, p. 279).

NOTE 4.19

Duhem made much of the distinction between the narrow but strong mind of the French and the ample but weak mind of the English (although it turns out that his example, *par excellence,* of the ample but weak mind is Napo-leon). He was writing in a time when it was still popular to write of national character. After noting differences between the heroes of French and English literature, he attempts to show that Englishmen's "shallow" (not in the pejora-tive sense!) proclivities for empirics lead in physics to a weakness for me-chanical models. Duhem's essay on the subject (Part I, Chapter IV) is too long to give in any detail, but the following gives the spirit of his thesis:

> In the treatises on physics published in England, there is always one ele-ment which greatly astonishes the French student; that element, which nearly invariably accompanies the exposition of a theory, is the model. Nothing helps us better understand how very different from ours is the manner in which the English mind proceeds in the construction of science than this use of the model . . . (1962, p. 69).

Speaking specifically to a science of electrostatics, Duhem writes:

> The whole theory of electrostatics constitutes a group of abstract ideas and general propositions, formulated in the clear and precise language of geometry and algebra, and connected with one another by the rules of strict logic. This whole fully satisfies the reason of a French physicist and his taste for clarity, simplicity, and order.
> The same does not hold for an Englishman. These abstract notions of material points, force, line of force, and equipotential surface do not

satisfy his need to imagine concrete, material, visible, and tangible things . . . (1962, p. 70).

And in reference to the work of Oliver Lodge:

Here is a book intended to expound the modern theories of electricity and to expound a new theory. In it there are nothing but strings which move around pulleys, which roll around drums, which go through pearl beads, which carry weights; and tubes which pump water while others swell and contract; toothed wheels which are geared to one another and engage hooks. We thought we were entering the tranquil and neatly ordered abode of reason, but we find ourselves in a factory . . . (1962, p. 70).

NOTE 4.20

To make his point, Campbell allots himself "about a quarter of an hour" to elaborate a formally adequate but meaningless theory for deducing a theorem which in its dictionary translation states that "the ratio of the resistance of a piece of pure metal to its absolute temperature is constant" (1920, p. 122). To emphasize that formal sufficiency alone is not all that we require of a theory, we can take Campbell's vacuous formal theory (as a kind of formal analogue) and apply it to the deduction of Fechner's law. Consider the following:

  u, v, w are independent variables;
  a, b, are constant for all values of u, v, w;
  c, d are intervening variables such that $c = d$ and $cd/b = \log R$, where R is stimulus intensity; $(c^2 + d^2)\, a = S$, where S is the subjective estimate of the physical stimulus.

Then

$$\frac{(c^2 + d^2)a}{cd/b} = \frac{S}{\log R}$$

Since, with $c = d$, the left side of the equation reduces to the constant $k = 2ab$, we obtain Fechner's law

$$S = k \log R$$

Quite simple! We have a formally satisfactory theory of psychophysics. It even possesses purely formal analogy with Campbell's theory of electrical resistance. All the same, as a theory, it is quite meaningless. It has no analogy by which we can comprehend it in the context of established theory which is understood.

NOTE 4.21

As Attneave (1959) is careful to point out, information theory is not a psychological theory but rather a technique for handling data. Nevertheless, what distinguishes it from such techniques as chi square and the analysis of variance is the analogy that $T(x,y)$, transmitted information, $Hy(x)$, equivocation, and $Hx(y)$, ambiguity, have for all systems which fail to utilize or to process all information available to them; i.e., its analogy for all input–output systems.

It is perhaps a point for debate whether researchers and theoreticians come to informational analysis because of phenomenological analogy or because information theory has been elevated to the position of an ontological probe. One senses that the general popularity of information theory stems partially from people being first enamored of the tool and then going out in search of an application.

NOTE 4.22

The discussion here is strikingly reminiscent of that between nominalism and realism. For nominalism, analogy inheres in objects; classes are conventions by which objects are grouped according to perceived similarities. For Platonic realism, the analogy inheres in the formal archetype of which phenomena are their partial empirical exemplifications; thus, for example, the emphasis upon calculi, formal models, and mathematical training for the philosopher-scientist.

Whether this dichotomy of labels applies to contemporary writers on theory and models is debatable. Few formalists nowadays endow their formal models with any more than a conventional status. At least the defense of mathematical models does not reveal the faith of a Galileo, who expected that his researches would reveal the underlying formal structure (the mathematical laws) of which all phenomena were manifestations.

CHAPTER 5

Explanation

ALTHOUGH much has been written on the subject of explanation, the literature is frequently less incisive and less definitive than that on theory and reductionism. The reasons for this are not hard to come by. Curiosity and the seeking of explanations are characteristic of us all, scientist and nonscientist alike. Logical attempts at explication aside, explanation is largely a personal matter. Curiosity and the need for explanation are the products of our intellectual development. Early in our lives we ask why? what? how? And, in turn, we accept "explanations." These explanations have this in common, they satisfy us. In some sense of cognitive completion, they satisfy. Yet it remains a source of puzzlement and amusement as to why the explanations we accept do, in fact, satisfy: why some people will accept a casual allusion to a general principle or to a causal agent while others pursue their inquiries into first principles, unmoved movers, ultimate unexplained explainers. In a sense nothing is explained; a thing or an event simply is, it needs no explanation. Yet what we accept as explanation gives us cognitive closure. Explanations terminate our curiosity and we are left free to attend to other events and move on to other inquiries.

Still this token of cognitive satisfaction is not easily codified. Satisfactory explanations are not always "true" descriptions of affairs. Hypotheses explain, so do fictions and lies, as well as what we might presume to be true descriptions. However, the language of truth is in doubt here. Since in science so much of explanation is of an hypothetical nature, it would be better to avoid making truth judgments at all concerning explanation and rather reserve such judgments solely for the domain of observation statements. Accepting this as the case, it is then important to distinguish between the cognitive requirements of explanation, on the one hand, and the formal or logical requirements of explanation, on the other. Failure to appreciate this distinction has led to much fruitless discussion over the meaning of explanation.

Consider, for example, the question of causation—a central issue for some although as Russell (1917) and others have pointed out (e.g., Campbell, 1920, 1921; W. H. Watson, 1938; Toulmin 1953) causality and causal laws are hardly mentioned in modern treatises of science. Still causality enjoys some precedence in matters of explanation. Causal antecedents are accepted as natural explanations of the events that follow. Consequently empiricists from the time of Bacon through Mill (1884) to the contemporary J. O. Wisdom (1952) have stressed methodology for the induction of causes; as if some algorithm of inference will assure us of isolating the antecedent event-complexes which in a very real sense serve to explain the effects that occupy our attention. There is something explanatory about concomitant variations, functional relationships, interdependence. The satisfaction we derive from such relationships is hard to overcome. And Humean skepticism has to be reaffirmed in each generation in order for us to see clearly that events just do happen, without necessary connection and without the occurrence of one event, alone and unaided by our principles of general inference, explaining the occurrence of another (Braithwaite, 1953).

By a cognitive requirement of explanation, then, I mean that an explanation is cognitively satisfying if its statement is accepted as an adequate answer as to "why" the occurrence of the event in question. The "why?" is a perfectly legitimate question. Still what is cognitively satisfying may be quite a personal matter. To hear that a virus is the "cause" of a disease may be quite a satisfactory explanation to the man who suffers the infection but it is hardly an adequate answer to the why that is posed by the biochemist. A falling barometer may explain the change in cloud cover to a backporch weatherman but to the meteorologist it is little more than a symptom in a large complex of relevant events. What the biochemist, the meteorologist, and the scientist in general want is not explanation based upon our pointing to empirical events with which we are familiar, but rather explanation based upon some larger deductive schema that generates inferences concerning many events not heretofore related. In such cases, our sets of explanatory statements must fulfill certain formal requirements.

By the formal requirements of explanation, I mean that an explanation is formally satisfying if the statement of the event to be explained is shown to be a logical consequence of principles, laws, and theories in generalized scientific systems. Thus a formal explanation may be one in which a theorem is derived within a scientific system such that the event to be explained is an instance of what the theorem stipulates. In the case of these hypothetico-deductive explanations, we are likely to come to greater procedural agreements as to what constitutes an explanation, yet we may not be cognitively satisfied with the character of the explanation. All formal treatments of explanation rest upon a deductive inference leading from either a theory or a law to a statement about a particular event. The details of the inference can be rigorously spelled out. However, the *explicans* (the set of statements which constitute the argument for the *explicandum*—the event to be explained) may be neither interesting, satisfying, nor otherwise psychologically adequate. Children, for example, seldom appreciate our adeptness at hypothetico-deductive explanations.

Now it is not just children who may disdain formal explanations. In psychology and other personalistic sciences, questions have been raised over whether any unique event such as the behavior of a given individual can be explained by recourse to hypothetico-deductive procedures or to the individual's being an instantiation of a law or set of laws. According to a more intuitional point of view, the explanation of behavior can only be achieved by its detailed, highly specific description accompanied by the observer's empathetic understanding. Thus only by projecting oneself into the event sequence will an explanation supported by an essential sufficiency of understanding be achieved. Laws, hypotheses, theoretical constructions, and all other classificatory schemata of the deductive procedures only serve to obfuscate description of the thing to be explained. This is a theme iterated by mystics, by existentialists, and by some personologists. It is argued on grounds that the classificatory schema does violence to the unique character of individual events. Only unique events have ontological substance, not classes, laws, or other abstractive repositories. This is a viewpoint that requires attention and in time we shall want to examine it further.

As a preview, we may list the types of answers and disquisitions that have been acceptable as explanations. First, the child's world, for this carries over into our subsequent demands for explanation. A child learns efficient causation largely through his early experiences in manipulating objects—by his causing them to move and to behave. He readily learns simple principles of mechanics, of the elements of momenta transfer. Thus he can understand why some objects move, why some fall, and how some objects cause other objects to move. Easily deceived by legerdemain, he is also easily satisfied as to how it all happens. It is as simple as the dynamics of the jumping bean. The child may be puzzled by the movement of iron filings on the table top, but if he is shown the magnet that is being manipulated under the table, he may appear quite satisfied that he understands the dynamics of the phenomenon—even though he has not the slightest conception of the principles of molecular structure. Another distinctive feature of the child's world is that he is likely early in his experience to accept as explanatory the omnipotencies that only later he refines into the arguments of first cause. Birth phenomena; the elementary economics of where does money come from; questions like that of Red Chief (O. Henry), why are oranges round?—all these are dispatched by facile references to God, banks, the government, daddy, and other agents of omnipotency. The etiology of such explanatory types is perhaps not difficult for the psychologist to discover but what is more interesting perhaps is the ease with which one moves from explanations by the omnipotent to explanations by the familiar.

Another phase of the child's cognitive development comes with his awareness of black-box agencies. This, we might say, is typically the jumping bean phase of explanation. Something is happening inside the box which accounts for its behavior. Thus, if the mechanical toy is opened so that wheels and springs are found, a primitive level of explanation is achieved. Considerable sophistication is, of course, required for thinking in terms of mechanical linkages. Still, if we can see the linkages and other media of concatenated events, we may find the gross behavior of the mechanism explained, even though explanation by phenomenological concatenation (i.e., of the familiar chaining of events) may be relatively primitive and leave entirely unexplained why such concatenations should occur. It has been argued that ablation studies in psychoneurology have frequently done no more than to exploit our primitive black-box criteria of explanation.

When the child has learned to structure sequences of events in terms of concatenation, concomitant variation, and other complexes of contiguity, he has gone a long way in becoming perceptually prepared for dealing with the problem of explanation. So long as he confines himself to his perceptual frameworks, his explanations, even his sophisticated explanations, will lead him to the problems of causal analysis. Thus to explain an event-sequence is critically to examine the "causal structure."

By then, of course, the child has become a relatively sophisticated philosopher. It is interesting perhaps to lay out the itinerary of his intellectual odyssey. First, he looks for linkages of events, which become familiar to him. Thus he takes for granted certain basic sequences of events. They become "unexplained explainers," as it were. And, if some event to be explained is found to be an exemplification of these basic patterns, that event is explained in at least a cognitively satisfying way. As a second adventure he may begin to wonder why such basic patterns actually obtain. He carries the refinement of inspection to a different level and begins to examine the microstructure of the events that appear to conform to the basic patterns. Thus as a relatively naive psychologist, he may direct his inspection from crude stimulus–response patterns of the object and behavioral world into the microstructure of the nervous system. As a naive physicist noting the phenomenological law of increasing entropy, he may wish to look into the structure of gases in order to find out why the second law of thermodynamics holds. The two examples here are somewhat different, for in one the microstructure is readily accessible, whereas in the other it is not; the microstructure is more hypothetical. Still the explanatory significance of the two microstructures is, in one sense, the same. If we were to see ·the given microstructure or to verify its hypothetical character (by microscopes, etc.), what would emerge is a finer grained picture of concatenated events; but in no sense would the psychological or the logical character of our causal analysis be altered. From crude contiguities, we go to finer grained contiguities. Still we get no closer to an agency of causal process transpiring in the finest grained of event sequences. This predicament leads the adventurer of our intellectual odyssey to his third and Humean port of call. There is nothing compelling about contiguity. The satisfaction of explanation arises from habit-established perceptual expectancies. Thus, the finest grained phenomenal conformities are described more than they are "explained." There is the uneasy feeling that the world need not oblige us by conforming to our descriptions and that if an observation violates our principles or our laws, the solecism will rest with us and not with the event.

For the radical empiricist, the end of the odyssey is Humean skepticism. Indeed, explanation and causal analysis can penetrate no further than the inevitable barriers of contiguity. We are often told that correlation does not mean causation, but as good Humeans, we can discount the argument by introducing certain space and time provisos with respect to stipulating the antecedents and consequents in a causal sequence. Correlation may not be causation; but causation *is* correlation unless, of course, we leave the domain of pure empirics—in which case it would be as well that we drop the language of causality altogether.

No effort has been made here to distinguish between causal relations and explanations. That is because I have concentrated on cognitively satisfying explanations and have proposed that what is satisfying is the perceptually familiar organization of experience. That causal analyses are explanatory is apparent not only from the work of empiricists but also of phenomenologists (from Kant to Michotte, 1963). However, if we wish to place explanation on firmer grounds than the nebulous standards of cognitive satisfaction, we will have to leave the psychological aspects of explanation and turn more directly to the practice of explaining events within science itself.

LEVELS OF EXPLANATION

Lower-Level Explanations

In *The Logic of Scientific Discovery*, Karl Popper writes: "To give a *causal explanation* of an event means to deduce a statement which describes it, using as premises of the deduction one or more *universal laws,* together with certain singular statements, the *initial conditions,"* (1961, p. 59).

Since the qualifier 'causal' is unnecessarily restrictive it can be removed and without substantial loss of meaning. What we have then is a formal description of lower-level explanation; that is to say, of explanation by instantiation.

Let us be explicit. Suppose we wish to explain the behavior of a pigeon in a Skinner box. He has learned to peck the target in order to get food, or better, because the response is accompanied by a reinforcing state of affairs. Or perhaps better still, his pecking the target is an instantiation of the law of reinforcement. The paradigm for this case might be as follows: Let x be any response, let Sx be "the response x accompanied by reinforcing stimuli," and let Rx be "the response x acquires an increment of habit strength." Then the paradigm

$$(x) \ Sx \supset Rx$$
$$\underline{Sx_i}$$
$$\therefore \ Rx_i$$

is simply the familiar *modus ponens.* We assume that if a response is repeatedly emitted it has habit strength. The habit strength, as expressed in Rx_i, is then inferable from the general *law of effect,* $(x) \ Sx \supset Rx,$ and the statement of the initial conditions, $Sx_i.$

At first glance such explanations may seem trivial. One notes an element of circularity here. If one defines response in such a way that all response is accompanied by reinforcing stimuli and that the general law of effect holds for every event we classify as a response, then indeed it seems somewhat circular to explain an event by what amounts to an arbitrary classificatory procedure (cf. N5.1). This may appear as trivial as saying, for example, that we explain the fact that a particular swan, Hisser, is white from the conjunction of "All swans are white" and "Hisser is a swan." One might as well explain some particular as having some characteristic (such as "John is accident prone") by saying that all particulars like *that* particular have the given characteristic ("All people just like John are accident prone").

Two comments are in order as concerns this conventionalistic or circular aspect of explanation by instantiation. First of all, the general law (or laws) takes precedence over the examination of a given particular. As scientists, for example, we are familiar with these general laws and classificatory schemata. If in fact a particular is found to exemplify a law, then we do indeed understand that particular in light of our comprehension of a law that is part of our domain of familiar discourse. The law of gravitation does explain events, although even the gravitational physicist is pressed to tell us why objects do appear to "attract" one another as a function of their masses and distances. The language of gravitation is a familiar one. It has the status of an explainer (an explicans) of falling objects, even though it presents a mere description of what we classify as free-falling objects. Why this language should prove a cognitively satisfactory explainer is not a question to be answered by a logic; it is a psychological question (cf. N5.2). Secondly, the element of cognitive enlightenment, of comprehension, of understanding, which is essential as the psychological qualifier of explanation, derives from the empirical inspection which results in our finding that a given event belongs to the class of events covered by the explaining law. In the general law, (x) $Sx \supset Rx$, whatever it is, the element of cognitive enlightenment comes in our recognizing that some event can be assigned to a class of events designated by 'Sx'. We first recognize that the event is a particular of the class of all particulars, x, to which we can assign S. This may not be immediately obvious to us, any more than it was immediately obvious to early scientists that magnetic and electrical events were describable by the same set of equations, or that judgments of value and judgments of sensory magnitude were describable by the same psychophysical laws. Lower-level explanations of the type we have been discussing would be circular only if we manufactured a law for each particular and its properties to be explained (cf. N5.1). But as we have seen, the laws take precedence. Explanations are achieved only when we find how to classify our explananda. At the level of instantiation then, explanation is a matter of putting our events to be explained, our explananda, into familiar slots, where the slots are general laws enunciated in the progress of science.

Superficially, these procedures of lower-level explanation look embarrassingly like the typologies which have been the scandal of psychology. A person displays such and such behavior because he possesses such and such a faculty, disposition, or personality type. The difficulty here is that one begins with behavior and from the classes of behavior "types" attempts to ascertain correlated characteristics in physiognomy, modes of expression, verbal report, etc. There may or may not be substantial correlations between, say, temperament and body type, but such correlations, even though they express "laws," cannot serve as satisfactory explanations in the sense discussed here. To find that all mesomorphs are aggressive is hardly an adequate explanation of why Hank is aggressive, even though Hank may be a mesomorph. The law does not take precedence over the class of particulars it now explains. That is to say, the law is not now found to hold for (and explain) a class of events not included in its initial formulation. Psychologically, what is satisfactory about lower level explanations is that a law (or laws) is extended to cover classes of events not visualized as being covered in its initial formulation. This aspect of lower-level explanation suggests: one, the explicandum is explained by a law not restricted to the class of events that are similar in all (cognitively germane) characteristics to itself; and two, the extension of the law itself is enhanced by virtue of the successful explanation.

Higher-Level Explanations

The hierarchy of levels in explanation rests upon the regress in explanatory pursuit. Thus, if the explicandum E is explained by the explicans L_1 and in turn we explain the predicates in the general laws of L_1 by another set of propositions L_2, then L_2 constitutes a higher-order explicans. Not only do we derive the sentences that truly describe E, but we derive in turn those laws and principles that are the instruments of inferring the description of E. Thus, for example, one can derive specific behaviors of the planets from Kepler's three laws of the planetary orbits; but also one can in turn derive Kepler's laws within the rubric of classical Newtonian mechanics. The explicans in the lower-level explanation is itself explained. Or again, we can explain certain changes in response pattern as an instance of the law of effect. But the law of effect might be explained in turn by a theory that postulates activation of cell congeries by the presence of reinforcing stimuli, thereby facilitating the emergence of cell assemblies that mediate the habitual response (e.g., Hebb, 1949; Milner, 1957; Rosenblatt, 1958).

In general then, theoretical explanations are higher-order explanations. The experimental hypotheses which are derived theorems within the theory are expressions of laws. These laws in turn might be the general principles serving in the lower-level explanations of particular events. Thus the idea of a hierarchy of explanations is simple to comprehend. However, the idea of higher-order explanations becomes particularly interesting when we consider explaining laws of one science in terms of the theoretical formulations of another. This is the familiar problem of reduction. It will occupy our attention to some considerable extent in subsequent chapters. But upon initial inspection, it is significant that reductive expansions themselves imply a hierarchy of explanations. A reducing science which constitutes the argument of an explicans is, in some sense, thought to be more inclusive or more basic than the reduced science. A successful reduction thereby provides us with a cognitively satisfying explication of events and laws in the domain of the reduced science.

LOGICAL REQUIREMENT OF EXPLANATION

In the discussion of levels of explanation, we have been concerned with deducibility of the explicandum. It is time to give the rubric of deducibility a more explicit formulation.

The classic treatment of the logic of explanation is to be found in an article by Hempel and Oppenheim (1948). Their schema follows that suggested by Popper (1959) and is given in the following summary statements (1948, p. 138).

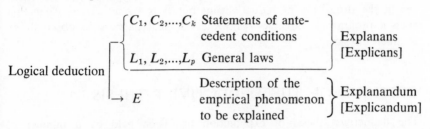

In light of the foregoing discussion, the elaboration of the summary statement should be obvious. 'Instantiation', 'deducibility', 'derivability', all are terms designating the procedure by which we arrive at a description of the event to be explained. Hempel and Oppenheim also prescribe the following logical conditions for the adequacy of the explanation:

R(1), The explanandum must be a logical consequence of the explanans. . . .

R(2), The explanans must contain general laws and these must actually be required for the derivation of the explanandum. . . .

R(3), The explanans must have empirical content; i.e., it must be capable, at least in principle, of test by experiment or observation. . . .

R(4), The sentences constituting the explanans must be true. . . . (1948, p. 137)

Strangely perhaps, this last requirement is the most curious of the four. As the requirements stand they imply that the schema applies only to what we have treated as lower-level explanations. What of higher-level explanations? The given schema would then have to be altered to include the possibility of hypothetical constructs among a set of postulates. (The completed theory need not include such constructs, but then, in the sense of a complete microreduction, no theory is itself complete.) Thus the explanans would include statements of antecedent conditions, general laws, *and* a set of postulates including whatever hypothetical constructs are sufficient for deducing all the theorems (experimental laws) of the science. This being the case, then there is some puzzlement as to the applicability of condition R(4).

Initially, the hypothetical constructs are theoretical entities of somewhat dubious existential status. They serve as devices in an if-then chain of reasoning. However, the only observational anchoring by which we may judge the truth of such hypothetical statements rests in the consequents of the chain of deduction. We thereby have necessary observational conditions for the truth of the hypothetical statements in the explanans, but we do not have the sufficient conditions. It is difficult then to see how we can hold consistently to condition R(4), unless, of course, we undertake a program to reduce all hypothetical terms to empirical entities. There is good reason for aspiring to such a program, as we shall see in the discussion of reductionism; but it is by no means clear that such a program is possible—as witness logical barriers to observability in microphysics.

CRITIQUE OF THE DEDUCTIVIST THESIS

The deductivist thesis of explanation has been held by a number of distinguished scientists and philosophers (cf. N5.3). It ignores the subjective aspects of cognitive satisfaction and concentrates on the less equivocal requirements of deducibility. It forms an integral aspect of hypothetico-deductive method in the sciences. Still in spite of the pervasive character of this methodology in all ot the philosophy of science, serious objections have been raised against the gospel of deducibility. Some of these objections are as old as the systematic attacks on modern science, some are more recent. We shall attempt to sift them out by attending to the following questions: (1) Does deducibility in fact serve as the touchstone of explanation in scientific practice? (2) Are prediction and explanation symmetric, as the Hempel–Oppenheim thesis of deducibility maintains? (3) Are there events which in principle are unamenable to, or are otherwise refractory to, deducibility?

Deducibility and the Analysis of Explanation

Several contemporary philosophers of science (Scriven, 1958, 1962, 1963; Goudge, 1958; Yolton, 1958, 1959; Hesse, 1963; Sellars, 1962; Feyerabend, 1962) have been critical of the deductivist analysis of explanation on grounds that the actual practice of scientific explanation is not so amenable to neat logical treatment as the deductivists claim. Of these, Scriven has been the most persistent in his criticism, and for the sake of brevity, we shall follow the line of his attack. First of all, if we look at the usages of 'explanation' we find that the term is used to designate quite diverse activities even in the restricted range of its applications in science. Not all explanations are deductive in nature; some are descriptive, many are causal, and many carry with them a kind of certificate of "primeval" assurance from within on the conceptual framework in which they occur. The language of science itself creates the conditions of understanding, it breeds its own intelligibility. Secondly, the schema of deducibility oversimplifies the process of arriving at explanations. It subsumes a finished body of laws, principles, postulates, such that explanations always occur in a finished corpus of theory. But this, according to Scriven (also see Yolton, 1958, 1959), is seldom the case. Only in "complete" theories, such as that of Newtonian mechanics where there are no unspecified nuisance variables, can we aspire to this placid ideal. Rather in most of our efforts, explaining requires the interplay of experimental hypothesis, factual language, and theoretical construction. These are contextually interrelated. Not only are theoretical systems incomplete but they are contextually dynamical in that events, i.e., the explicanda, themselves, may inspire some modification of the theory. Thirdly, deductivism concentrates on the symbols of science, on its language and statements, rather than on events as such. Hypothetico-deductive methodology retains both its simplicity and integrity by attending only to statements; it refers to statements and not to the events as such, which presumably are capable of a more direct cognitive assimilation. Moreover, general laws are idealizations. Lawlike statements are both inaccurate and incomplete as descriptions of particular events to which presumably they apply.

Should the foregoing not be sufficient to reject deductivism, Scriven then mounts his attack on the Hempel–Oppenheim thesis with the following bill of particulars:

1. It fails to make the crucial logical distinctions between explanations, grounds for explanations, things to be explained, and the description of things.
2. It is too restrictive . . . [in that it excludes many examples of scientific explanation].
3. It is too inclusive and admits entirely nonexplanatory schema.
4. It requires an account of cause, law, and probability which are basically unsound.
5. It leaves out of account three notions that are in fact essential for an account of scientific explanation: context, judgment, and understanding (Scriven, 1962, p. 196).

Such an unrelenting attack on deductivism should be sufficient to bury it as a significant analysis of explanation; but, in many respects, this schedule of particulars is more contentious than convincing (cf. N5.4). The points Scriven makes here are poignant, but what is not given due emphasis is the fact that hypothetico-deductive explanation is a schema. As such, it is an ideal. Its only straightforward application is in a complete theory.[1] Few sciences, certainly not that of psychology, can offer complete theories without loose constructions and nebulous inference chains. Nevertheless, this fact does not obviate the need for rigorous specifications as concerns adequate explanation. In contrast, what is more distressing is what Brodbeck (1962) has designated the reliance upon "obscurantist" criteria of understanding and intelligibility. These

---

[1] By "complete theory" is meant one in which *all* relevant variables are accurately specified. Related terms are "closed systems" and perfect knowledge as related to scientific systems. See Bergmann, 1957; Brodbeck, 1962.

have their roots more in intuition and the feel for conceptual context than in logical analysis. Critique of deductivism is warranted, to be sure; it should prompt our care and our caution to achieve logically adequate explanations. But it does not disqualify the deductivist thesis. Intelligibility is secured by logical analysis more than it is by impressionistic reference to "understanding." The deductivist thesis subsumes the ideal of complete theories. As such, it is programmatic as well as prescriptive. Were the case otherwise, the contemporary stress on the axiomatization of theories would be gratuitous.

Explanation and Prediction

One of the implications of the Hempel–Oppenheim argument is that explanation and prediction should be symmetric. That is to say, the time context of the event to be explained is irrelevant so far as the criterion of deducibility is concerned. Commenting on their schema of explanation, Hempel and Oppenheim write:

> Let us note here that the same formal analysis, including the four necessary conditions, applies to scientific prediction as well as to explanation. The difference between the two is of pragmatic character. If E is given, i.e., if we know the phenomenon described by E has occurred, and a suitable set of statements C_1, C_2, . . . , C_k, L_1, L_2, . . . , L_r is provided afterwards, we speak of an explanation of the phenomenon in question. If the latter statements are given and E is derived prior to the occurrence of the phenomenon it describes, we speak of a prediction. It may be said, therefore, that an explanation is not fully adequate unless its explanans, if taken account of in time, could have served as a basis for predicting the phenomenon under consideration (1948, p. 138).

This is a strong statement and exception has been taken to its thesis (e.g., Scheffler, 1957; Rescher, 1958; Hanson, 1959; Scriven, 1962). For a complete theory, such as the Newtonian model of the solar system was once assumed to be, predictions and postdictions could be made with equal facility, and within the same logical schema (as demonstrated, for example, in the planetarium). However, it is not difficult to find exceptions to this simplistic treatment of prediction. In practice, predictions, however rational, seem to include an element of intuitive gambit in which the predictor commits himself against a background of risk or of chance which is not part of any rational structure of the theory. The uncertainty is a cognitive uncertainty belonging to the predictor; in no way is it part of the formal structure of a theory or other explanans. Furthermore, when we turn to microphysics, we find that quantum phenomena can be deduced *ex post facto* as the logic of explanation requires, but due to the uncertainty factors, they cannot be predicted with the same precision (Hanson, 1959). The specification and overall knowledge of the system is less perfect.

There is a significant difference in the character of the two lines of argument suggested above. The elements of intuitive gambit and cognitive uncertainty, so to speak, represent lacunae in the chain of inference. They betoken the inchoate character of the theoretical system which serves as the logical foundations of inference. As such, they can be overcome by completion of the system of inference, by our having available a theory with complete specification of all variables germane to the events in question. In principle, then, perfect knowledge is possible and prediction would indeed follow the hypothetico-deductive schema. However, the deducible-in-principle outlook is obliterated in the argument as presented by Hanson. The character of predictive statements is uniquely different from *ex post facto* explanations. Predictions necessarily carry with them uncertainty effects due to feedback (interference) in our ascertaining the initial conditions and the state of the system. There is no way to overcome this predicament in quantum physics. Even with perfect knowledge (as allowable within the premises of the theory) we cannot in principle predict with the same precision that we can explain events after the fact.

Since the status of the uncertainty principle is still being debated, perhaps one should be cautious in accepting this latter argument as dogma. But there can be little question that gaining knowledge of the state of a system to be predicted is uniquely different from hypothesizing what the state of the system has been in order for certain phenomena to obtain. For example, a neurophysiological explanation of behavior might be such as to assert that if the state of the system could be represented by $S_1, S_2, \ldots, S_j$, then we could infer E_r as a description of the actual behavior. The explanation is hypothetical. No interference effects (e.g., scalpel cuts, electrode implants) have been introduced to affect the states signified by $S_1, S_2, \ldots, S_j$. It is clearly different in the case of prediction. In order to predict behavior, or rather, to predict its description E, we must empirically ascertain the state of the system. Thus not only do we need statements of the order $S_1, S_2, \ldots, S_j$, but we will require additional statements of the character $S_k, S_l, \ldots$ which specify the effects that gaining knowledge of the system will have on the system. In principle, it might be possible to build perfect predictive theories incorporating the interference effects but the theory and chain of deductive inference would differ in this respect from those of explanation: they would include interference variables for which there is neither place nor need in explanation.

Even admitting this line of argument, the deductivist may wish to assert that his thesis of the symmetry of prediction and explanation is inviolate. Both explanation and prediction adopt the same schema of deduction. How the initial conditions are determined is irrelevant to his inquiry. He is interested only in the fact that from C-statements and

L-statements (Hempel–Oppenheim) he can deduce *E* statements descriptive either of past or of future phenomena. This line of argument can only be pursued at the risk of suppressing vital methodological distinctions. In principle, we might think both psychology and mechanics are capable of complete specification of variables and perfect knowledge. Nevertheless, the class of predictions includes a set of variables not included in the class of hypothetico-deductive explanations. Predictions involve interference variables which need not be, and usually are not, included in explanations.

Mention should also be made here of the troublesome reflexive aspects of certain classes of predictions. In complete systems with perfect knowledge, specification of the values of *all* variables will, through the deductive chain, yield a statement exhaustively descriptive of the event to be predicted or explained. But what of systems wherein the statement E_r itself becomes a value of a significant variable in the state of the system, thereby yielding a different *E,* say E_s, and different state of the system, then a different E_t, and so on *ad infinitum?* This is the familiar problem of reflexive predictions (Merton, 1957; Buck, 1963) wherein the prediction itself serves to enhance or to mitigate the event predicted. Witness, for example, the effect that a precision prediction of the stock market might have on the subsequent behaviors of investors.

This problem is too involved to pursue here. There can be little doubt, however, that it suggests difficulties for the behavioral scientist, not met, say, by the macrophysicist. Reflexive predictions can be shown to be trouble free in this context only if they can be incorporated into what have been designated complete theories.

Yet all this is a rather fruitless debate. There is no question but that scientists and nonscientists alike proceed differently in making predictions and in producing explanations. If taken seriously, the task of prediction is the more difficult. In explanation, all the data, all the information, is before the person; but in prediction this is not the case, the events are yet to happen (cf. N5.5).

Nondeducible Events

Our third and final question in the critique of deducibility is: Are there any events or classes of events which in principle are nondeducible? Three lines of argument can be entertained as proposing affirmative responses to the question. They will occupy us for the remainder of this chapter. One, statistical laws refer to probabilistic relations between classes of events. No inference can be made concerning individual events. Therefore, no derivation, no explanation (or prediction) in terms of statements about individual events is possible. Two, events occur with putatively emergent properties. What distinguishes emergent from nonemergent properties is their nonpredictable character at the time of their emergence. And three, all individual events are unique. Classification is undertaken as a matter of procedural convenience. One does not suffer from this loss of specificity in the physical (or other nomothetic) sciences, but in psychology and other personalistic sciences the loss is fatal, so it is argued, both to understanding and to prediction. Statements about unique individuals are not deducible from general laws.

(1) *Statistical explanation.*   When describing individual events, we must always think in terms of assigning a property or a set of properties to some particular. Either the particular is to be assigned a given property in the catalog of all properties or it is not. A two-value logic applies. Aside from some subjectivist treatments, probability relationships and predicates are always thought to apply to collectives. Thus statistical explanation within the deductive schema permits our deriving statistical laws and statements of relative frequencies but it does not permit us to deduce whether or not a given particular (event) within the collective will have a given property.

As stated here, the argument is quite correct. Our concern need only be as to whether on such grounds the deductivist schema is disqualified as the basis of explanation. At the outset, we should note there is no questioning our not being able to explain or to predict individual events on the basis of laws that are predominantly statistical. Consider the behavior of the die described in the preceding chapter. The die has some propensity to respond, which we have called a disposition. The laws describing that disposition are probabilistic ones. Suppose for all such dice the probability of throwing an even number is twice that of throwing an odd. Thus if some given die is a member of this class of dice, it will fall even with a probability of two-thirds. Translated into the collectivist's language, this means that out of the class of many such tosses, our expectations are that two-thirds of them will be even. But note that neither the property of being even nor the property of being odd is excluded by this lawlike description. Thus, following the deductivist schema, regardless of what the outcome is, it is "explainable" by the same set of laws. Explanations of individual events would therefore lose the precision we expect. In fact, there is no precision in dealing with individual events; that is just the point.

This example is, of course, a trivial one. We could better have taken as our example choice behavior and some stochastic model of learning. Theorems derivable within the model are expressed in terms of probability of response. In the dichotomous choice situation, say, both response R and response $\sim R$ are covered by the theorems of response. Yet which of these two responses is to occur on a specific trial is neither to be predicted nor explained.

This is a poignant criticism and it needs to be taken seriously (see, for example, Hempel, 1962). However, it is fatal to the deductivist point of view only if we assume that science must predict and explain individual events. A law is nonetheless a law because it expresses a probability relationship rather than some categorical assignment of a property. And a prediction is nonetheless a prediction even though it asserts only that some proportion p of all events will have the property. But what is more important, the schema of the argument is the same both in complete systems with perfect knowledge and which permit prediction of particular events, and in relatively incomplete systems with imperfect knowledge and which incorporate probability and uncertainty into their predictions. An analysis of the application of such stochastic models shows that they fit the deductivist schema. From statements of initial conditions and statistical laws, one derives statements about classes or collectives of response. It is of interest to note that among the few attempts at axiomatization of psychological theory is that concerning a statistical learning theory (Estes and Suppes, 1959). Successful axiomatization assures us that the deductivist schema of explanation will hold (cf. N5.6).

(2) *Emergent events.* Another class of occurrences which is presumed to be problematical for the deductivist schema of explanation is that of emergent events. The concept of emergence is difficult to define and examples of emergent events which carry ontological pedigree over and above the mere symptoms of novelty are all but impossible to verify. Let us be somewhat lenient in our specifications then and define as emergent any event whose occurrence is not deducible within any extant theory. By definition then, emergent events are indeed problematical for those who stress the indispensability of deduction in matters of scientific explanation.

We can, however, be somewhat more explicit. We can focus upon two alternatives allowable within the scope of this definition. One, we may speak of emergent properties within the language of science, such that statements of emergent properties are not derivable within the science from any of the statements of the properties of known particulars. And two, we may speak of emergent properties precipitated, as it were, in the emitive process of creative, cosmic, hormic, or other type of emergent evolution. In the first case, the issues of emergence are primarily epistemological; in the second case, they have ontological significance.

Consider the first of these. From a corpus of theory and fact, all known properties of events can be represented in the set of all predicates, $\{P_1, P_2, \ldots, P_n\}$. An emergent event is then one to which we must assign some new property or predicate, P_{n+1}, which is neither deducible or otherwise assignable within the corpus of the science. The ingredient of unpredictability presumably signifies a genuine emergent novelty. A classic presentation of this line of argument can be found in Broad's *Mind and Its Place in Nature* (1925), where he argues that our knowledge of the properties of constituents in chemical compounds may not be sufficient for us to predict the properties of the compound events. Thus he writes:

> The characteristic behavior of common salt cannot be deduced from the most complete knowledge of the properties of Sodium in isolation, or of Chlorine in isolation, or of other compounds of Sodium, such as Sodium-Sulphate; or of other compounds of Chlorine such as Silver-Chloride (p. 59).

After similar examples from chemistry, he goes on to say,

> . . . in abstract terms the emergent theory asserts that there are certain wholes, composed (say) of constituents A, B, and C in relation R to each other; that all wholes composed of constituents of the same kind as A, B, and C in relations of the same kind as R have certain characteristic properties; that A, B, and C are capable of occurring in other kinds of complex where the relation is not the same kind as R; and that the characteristic properties of the whole R (A,B,C) cannot, even in theory, be deduced from the complete knowledge of the properties A, B, and C in isolation or in other wholes which are not of the form R (A,B,C) (p. 61).

We may supplement Broad's examples from chemistry with the following two. If we allow the unreal assumption of an extant science prior to the origins of life, we could hardly have predicted the origins of life from properties of the pre-viable carbons. Or, apropos of the Ladd–Franklin theory of color vision, we could hardly have predicted the qualities of red and green prior to the emergence of the red-green receptors, any more than we could now predict the qualities, say, of ultraviolet were an ultraviolet visual receptor to emerge. Our examples here do not distinguish between properties and qualities of experience. This is a fact we shall have to keep in mind as we examine the response to Broad's argument.

Two lines of argument have, I think, proved all but fatal to Broad's treatment of emergence as an attack on deductive explanation. One, Nagel (1961), has stressed that scientific explanation always concerns the derivation of statements and never the events as such.[2] Thus, for a deductive schema to be adequate to the task of explanation, it must contain statements of all events and properties to be explained within the theory. This is a truism. If some novel property were "emergent," then indeed, if there were no expression for it, if some statement describing or even naming it were not part of the language of the science, that property could neither be predicted nor explained. But in this case the

---

[2] The present discussion of emergence owes a great deal to the reading of Nagel.

concept of emergence tends to be a trivial one. It merely implies that the science is immature and relatively incomplete. One would then have only to extend the set of predicates and the set of propositions to include statements about the novel property. Explanation of the "emergent" event might then be achieved within the familiar deductivist schema. Suppose, for example, that of some species of primitive organisms the only known properties of response in its native environment were reflexive ones. And suppose further that now under some radical alteration of their environment individuals of the species were observed to display emergent properties of learning. Obviously our theory of these organisms would have to be expanded to include learned response in the set of all response properties. Explanation is not ruled out by emergence of new response properties. Indeed, it becomes imperative to explain the emergent properties through a modification of the theory. As Nagel states the argument:

> Accordingly, all descriptive explanations occurring in a statement that is allegedly deducible from the theory must also occur among the expressions used to formulate the theory or the assumptions adjoined to the theory when it is applied to specialized circumstances. Thus a statement like "Water is translucent" cannot indeed be deduced from any set of statements about hydrogen and oxygen which do not contain the expressions 'water' and 'translucent'; but this impossibility derives entirely from purely formal considerations and is relative to the special set of statements adopted as premises in the case under consideration.
>
> It is clear, therefore, that to say of a given property that it is an "emergent" is to attribute to it a character which the property may possess relative to one theory or body of assumptions but may not possess relative to some other theory. Accordingly, the doctrine of emergence (in the sense now under discussion) must be understood as stating certain *logical* facts about formal relations between statements rather than any experimental or even "metaphysical" facts about some allegedly "inherent" traits of *properties* of objects (1961, p. 369).

A second and equally convincing line of argument has been proposed by Kurt Grelling (an early positivist and victim of Nazi tyranny). Taken at face value there is an inconsistency implicit within Broad's type of part-whole argument. In effect, that argument asserts that properties of the emergent whole cannot be predicted from our knowledge of the properties of the constituent parts. It is short-sighted to assert that properties of the whole are unpredictable from knowledge of properties of the parts, for an exhaustive denumeration of the properties of the parts include all those combinatorial potentialities which are reified (i.e., emerge) when such parts combine to form wholes.

It should be noted that Broad (1925) himself protects against this argument by deliberately excluding the properties of potential combination in the emergent from the set of properties attributable to the constituents. But this is not an allowable safeguard. It spares the doctrine of emergence by keeping the constituents in epistemic isolation. It succeeds only in restricting the discussion to that class of emergent situations where extant theory is insufficiently explicit to permit derivation of the emergent properties of the events. As the quotation from Nagel intimates, emergence in these terms reflects only a logical limitation.

Earlier it was asserted that one must distinguish between properties of objects and those qualities which we regard as the contents of consciousness. Broad's argument has sometimes been interpreted as saying, for example, that from all the properties of hydrogen and oxygen, we cannot infer those combinatorial properties of water such as its translucence and taste, which are qualities of our perceptual experience. This is a mistaken application. Be that as it may, it is quite in order to say that qualities of our subjective experience are never strictly deducible from statements about physical events. It is one of the recurrent themes of logical empiricism that qualia, as it were, are given. They are not deducible or otherwise explainable. The only way it would make sense to incorporate them into the schema of explanation would be to replace them by statements such as those reflecting postulates of psychophysical parallelism. Following this tack, we would not, of course, concern ourselves with qualia, as such. In one of the earliest discussions of emergence, Pepper (1926) discounts all doctrines of emergence which concern themselves with epiphenomena rather than with physical events subject to public and lawful description. It is the nature of epiphenomena to be unexplainable. That is why they, in their pristine isolation, are not the proper subject matter of science.

The foregoing discussion has treated emergence primarily as a problem in epistemology. What if we were to treat it as a doctrine of ontological significance? According to this latter thesis, the universe of laws and relations is itself the subject of ontogenesis, forever developing new "habit patterns," ever building on the fund of its childhood, always emerging into yet another adulthood. Thus the changing, evolving, emerging universe. This theme has been the subject of literature and science alike. It is to be found in the prefaces and plays of Bernard Shaw, in the writings of the biologists C. L. Morgan and J. B. S. Haldane, in the philosophical writings of Alexander, Bergson, Boodin, and Whitehead. It is the subject of debate and counterdebate in modern physical cosmology. It is an enticing doctrine, it appeals to the Heraclitean mystique. Yet, two observations can be made at the outset. One, there is no reliable means of testing this doctrine. And two, nothing in the doctrine precludes our adopting hypothetico-deductive methodology as the instrument of understanding.

Consider first the matter of verifying the hypothesis of cosmic emergence. In order to attest to genuine emergent properties in the universe, we must be able to distinguish such properties from those which are merely novel and from those which by virtue of our epistemological limitations are merely unpredictable. In an article on "The Status of Emergence," Henle (1942) addresses himself specifically to this problem. First, he notes that unpredictability cannot serve as the critical property of emergence, ". . . predictability, far from being a mere predicate, is at least a tetradic relation and we must say, not that quality A is predictable, but rather that quality A is predictable by person B on evidence C with degree of assurance D" (p. 489). Thus, "any characteristic past, present, or future, not related to a given body of evidence would be unpredictable on that evidence." However, novel events, such as the accidental discovery of a new planet, and inadequate theories both imply unpredictability without at the same time implying emergence. Novelty clearly exists, but whereas emergence entails novelty and unpredictability, the latter do not entail emergence. Henle then maintains that a formal definition of emergence requires, (1) that the emergent event must be logically novel, in the sense of its being unpredictable within extant theory; and (2) that it be not merely a spatio-temporal accident, such as the discovery of the new planet. Seemingly such criteria could be applied to the evaluation of novel events. However, the issue of "ontological versus epistemological significance" is left hanging. The ultimate analysis is logical. Emergence is judged in the context of theory and theories are evaluated in terms of their comprehensiveness and simplicity. But logical simplicity relates to the language of science. It possesses no substantive, hence no ontological, significance. Cosmic emergence cannot be conclusively verified.

Be that as it may, even were we to grant the possibility of cosmic evolution, i.e., a dynamic cosmogony, we might wonder whether there would be efficacious alternatives to scientific explanation. To be sure, Bergsonian intuitionism has been proposed as an alternative (cf. N5.7). But then we must enter a different realm of knowledge wherein language can play no part. For example, Bergson (1911) writes, "We do not *think* real time. But we *live* in it because life transcends intellect." Transcendence thus removes the object, the process, from the realm of explanation and thereby accomplishes its own irrelevance for discussions like the present one. However, what is sometimes overlooked is that Bergson was, himself, an astute analyst of abstractive science. His cognizance of the role of invention and representational devices was the source of the sympathetic bonds that existed between him and James and the pragmatists. As such, the rigors of scientific explanation were not to be discounted within the realm of scientific understanding itself. If one were committed to the language of science, then what limited discussion of emergence would be at all possible must be accomplished within the syntax and limitations of that language.

We may visualize two situations in which it might be appropriate to use the language of emergence. Our concern is to show that in neither case is the deductive schema of explanation rendered inapplicable to the task of bringing emergent phenomena within its purview. First, suppose we grant the evolution of the terrestrial universe from the primeval to the complex. This evolutionary process signals the emergence of ever more complex structures out of primeval substance. Thus, for example, in Oparin's conception of the origin of life (1938), primitive life forms (emergents) evolved when the impact of cosmic radiation on primeval carbides instigated a chain of events eventuating in the production of self-duplicating organic compounds. Each event in the chain might be regarded as emergent in that new substances with new properties came into production where there had been no such substances before. In this context it is little more than a quibble to debate whether emergence is an epistemological or an ontological hypothesis. In either case, novel events have to be incorporated into a science which at each epoch of emergence could not be sufficiently complete to explain the emergence of the new properties. Awaiting its emergent fund of knowledge, science would have to be retrospective. Still its explanatory function would be achieved deductively and would be expanded as the ingress of emergent properties made it imperative to enlarge the fund of basic predicates.

The second situation is more dramatic. Suppose the universe were such that it could be understood only as a succession of epochs. Not only would we have to contend with emergent properties but with ever-changing laws as well. Engaging as this possibility might be in the realm of science fiction, it is difficult to see how its possibility would in any way alter the scientific enterprise. Laws, to begin with, express relations between variables that designate properties or other classifying characteristics. Thus if one of the variables were time, a law might express change in some property as a function of time. At some higher-order level of complexity, we might find that the function expressed in the law is itself a function of time. We might have a succession of epochs, E_j, E_k, . . . , E_n, . . . such that each epoch contained a unique law over some distinguishable or otherwise enduring classification of phenomena. Under the circumstances we would hardly have any alternative but to proceed as we do under the assumption of a constant universe. We would look for some law descriptive of the epochal changes (i.e., a law of epochs), and make that law the instrument of explanation and prediction. Should no orderly progression of epochal change be in evidence or should assumptions of the constancy of "nature" not be applicable (as, for example, a random change in universal constants), then our law of epochs would become a stochastic law, incorporating the properties of randomness.

In summary, then, a defense of the deductivist schema of explanation is maintained against the proposals and arguments of emergence.

The deductivist, as we so style our partisan here, does not on any grounds rule out novelty. Nor does he ever claim that theories are even approximately complete, sufficiently so that novel phenomena are invariably predictable in advance of the actual occurrence of the emergent properties. Nor does he necessarily rule out on any grounds the possibility of ontologically significant doctrines of emergence. What he does claim is that there is no alternative but to formulate his explanations in terms of laws and formal theories. The critique of scientific explanation often involves discussions of how science is actually done. Doubtless intuition has played a role. The history of science has shown that scientific thinking has been at times haphazard and irrationalistic. But eventually we seek simplified formulations, a tidying up of scientific thinking, not just in the domain of experimental confirmation but also in that of logical analysis and clarification. On these grounds discussions of the methodology of deductivism and schemata of explanation will never lose their relevance. To think otherwise is to retreat into irrationalism, against which the scientific revolution has been the obdurate and incessant countertheme.

(3) *Idiographic versus nomothetic descriptions.*   The third argument is not so much an attack on deductivism as it is an effort to show that explanation is not the only means to understanding. One understands not alone by explanation, he also apprehends meaning directly through a meticulous description of the event-complex as a unique historical phenomenon. Indeed in history, psychology, and political science, direct knowledge by description is indispensable to understanding.

The issue is frequently drawn on the distinction between *nomothetic* and *idiographic* descriptions. Nomothetic descriptions involve statements of general laws, principles of inference, and the language of classes applying to many particulars, whereas idiographic descriptions involve statements explicitly describing the individual as a unique phenomenon in some spatio-temporal section. In scientific explanation understanding is achieved by our utilizing nomothetic statements as tools of description and inference. But inference is always from one class symbol to another. Therefore, in such context, an individual event assigned class membership can be known only by the attribution to it of the defining general property. This obliterates its individuality. And, we are told, it is this individuality which we are concerned to understand. Nomothetic devices may function well for the physical sciences where historical origins and individuality can be ignored, but this is not the case for history and psychology where the unique nonrepeatable history of the event to be understood renders all but the crudest of class identifications impossible.

The alternative, of course, is idiographic description. However, it is not always clear in the arguments whether idiographic understanding is a special kind of intuitive, nonlinguistic understanding, *per se,* or whether it designates a special kind of nonlogical inference. If it is the former, we need hardly concern ourselves with it in a treatise on explanation. Intuitive understanding, if it is beyond the pale of language and its class structure, could neither be communicable nor an instrument of explanation: "Whereof one cannot speak, he must be silent." On the other hand, if it is the latter, then the idiographic approach to knowledge results in a state of understanding which follows from this special kind of nonlogical inference. In this case, we would not have to keep our silence; and the understanding, if it were shared by several observers, might become the instrument of explanation. At any rate, from awareness and the idiographic description of an event complex, $E_1 \ldots E_n$, and some nonlogical instrument of inference, I_f, we could infer, predict, understand, comprehend, or otherwise intuit the state of affairs which is the object of curiosity. What that "nonlogical instrument" is, is of course, the crucial item. It cannot be any kind of analogy, for that would throw "idiographic inference" back in the clutches of abstraction, nomothetics, and the class struggle. That is why appeals to *empathy* and to *verstehende* remain so unconvincing as tools of inference; they show their kinship with analogy. As in the cases of identification and projection they reveal their psychological origins as cognitive supports. Experientially derived, they implicitly afford us general principles of inference that we as individuals bring to focus upon individual events.

There can be little question but that some subconsciously processed fund of experience serves us in our individual worlds as the nonformalized instruments of inference. In brief, this is the heart of the doctrine of apperception. Any unique event sequence is meaningful to us to the extent we can assimilate it to the complex system of cognitive schemata. There is, however, an alternative to the empirical origins of the schemata. It renders the doctrines of idiographic intuition and *verstehende* somewhat more poignant than they would otherwise be within ordinary psychological analysis. According to Windelband (1921), to whom the nomothetic–idiographic distinction is due, perceptual schemata are *a priori.* Like the Kantian categories and the transcendental aesthetic, they are the indispensable agents for the reification of experience. Consequently, to attend to the unique event as it happens, to understand it, is to know that that experience *must* be ordered, *must* occur, in just the way it does. Not only do we experience A and B, but in experiencing A and B, we know that B must have the relations (e.g., cause–effect) to A that it does.

Now the Kantian argument for cognitive predispositions has always been an enticing one. However, in spite of some dissent (Michotte, 1963), empiricist psychologists remain unconvinced. They remain good Humeans and make of intuition and apperception nothing that cannot be accounted for in terms of the person's processing information by his experientially derived perceptual categories. Nevertheless, a number of psychologists, primarily personologists, have held out for a special license for idiographic descriptions. Influenced by the writings of philosophers like Dilthey, Windelband, and Rickert, they see in idiographic descriptions an instrument of knowledge different from and compensatory to the nomothetic formula of general theories. In an early paper, Klein (1932) lists four types of understanding: (1) a structural continuity type (e.g., diagrams and models); (2) a functional unit type (e.g., cybernetics, Deutsch, 1960; Gregory, 1961); (3) an implicative type (e.g., by *modus ponens*); and (4) empathetic understanding (as in idiographic description). Of these, the first three fit our schema of scientific explanation. The latter is unique. But doubtless it is Allport (1937) who has placed the greatest emphasis on the idiographic study of personality. Faculty psychology, typologies, trait profiles, attitude scaling, all of these bring with them the suppression of what is unique to the person as an individual. And in a different theoretical setting, Lewin (1935, 1936) has emphasized the individual as being best pictured as a unique field construct of personal and environmental variables, in which his unique genotype can be understood only by probing behind the nomothetic aspects of the phenotype.

For a time, much of this sounded like a radical thesis, almost a rejection of the familiar principles of scientific description and explanation. On closer inspection, however, (see, for example, Skaggs, 1945, and Allport's reply, 1946) it has appeared that the issues are not at all clearly drawn. Both idiographic and nomothetic methods of description and understanding are essential. One is to supplement the other. Thus Allport writes: "Where my view is 'unorthodox' is in my contention that psychological science (and I mean here the total course of psychological inquiry) cannot stop with common traits, factors, IQ's, and like nomothetic dimensions, but must admit additional methods and theories to handle the organic interrelation of the artificialized variables with which nomothetic science deals, and must represent better than it has the personalized coloring of these variables in the individual life" (1946, p. 133). And what constitutes the idiographic personalized coloring of the descriptive variables? It is Lewin who points up the issue which both friend and foe of idiography have come to regard as significant. He writes:

> Even if all the laws of psychology were known, one could make a prediction about the behavior of a man only if in addition to the laws the special nature of the particular situation were known . . . [A task] of equal importance and inseparably connected with the determination of laws, involves the task of representing concrete situations in such a way that the actual event can be derived from them according to the principles which are given in the general laws (Lewin, 1936, p. 11).

Even granting that Lewin's psychology should stand apart in its own right, the issue as drawn seems not to be so critical after all. If by the meticulous descriptions of idiographic methods (e.g., Allport's case study and personal documents) one seeks only to refine the concrete situation so as to apply principles of valid inference, there can be little quarrel. This is precisely what the physical scientist, the biologist, and any other nomethetic methodologist would agree to.

It is also interesting to note that this is the issue at stake in the arguments of statistical versus clinical prediction (Meehl, 1954; Sarbin, 1944). The issue of the validity of method aside (nomothetics apparently has the edge), clinical intuition is nothing if it is not the application of general rules of inference to highly specific classes of events arrived at through the clinician's careful inspection and evaluation of personal data (cf. N5.8).

RETROSPECT

We may close out this chapter in the same tone with which it was opened. Discussions of scientific explanation are not very reassuring. Although we can give fairly explicit analyses of explanation (as in the writings of Hempel or as in the even more impressively formal constructions of Braithwaite, 1953), few dissertations which pass for explanation in the sciences satisfy the ideal form. At best deductive explanations are reserved for relatively simple, strictly determined systems which are characterized by completeness and perfect knowledge. There are, to be sure, no such systems in psychology. Furthermore, there can be little question but that hunch, wistful hypothesizing, and other intuitive gambits play a large part in filling the lacunae of our deductive schemata. That is why the explicit examples in treatises on the logic of explanation often seem so trivial.

In addition there is always the specter of imperfect knowledge. It is not only that many of our laws are statistical, or that all laws are nomothetic in character (we can learn to live with abstractions), but as Scriven has ceaselessly pointed out, even descriptions of the particular phenomenon are subject to the ambiguities of abstraction. Every particular statement, Sx, is such that some property S is assigned to some particular, x. Yet properties, it must be emphasized, are not particulars. To assign a property is to assign a class membership. And classes are abstractions, wherein the name of the class imposes just that ambiguity we must invariably face in our letting symbols represent particular phenomena.

Be that as it may, it is defeatist to reject the ideal format of deducibility on the grounds that symbolic representations do violence to unique events, whatever they may be. A more ameliorative attitude, for example, has been adopted by Körner (1964) in an attempt to incorporate imperfect descriptions into the deductivist schema (cf. N10.9). Körner argues that the deductive schema is a presumptive bridge spanning our descriptions of events. The statements about events are essentially ambiguous. Even the two-valued logic of predicates fails us. Still, science has no alternative but the idealization of its chain of inference. And the presumptive bridge between the language of fact and the ideal language of the deductive schema must be established if we are to systematize knowledge.

As a final note, it seems singularly fruitless to stress the inadequacies of formal logic and formal explanation as applied to scientific endeavor when the only alternative, it would appear, is to embrace those kinds of *verstehende* which presumably come with the analysis of common usage and the direct contemplation of causal nexus. Knowledgeable intuitionists from Bergson to Marcel have never tired of telling us that there is another more direct understanding than that of abstractive science. No doubt there is. But it is the kind of understanding one should honestly suffer in silence!

NOTES

NOTE 5.1

Leo Postman opened the issue of the circularity of the law of effect in his article "The History and Present Status of the Law of Effect" (1947). Should we fail to define reinforcement and effect independently of learned response then we run the danger of defining the law of effect in terms of response which itself is defined in terms of effect. Examining Postman's comments and others as well, Meehl (1950) has maintained that the charge of circularity is to be avoided if we can in fact define effect and reinforcement independently of response or habit increment. First, Meehl distinguishes between circularity in definition of a term and circularity in proof. A definition is circular if the definiens includes the definiendum among its set of predicates (i.e., if we define X in terms of Y where Y includes X in its meaning). A proof is circular if in establishing the validity of a proposition P, P itself is included in the set of premises of the argument. He then argues that in neither sense need the law of effect be circular. Rather than defining a reinforcer as that which strengthens a response, we define it independently, say, as a stimulus related to drive, to satisfaction, or to expectancy. Then the law of effect states that responses emitted in the presence of such stimuli will be strengthened. But the law of effect does not entail our defining response just in terms of those reinforcing stimuli. The search for those reinforcers is empirical. The assumption is that the class of reinforcers will have the property of being "trans-situational." That is to say, a given reinforcer will be effective in many different response situations wherein the classes of response are defined independently of the applicability of the law of effect.

From the conventionalist point of view (Schlick, Ryle, Toulmin) laws are thought to hold for just those classes of events for which they are indeed found to hold. This would seem to imply circularity of a most insidious kind. However, the argument here begins with the question: Are laws true? Of course they are—for just those cases, for those classes of events, for which they are found to be true descriptions. But this renders trivial the meaning of truth evaluation. A law cannot help but be true. What we do not know is its truth range. Thus a law is a good "inference ticket" and a good explainer to the extent it functions to extend the range of its application. The initial statement of the law, however, is made independently of our knowledge of its range. In effect, what we discover from the application of a law is that what holds for one class of events also holds for another. This is what we mean by extending the range of a law. It is also implicit in lower-level explanation.

In brief, we may avoid circularity in our statement of the law of effect, if we define reinforcers and response strength independently of one another. Although the law may be a conventionalistic formula, there is nothing in that formulation which foretells the range of its application.

NOTE 5.2

Many writers have stressed the role of the familiar in explanation (see e.g., Campbell, 1920, 1921; Hospers, 1946). What is accepted as familiar is a general principle or law which has the status of an unexplained explainer. For most of us, the law of gravitation is an unexplained explainer, even perhaps the law of reinforcement (e.g., for Skinner). It explains but is unexplained. Should one counter that such laws themselves need explanation, he is proposing a legitimate problem. The law needs then to be explained as a deductive consequence of other principles and laws that may constitute a theory. However, the indispensable element of all explanation is the set of first principles which themselves are unexplained. The predicament of explanatory assumptions is that no explanation is complete. One can never explain the particular event and simultaneously all the assumptions, laws, principles, etc., which are the logical components of the explicans. The regress in explanation often stops with the familiar. It is a decision dictated by cognitive appeal and is thereby psychologically arbitrary.

NOTE 5.3

The rudiments of hypothetico-deductive methodology can be found in the works of Mill, Whewell, and Jevons. However, in recent times the argument was taken up by the positivists Feigl (1949) and Carnap (1936). Substantial accounts are given by Popper in *The Logic of Scientific Discovery,* by Braithwaite in his *Scientific Explanation,* and by Nagel in his *The Structure of Science.* Hempel has been a consistent proponent of deductivism in all of the sciences, deterministic and stochastic, physical and historical (1942, 1948, 1962, 1963). Hull's statement of hypothetico-deductive methodology (1943, Chapter I) has been influential in psychology.

As used in the present chapter deductivism refers to the hypothetico-deductive schema of explanation. Debates over deductivism versus inductivism which one finds in the literature do not refer precisely to the issues of explanation and prediction as discussed in the text. Rather, at stake is the matter of the origin and precedence of hypotheses in empirical contexts. Inductivism tends to stress the priority of data and experience; deductivism (Popper, 1935), the priority of hypotheses. See for example, Kotarbiński (1962) for a discussion and defense of inductivism. For a recent defense of deductivism see Brodbeck (1962).

NOTE 5.4

For a clear and incisive (and sometimes acid) defense of deductivism against its critics see Brodbeck's article, "Explanation, Prediction, and 'Imperfect' Knowledge" (1962). Responding primarily to arguments of Scriven, Brodbeck makes the following points:

(1) Stress upon the analysis of common usage reflects a rejection of formal logic. The understanding one gets from such analysis cannot be made explicit. Meaning and understanding of scientific inference require the rigors of syntactical and semantical analysis. As a result votaries of common usage lay emphasis upon subjective rather than objective aspects of scientific knowledge.

(2) A requisite of explanations and predictions is that they be certain. That is to say from a set of premises some one prediction or explanation should be reached and not another. We justify our explanations by reaching certain conclusions. "Either an explanation is deductive or else it does not justify what it is said to explain" (p. 239).

(3) Factors of uncertainty and imperfect knowledge do not obviate deductive models of explanation. Uncertainty effects can be described in statistical laws. In such a case an explanation would refer to a class of events not to some particular. Statistical explanations may not enable us to derive statements about singular events but they do follow the deductive schema all the same.

(4) Belief that "cause" is unanalyzable and therefore basic in our understanding (Scriven) ignores the fact that the foundations of justification rest in logic. Causal imputation is not independent of laws. Explanation is by laws, not by "causes."

(5) Presentation of nonpredictive historical explanation as the paradigm for explanation is grossly misleading. If history either implicitly or explicitly utilizes laws or rules of inference, then its explanation can be for-

malized in the deductivist schema. Historians may be able to explain where they cannot predict but "historical" explanation is like all scientific explanation; if it is to warrant the credentials of justification, it must be deductivist in nature.

(6)   Inference is a matter of language and logic. One cannot infer one object or state of affairs from another. Analysis of common usage reveals no principles of inference not formalizable in logic.

NOTE 5.5

A relatively concise summary of the argument against the Hempel–Oppenheim symmetry between explanation and prediction can be found in Scheffler (1957). He would differentiate between prediction and explanation on the following grounds:

(1)   We explain (i.e., deduce) laws but we predict events; abstractions such as laws are not predicted.

(2)   Predictions can be false but explanations cannot be.

(3)   Predictions can be made without sufficient rational support, explanation cannot be.

(4)   Predictions do not explain actual occurrences.

(5)   And, of course, predictions are of the future, explanations are of the past.

It should be noted that no one denies that predictions, actual or in principle, are nondifferentiable from explanation. The important question is whether scientific explanation and scientific prediction have similar logical structure. It is on this question that the Hempel–Oppenheim thesis should be evaluated.

The distinction between events, as such, and the language of science wherein explanation takes place is a significant one (as noted in N10.4). Scriven (1962) has made much of this distinction in his own critique. It is difficult to see, however, that predictions always deal with events, *per se*. What they do involve, of course, are statements about particular events occurring in stipulated space–time coordinates. Expressed predictions like explanations involve language, albeit they may be singular statements. It is not at all clear what it would mean to say that we predict the event as such rather than a statement which is the description of an event.

Argument based on the distinction between events and statements has further ramifications. Toulmin (1953), Ryle (1949), and the Wittgensteinians in general have maintained that statements and logic are one thing; events and phenomena are quite another. We do not deduce events, only statements about events. As such, deduction and logical relationships are not part of the event world. Events do not obey logic, they do not have logical structure, only thinking about events can be endowed with the properties of rational structure. Borrowing from the conventionalist treatments of law by Schlick (1938) and by Ramsey (1931), both Ryle (1949) and Kneale (1949) treat laws not as structures inherent in events, but as inference tickets, as pragmatic devices for finding one's way in the world.

Brodbeck (1962) is critical of this tack not on grounds that we can speak of events without concerning ourselves with statements about events, but on grounds that language and logic reflect the structure of the events themselves. She maintains that language and explanation do in fact indicate to us what is ontologically fundamental in the world.

At first glance it may appear that there is not much to choose between in this argument. Brodbeck, however, expresses the fear that a purely pragmatic evaluation of the role of language demeans the significance of language and logic for ontology. The significance of logic is underplayed in favor of obscurantist insights and understanding which are presumed to emerge in the meticulous analysis not of logic but of common usage.

NOTE 5.6

As a statistical example of lower-level explanation (*modus ponens*) we have:

$$(x) \; Sx \supset [P(x \in R) = p]$$
$$Sx_i$$
$$\therefore P(x_i \in R) = p,$$
$$P(x_i \in \sim R) = 1 - p$$

The first premise is a statement of the statistical law. The second premise asserts that the particular x_i has the property S. The conclusion states that the probability that x_i has the property R is p. But this is an elliptical statement. Ruling out subjectivist notions of probability, as we shall do here, the interpretation of p is only in terms of a relative frequency applying to the class of all x's. A given x, x_i, either possesses the property R or it does not, but regardless of which property, the event would have to be covered by the same statistical law. It is this fact that renders statistical explanations imprecise when applied to individual events. Only when we treat the class of many such particulars do we achieve precision of statement in statistical explanation.

Clear presentations of statistical explanation can be found in articles by Hempel (1962) and Rescher (1963). In the former work, Hempel offers the appropriate modification of his earlier views on explanation. In the latter work, Rescher addresses himself to the subject of stochastic processes and Markov chains. For strictly deterministic laws, if a particular x is in state S_i at time t, then it can be inferred that it will be in state S_j at time $t + \Delta t$. But for stochastic laws, if x is in state S_i at time t, it can only be inferred that x will be in state $S_j \lor \ldots \lor S_k \ldots \lor S_n$ with probabilities $p_j \ldots p_k \ldots p_n$ where $\Sigma p_k = 1$. Assuming successive states for the system, then the transitional probabilities can be represented by a square matrix. Only if the nonzero elements in the matrix are 1.0 will the discrete state system be deterministic. If the system is deterministic then explanation is straightforward and the given sequence of events is strictly deducible. If it is nondeterministic, then any event sequence with $0 < p < 1$ is deducible. Consequently precision of interpretation for stochastic processes is achievable over the class of many trials.

Rescher points out, however, that statistical explanations may fail to contribute much to scientific understanding. Systematization and rational models rather than explanation are required. Needless to say, however, rigorous deductive models are essential to the task.

NOTE 5.7

The writings of Henri Bergson remain of interest both to psychologist and to philosopher of science. With the possible exception of the popular *Creative Evolution,* the best introduction to his writings is the brief *An Introduction to Metaphysics.* Here one finds crisp and literate statements of his critique of analytic consciousness and of his pragmatic philosophy of science. Bergson came to his views by way of the continental revolt against rationalism and empiricism. But rather than reject science, he delegated to it the instrumentalist role of concretizing, analyzing, and abstracting experience. Hence science was to be regarded as a tool both to apperception and to action. In this, he was a pragmatist. Compare, for example, his "to label an object with a certain concept is to mark in precise terms the kind of action or attitude the object should suggest to us" (1913, p. 35) with Charles Peirce's: "Consider what effects, that might conceivably have practical bearings, we conceive the object of our conception to have. Then our conception of these effects is the whole of our conception of the object" (1878, p. 31).

In the overview, Bergson's philosophy is cosmological. The central thesis is Heraclitean. Duration is the nonanalyzable core of all experience and of all existence. Duration is the ceaseless, noncrystallizable process of fluid states merging one into another. Duration implies mobility throughout; no durational event can be given spatio-temporal coordinates. Abstraction is the means by which we precipitate events from the unanalyzable fluid, and intuition is the means by which we synthesize the multiplicity of states and the unity of consciousness. In the philosophy of life, as against that of knowledge, inner duration is the continuous life of memory which prolongs the past into the present.

One must distinguish between metaphysical knowledge which we know by intuition and symbolic or conceptual knowledge which we know by analysis. Thus the fundamental distinction:

> By intuition is meant the kind of *intellectual sympathy* by which one places oneself within an object in order to coincide with what is unique in it and consequently inexpressible. Analysis on the contrary is the operation which reduces the object to elements already known, that is, to elements common both to it and to other objects (1913, p. 6).

Now it is important to note that Bergson does not dismiss science and retreat into irrationalism. Rather one brings intuition to focus on the same experience that we symbolize and conceptualize within the language of science. Intuition is synthetic. It gives us direct access to the flux and connectedness of what in scientific descriptions are cinematographic reports and presentations. Bergson, quite naturally, is sympathetic to Kant. But he will have nothing of categories and absolute time and space schemata. For him the transcendental schemata are dynamic. They reify all change, and through intuition, they afford the individual his direct access to duration and metaphysical knowledge.

The Bergsonian metaphysics is obscure, to be sure; few philosophers of science care to take it at all seriously. Yet it is of interest to note that some of our contemporaries, disenchanted as they are by the deductivist amplification of Humean skepticism, have sought for something like intuitionism to give to causal relations a seal of ontological approval (e.g., Scriven, 1962; Kneale, 1949).

Bergson himself stressed that scientific analysis is abstractive. It is instrumental in prediction and scientific understanding, but it does not aid intuition. Both the antinomies of philosophy (e.g., Zeno's paradoxes) and bad metaphysics stem from our making ontological claims for scientific concepts. Science analyzes, it cannot construct. It detaches the object of experience from its surrounds, it fractionizes, it crystallizes. The thing in duration succumbs to analysis, symbolization, abstraction. It can never be reconstructed. Abstractive symbols are not component parts but only partial experiences. Applying his skepticism to introspective psychology, Bergson, like James, discounts any ontological basis for the ego-concept:

> On the level at which the psychologist places himself, and on which he must place himself, the 'ego' is only a sign by which a primitive, and moreover very confused, intuition which has furnished the psychologist with his subject matter is recalled; it is only a word, and the error here lies in believing that while remaining on the same level we can find behind the word a thing (1913, p. 26).

NOTE 5.8

The importance of idiographic method is perhaps even more significant when we consider history. The poverty of historicism as a nomothetic discipline (Popper, 1957) being what it is, historical epochs are even more unique, if that is possible, than the lives of individuals. Efforts to classify them are singularly Procrustean. Be that as it may, Hempel (1942) and Nagel (1952, 1961) among the empiricists continue to insist that classical procedures of scientific explanation can be applied to the understanding of historical events. History holds no special problems not also to be met, say, in astronomy, paleontology, meteorology, and psychology.

Mention should be made of Sellars' fine paper "The Language of Theories" (1961). Critical of overly formalized accounts of scientific explanation like those of Hempel and Braithwaite, Sellars maintains that what is significant about a scientific explanation is not that it is an adequate covering device for the deduction of laws and events, but that it explains why events conform, in so far as they do conform, to the appropriate laws. If we were given to pinning labels, we would have to say that Sellars is a semantic realist. That is to say, he believes that theoretical terms take their meaning in the context of the observational framework and are not mere reductions or logical constructions out of sense data. Granting theoretical terms surplus meanings and a potential for reification through observation, then the fact of deducibility carries with it the realization that it was just this postulate, this theoretical term, which made the deduction of the event to be explained possible. There is, of course, no need to introduce intuition, *verstehende,* or other obscure agents of understanding to achieve the insight Sellars prescribes. But it is interesting that hypotheses do provide such insights over and above the fact that they are the logical intermediaries of confirmed deductions.

NOTE 5.9

In his article "Deductive Unification and Idealization" Körner (1964) opts for a moderate Humeanism in which deductive schemata serve to order rather than to structure (modify in a constructual sense) experience. He argues, however, that a deductive schema is not a mere ordering of experience but is an idealization as well.

Körner schematizes hypothetico-deductive method by

$$(b_1 \text{ and } T) \mid_{\overline{L}} b_2$$

where 'b_1' and 'b_2' designate basic propositions; 'T', a theory; '$\mid_{\overline{L}}$' deducibility within a logic L comprising two-valued logic, quantification theory, theory of equality, and the theory of real numbers. Predicates of T are either empirical or nonempirical, whereas the predicates of b are empirical only. Extension and modification of the theory can be achieved by adding to its logical terms and by predicating additional substantive terms for the field of empirical inquiry. Application of the schema imposes the following restrictions on T.

(1) The mathematical notion of continuity is an idealization of actual measurement.

(2) The empirical notion of equality is not the same as logical and mathematical equality; e.g., perceptual equalities do not always obey the law of transitivity.

(3) The schema embraces two-valued logic whereas many other schemata with different logics are possible.

The originality of Körner's analysis concentrates on item (3). It is worth giving in some detail. Speaking of "resemblance classes" and "resemblance predicates," he notes that some classes are exact whereas others are inexact. Thus for any formal theory, its class structure represents an ideal. It is superimposed upon empirical predicates. In classical two-valued logic: if x is an individual and P is a predicate, then in assigning predicate or class membership, we have "$x \in P$" or "$x \in \sim P$". But with indefiniteness of individuals, so far as resemblance predicates are concerned, one should have another category for propositions, say, "$x \overset{\epsilon}{\in} P$" which asserts that x is a neutral or indeterminate candidate for P. Here Körner adopts certain ideas of Kleene (*Introduction to Metamathematics,* §64) rather than the three-valued logic of Lukasiewicz. Neutrality in predicate assignment is to be stressed rather than uncertainty.

We are still to operate within the dichotomous class structure P and $\sim P$; but rather than just two truth values 't' and 'f' for true and false, we introduce a third symbol '*' which designates neutrality as concerns assigning P. Körner proceeds to develop truth tables for the usual logical operations only now incorporating the neutrality value, and also to extend the schema so as to include quantification operations. The argument is too detailed to include in this note, but Körner then proceeds to show that a modified two-valued logic cannot serve as an instrument for deducing neutral statements. $[p \cdot (p \supset q)] \supset q$ is a correct inference in *modus ponens*. However, if any of the premises were neutral, then an inference is possible only if we treat such premises as true. Thus an idealization is always implicit in our adopting the two-valued convention of logic, when in fact the neutral value might well be included.

The argument is an ingenious one. Inexact predicates must be replaced by exact ones. Against the backdrop of neutrality this forced exactness represents an idealization. Strictly speaking, it is false to assert identity between the basic propositions of a theory and the empirical propositions of which they are the idealizations. We need, therefore, the expression '$b \approx e$' for 'b is an idealization of e'. Then for

$$(b_1 + T) \mathbin{\vert_{\overline{L}}} b_2$$

we have

$$[e_1 \approx b_1 \ (b_1 + T) \mathbin{\vert_{\overline{L}}} b_2; \ b_2 \approx e_2]$$

where the e_1 and e_2 are not deducible from b_1 and b_2, but $e_1 \approx b_1$ and $b_2 \approx e_2$ are expressions of the presumptive idealization of explanation and prediction. In summary: (1) the entire bracketed proposition, from e_1 to e_2, is the statement of an empirical proposition employing as an idealization a logical bridge between its parts; (2) one does not, strictly speaking, disconfirm a theory, but rather the whole empirical proposition $[e_1 \ldots e_2]$; (3) scientific propositions such as $[e_1 \ldots e_2]$ differ from ordinary propositions only in terms of their logical structure. They are part idealization. Like all such propositions, scientific explanations are idealizations.

CHAPTER 6

Reductionism: I

THE VOCABULARY of reductionism has been a popular one in logic, philosophy, and science; and for this reason, it has often lacked precision in its use. The idea of reduction is, of course, an elementary one. Linguistically, a statement or set of statements, $\{S_R\}$, is reducible to another set of statements, $\{S_r\}$, if the latter can be substituted for the former without contradiction and without loss of content,[1] and if the latter is in some sense more basic than the former. This attempt at a definition is itself not very precise. It is not intended to be. Initially all that is required is some statement which, by and large, covers the many reductive activities of philosophers and scientists.

Generally then, we recognize as reductive any activity wherein the person seeks to substitute for one set of assertions another set whose members are more basic than those of the original. Thus, in philosophy, the theses of phenomenalism and physicalism are both reductive. In phenomenalism, every statement about objects purports to be reducible to statements about sense data. In physicalism, all significant statements, which are not strictly logical statements, are reducible to statements in the physical thing-language. On the other hand, in logic, a symposium on reductionism may be the occasion to debate whether all of arithmetic can be reduced to the language of classes, or whether reductionism is simply the possibility of analysis (Thomson, Warnock, Braithwaite, 1952). The thesis of extensionality, which we found to express the analytic paradigm of logical atomism, is, of course, reductionist. The truth of every molecular proposition reduces to the truth functions of its atomic constituents. Modern empiricism, from its inception with Locke, Berkeley, and Hume, has been reductive in its epistemology. And now-

---

[1] "Without loss of content" requires merely that no subset of $\{S_R\}$ is without a substitutable subset in $\{S_r\}$.

adays the argument between nominalism and realism is debated on reductionist grounds.

"Nominalism versus realism"—this is one of the oldest acts to be performed in the reductionist arena. The question to be debated here is: Are there universal laws, entities, or transcendent hypotheses which are subsistent reals independent of, and not merely reducible to, our conventions in classifying particulars? Realists from the time of Plato have vouched for universals which, in their intension, transcend any finite set of particulars. This is the heart of Platonic doctrine of Ideas. Nominalists, on the other hand, maintain that all generalizations, all abstractions, so to speak, are reductive conventions. There are no capitalized Universals, no enduring Laws; there are only convenient classifications of particular events. This is an interesting issue, not because scientists or philosophers still debate the transcendental doctrines of ideal prototypes, but because it touches upon such basic conceptions as number, law, and inductive inference. Nominalists are necessarily finitistic. For them, the universal quantifier "all" can never reach into the unsampled universe. Their defense of scientific inference must inevitably be postulational and conventional. Although it is not necessary that it be so, empiricists have inclined toward nominalism.

TWO MEANINGS OF REDUCTIONISM

Our concern is with reductionism as it applies to science, specifically to psychology. The issues are no different for psychology than they are for other sciences, but for psychology they are perhaps more poignant and more timely. Let us begin by distinguishing between reduction as it applies to individual concepts and reduction as it applies to aggregates of concepts such as in a theory or a science itself.

Constructual Reduction

By constructual reduction is meant the reduction of some term (construct) that is not assumed to designate a specific object with existential status to a set of statements about objects that do have such status. The word 'object' here can be misleading, but it is important to recognize that the existential status of an object derives from its being empirically real and not inferred. Specifically, in psychology, 'construct' refers either to terms in the language of theory, or to terms requiring what is commonly called an operational definition.

Before turning to the use of constructs in psychology, it would be well to review briefly the concept of a logical construction as dating from Russell (1917, 1918) and Carnap (1928). Initially logical constructions were treated as constructions out of sense data. The primitives, i.e., the basic data statements, referred to sense data; and the problem of reductionism was essentially phenomenalistic. The important feature of such constructions is that their meaning is purely contextual. A logical construct does not refer to any identifiable thing as such, nor to any set of things as such. Rather it refers to some set of things upon which some conventional construction is imposed. Russell himself was very explicit that logical constructions were not indubitable entities like sense data. Nor should one make the mistake of inferring existential status for such constructs. Hence the occasion for his "supreme maxim in scientific philosophizing . . .": "Wherever possible, logical constructions are to be substituted for inferred entities" (1917, p. 155). We need to keep this admonition in mind in our discussions of theoretical terms.

As the language of physicalism began to supplant that of phenomenalism, the definition of logical constructions was loosened so as to incorporate basic observation statements as the language of the reductive primitives (e.g., Carnap, 1928; Pap, 1949). However, the status of logical constructs remained the same; they were to be regarded as symbols whose explicit meaning reduced to specific operations performed on the set of basic data. Thus, the "median response," which is the variable plotted, say, in experiments concerning subjective estimates of loudness (Stevens, 1956), is a logical construction. There is, of course, no response as such, no phenomenon we can point to as *the* median response. The value which obtains for our logical construct derives from our performing certain explicit operations upon a set of response data which are empirically basic. When Skinner defines drive in terms of a deprivation schedule or in terms of behavioral variability (1938, 1953), he is treating motivation as a logical construction. And when Hull postulates habit strength as a function of the number of reinforcements, he, likewise, is treating habit strength as a logical construction (cf. N6.1). It is important to note that in all of these examples one cannot point to any thing or set of things by which we can either ostensively or even explicitly define the construct. Nevertheless, the construct is meaningless without its empirical content. It is a content, however, which is subject to a set of constructional operations (cf. N6.2).

For the psychologist, the issues of constructual reduction obtrude when he considers the empirical status of his mediating variables. We have previously differentiated among types of mediating variables (Chapter 3). In the present context, we note that intervening variables are very like logical constructions, reductive and without existential status (in the phenomenalistic sense), whereas hypothetical constructs are not strictly reducible, carry surplus meaning with them, and may in fact pretend to potential existential status. The issue, as we shall see, devolves on whether intervening variables can do the job theory construction requires. Such variables are clean and tidy and are reassuring to radical empiricists like Skinner. Nevertheless, one may need something more substantive than a logical construct to implement S–R psychology; and in so needing, he may plead cause to invert the well-known Russellian maxim. In its place he writes, "Wherever possible advance your theory by the introduction of hypothetical constructs." Discussion of this matter will be taken up in a later section.

As for operational definitions and operationism (the "ism") the crusade fortunately has been put to rest. Psychology certainly must share in the responsibility for what Passmore (1957) calls the "embarrassing amateurism" in defense of operationism. What took on the aspects of a new metaphysic with the publication of Bridgman's *Logic of Modern Physics* was at a slightly earlier date proclaimed by Eddington (1920) as the seed for his neo-Kantian metaphysics. Actually, there is little that purportedly is original in operationism which cannot be found in the writings of all empiricists since Locke. Even Francis Bacon could write of "operative physics" (*Novum Organum*). What is more important is that operationism itself has succumbed to open-textured interpretations. Operations may only partially interpret some concept, thereby leaving the meaning of the concept open. For example, drives, attitudes, reactive potentials, etc., may be operationally measured, but there remains a thingness to what is measured that is not entirely exhausted by an operational description. Nowadays, operationism, if given a heeding at all, is discussed simply as the subject of empirical procedures. After two decades of critical analysis, the proscriptive role cut out for operationism has been abandoned (cf. N6.3).

Theoretic Reduction

By theoretic reduction is meant the reduction of the postulates, laws, hypotheses of one theory to those of another. Since the emphasis is on reduction, one assumes that the reducing science is in some sense more basic than the reduced science. Hence a "simplification" in the theoretical explanation of events is achieved by the reduction, whereby at the same time this reduction fulfills all the requirements of an explanation. The laws of the reduced science are thereby explained by the laws of the reducing science.

Before proceeding to a discussion of the formal requirements of complete reduction let us note some rather obvious implications of this reductive thesis. First, a hierarchy of sciences is assumed with respect to the inclusiveness and explanatory scope of scientific theories. Hierarchies such as those proposed by Auguste Comte (mathematics, physics, biology, psychology, sociology) are suggestive but misleading because mathematics is there ranked among the empirical sciences. One notes, however, that we often do speak of reducing biology to physics (biophysics), psychology to biology (psychobiology), and sociology to psychology (social psychology as a real socio-psychology). We do not, however, speak meaningfully of reducing physics to biology, or of reducing biology to psychology. There seems to be an ordering natural to our reductive efforts. Second, reduction seems to imply the assumption of a unity of science. If in the hierarchy any one science programmatically reduces to the next lower science, then ultimately all sciences reduce to the basic science—presumably to physics. This is not an unreasonable assumption for the reductionist, although it has often been thrown up as a scarecrow against reductive efforts. Why, it is asked, not teach our sociologists physics to begin with? The reasonable reply is that neither the hierarchical nor the reductive schema precludes our developing at every level of science concepts which are unique to the specific science. It can be argued, however, that the imperative for theoretic reduction comes into play primarily when questions between alternative conceptualizations within a given science need to be resolved. And third, the precautionary note needs to be sounded. In our sanguine espousals of reductive sciences there may be unwarranted pretentions to logical rigor, as if we were dealing with sciences more highly formalized than they actually are. The formalization of physics is impressive though incomplete. The biological and social sciences are in their infancies. Therefore, we may be premature in speaking out for theoretic reduction.

Although one may speak sanguinely of theoretic reduction, actual instances of reducing one science to another are somewhat rare. Sometimes what purports to be a reduction is no more than the development of a theory itself. For example, we hear of Newton's reduction of Kepler's laws of planetary behavior, or we may hear of reducing Mendel's laws of heredity (with their assumption of dominant and recessive characteristics) to a theory of genes. In both examples, however, basic phenomenological laws are found to be deducible within a developing theory. It is more a case of achieving a scientific explanation through development of a theory than one exemplary of reduction (cf. N6.4). The classic example, however, is the reduction of thermodynamics to statistical mechanics. Before the reduction, thermodynamics was a rather loose compilation of gas laws, thermal principles, and laws of conservation and entropy. As a phenomenological science, thermodynamics developed without definite commitments as to the nature of a gas. The relevant variables were temperature, pressure, volume, energy. By assuming a gas to be composed of perfectly elastic molecules behaving according to the laws of Newtonian mechanics, and by making certain statistical assumptions about the distribution and momenta of the molecules, one is able, for example, to deduce the Boyle–Charles law and the second law of thermodynamics (which states that for closed systems the tendency is for entropy to increase).

The physicist proceeds here by assigning an average velocity and mass to the N molecules in a given volume of gas. By assuming the correspondence of pressure and the product of density and square of the velocity of the particles ($p = dv^2/3$), he is able to make valid inferences concerning manometrically measured pressure. Likewise, by assuming the proportionality of temperature and the mean kinetic energy of the particles ($T = mv^2/3k$), he is able to infer thermometric temperature. More specifically, he is able to show that conditions which would influence the density and momenta of the particles are the conditions which affect measured pressure and temperature of the aggregate of particles. Derivation of the second law of thermodynamics (Gibbs and Boltzmann) in probabilistic terms leads one to expect the increasing homogenization of phase cells differing as to their kinetic energy. Entropy is converted from a deterministic law into a statistical one by the appropriate reduction in statistical mechanics.

What makes this reduction remarkable is its success in deriving phenomenological laws of gases from a set of postulates about the microstructure of the gas, indeed, in bringing these laws into the manifold of mechanics itself. The significance of the role of microstructure in explaining phenomenological laws should not be overlooked by the psychologist.

FORMAL REQUIREMENTS OF REDUCTION

Requirements for constructual reduction are simple ones. The reduction is achieved by explicit definitions, by operational definitions, by specific sets of biconditional reduction sentences. Either they are conventional equivalences or they represent constructual operations on a finite set of observational primitives. With the reduction of one theory to another we need, however, to go into greater detail.

Woodger in biology (1952) and Nagel in the physical sciences (1949, 1961) have given us the most explicit statements of reduction. Differences between them are minor ones and the account to be given here follows them in all essentials. We note initially that a formal reduction of one science to another calls for the axiomatization of each of the theories. Thus, let us assume that two sciences or theories that stand in reductive relationship are fully axiomatized so that all sentences are either postulates, laws, correspondence rules, or observation statements, and all theorems of the science are provable within its formal structure. Terms of the language are either logical terms, terms of particulars, or terms of properties or characteristics. Let T_1 be the primary or reducing science; let T_2 be the secondary or reduced science. Let us follow Nagel in speaking of a science rather than a theory, for a given science such as psychology will not only contain statements unique unto itself (e.g., sensation) but also statements in the language of physics (e.g., descriptions of physical stimulus intensity). Thus the language of physics may be common to both psychology and physiology. Let the functors (i.e., predicative expressions) of T_1 and T_2 be as follows:

$$T_1 = a,b,c, \ldots ,A,B,C, \ldots$$
$$T_2 = a,b,c, \ldots ,A,B,C, \ldots ,G,H, \ldots$$

where $a,b,c,$ are functors borrowed from other sciences and are common to both T_1 and T_2 (and other sciences as well); $A,B,C,$ are common to T_1 and T_2; and $G,H, \ldots$ are functors unique to T_2. Then for the complete reduction of T_2 to T_1 the following requirements must be fulfilled:

1. The vocabulary of T_1 is a subset of T_2, i.e., all functors and primitives of T_1 are also members of T_2. One might call this the principle of simplification since the reducing science necessarily must have fewer primitives and functors than has the reduced science.

2. Every expression G in T_2 not in the vocabulary of T_1 must satisfy the biconditional

$$(x)G_x \equiv P_x,$$
where $x \in P \equiv (. \, . \, . \, ,x,a,b,c, \ldots ,A,B,C, \ldots).$

That is to say, every unshared statement in T_2 but not in T_1 must be constructible from functors of T_1. Furthermore, the biconditionals must be well established theorems of T_2. (Nagel calls this the *principle of connectibility*.)

3. All expressions (postulates and functors) of T_2 not shared by T_1 must be reducible to expressions in T_1 by virtue of the above biconditionals (Nagel calls this the principle of *derivability*).

Fulfillment of these requirements assures us of an effective reduction. All laws and theoretical constructions of the reduced science are then expressible in the language of the reducing science.

The crucial requirement is (2): all theoretical expressions in T_2 must connect with expressions in T_1. Nagel's choice of 'connect' here is well considered. A word like 'derive' would be restrictive. The biconditional, $G_x \equiv P_x$, serves as a theorem to be established in one of three ways. One, such a biconditional may express the logical equivalence of synonymity. For example, a conditioned eyelid response might be regarded as equivalent to a set of responses in the appropriate efferents of neurophysiology. Two, the connection may be empirically established. For example, an expression of anger may be correlated with an increase in adrenalin content of the blood. Or three, the biconditional may be postulated as a convention connecting two expressions. For example, drive might be equated to reduction of blood sugar to some specified percentage of a "normal" level.

This last possibility differs from the other two in the sense that it involves an element of fiat and convention not contained in the former. That is, one might proceed preferentially and choose only theoretical terms in the secondary science which are indeed translatable in terms of the primary language. But as Woodger points out this is a Procrustean reducibility. We proceed by prior commitment to stay within the range of the primary science, when in fact the autonomous development of the secondary science may have resulted in a vocabulary unique to it. Reductionism in this case would be coercive and Woodger prefers to regard the matter as one of "interpretability" (of T_2 in T_1) rather than of reducibility (cf. N6.5).

REDUCTIONISM IN PSYCHOLOGY

The preceding discussion has been the groundwork for what follows. I will not attempt to assess the extent either of the successes or the failures in reducing the laws and theories of psychology to those of physiology. The failures have been many, the successes few. Psychology started out its experimental incarnation as a discipline prone to physiological explanations. Psychophysics, of course, invites this kind of emphasis. But Titchener defected from physiologism, as did even Watson. Furthermore, subsequent concentration upon phenomenology and behavioral studies encouraged the development of unique psychological languages, even though phenomenologists like Köhler and behaviorists like Lashley still preferred the reductive language of physiology.

One suspects, however, that in their wistful moments psychologists invariably come to think of physiology as the ultimate in explanation. Learning, memory, perception; all of these are very close indeed to organic functioning. If physiology is to be ignored, it is to be so only for methodological reasons. Yet even where pragmatic ingenuity is to prevail, such as in personality and in learning theory, it is suspected that new developments in neurophysiology will result in our modifying purely psychological conceptions. The old arguments over functional and organic disorders in psychopathology have to be rephrased. One does not say that aberrant function can be studied in a purely psychological language. If reduction is not required, certainly a joint psychological, physiological language is.

Still the arguments go on. We hear the calls to neurophysiology. We also hear that psychology suffers from the accidents of its stimulus–response, reflex-oriented vocabulary; physiological reference is clearly dispensable. Much of the debate would be avoided if we took Woodger's counsel (cf. N6.5): in order to meet the requirements of reduction, the revelant sciences much be axiomatized. Neither psychology nor physiology is sufficiently systematic so as to be axiomatizable. But not all of the debate can be avoided. Vocabulary and the conceptual framework do determine the direction of the psychological efforts. It is not just that we may cavalierly issue promissory notes on some future psycho-physiology; but the language of learning theory predisposes us now to thinking in terms of physiological equivalencies.

Methodological versus Metaphysical Reductionism

Before taking the issues of reductionism directly to psychology, it is necessary to make another distinction. We should be careful to distinguish between methodological and metaphysical commitments to reductionism. By *methodological reductionism* is meant the arbitrary decision, for whatever purpose, to confine the language of one's science to expressions which at least in principle are reducible to the language of a reducing science. For psychology this would mean restricting its theoretical constructs to terms reducible in principle to the language of physiology. The emphasis is one of methodological predilection (Hebb, 1949, 1955, 1959; Krech, 1950, 1951; Morgan, 1959). Of all the languages open to psychology that of physiology seems most promising, most disposed to implementing the complete interpretation of its mediating variables. It is acknowledged that purely psychological constructions of memory trace, cognitive structure, and drive can be invented and exploited to the exclusion of any other class of constructions. However, it is felt that evils of semantic diversification can be avoided only by restricting theoretical constructs to hypotheses reducible to the language of physiology. The subject matters of psychology are varied and complex. Theoretical psychologists suffer from the lack of one theorist understanding or utilizing the language of another theorist. Psychology needs a common theoretical language, and physiology is the language all can understand and use. The case is similar to that for methodological behaviorism. There, mental phenomena and consciousness are not denied. The language of private data is avoided in favor of the physicalistic language which is anchored in public observation and public report (Lashley, 1923). Communicational and observational agreement is achieved, perhaps at the expense of restricting the field of study.

In contrast, *metaphysical reductionism* is, in one sense, a stronger principle. It asserts that for psychology ultimately all questions of theory are to be resolved by physiological reductionism. That is to say, all arguments, crucial tests, and so on, concerning the nature of hypothetical constructs eventually are to be settled by reducing them to the microstructural components of physiology. Just as we foresaw in Chapter 4 that cybernetics is to be regarded as the bare prospectus for neurophysiological construction, the language of psychology will be refined through the history of successful reductive analysis and construction. This compares with a metaphysical behaviorism which assumes that all sentences in the mental language are really translatable into sentences in the physicalistic language; the language presumably of pure mental content is meaningless.

This distinction in philosophical types of reductionism is the source of much confusion. The most important misconception is to interpret metaphysical reductionism as a dogmatic defense of, nay, a call to, physiologizing. More likely, it is methodological reductionism which is the more dogmatic. The latter precludes all but physiological speculation on methodological grounds alone. Metaphysical reductionism only speaks of ultimate reductions and ultimate objectives. All black-box phenomenologists can, if pressed, embrace this type of reductionism, as can all pragmatists and inventive instrumentalists. As metaphysical reductionists their only firm commitment is that ultimately theoretical constructs will be interpretable in the reducing discipline, and *that no logical barriers stand in the way to the reduction of psychology to physiology*. It does not mean that psychology should give up its unique conceptions and theorizing as a macrobehavioral discipline.

Reductionism and Hull's Behavior Theory

Before turning to the objections to reductionism (Chapter 7) it may be well to have in mind what a program for reduction might be like. Consider for example, the theory of Clark Hull. It comes as close to an axiomatized macrotheory as psychology can boast. Hull (1943, 1951, 1952) presents a hypothetico-deductive system which starting with certain unspecified and undefined primitive terms is then structured according to its sets of definitions, postulates, and theorems. Empirical support derives from the theorems which are tested by virtue of coordinating rules. In order to establish the reducibility (in principle) of Hull's system, we would have to ascertain whether all functors in the system are derivable from functors in the physiological language (which we assume to be a subset of Hull's behavioral language). According to the requirements of connectibility and derivability, $(x)G_r \equiv P_x$ means that any functor G in Hull's theory must be reducible to a sentence in the neurophysiological language, i.e., constructed of functors admissible to that language. Reducibility would be precluded only if there were some sentence G_x in Hull's theory such that for all sentences $P_i x$ in the language of neurophysiology, $\sim(G_x \equiv P_i x)$ (where $P_i x$ is a possible molecular sentence in the language of physiology).

Without laboring the reductive program point by point, I think it is safe to assume that such a program is in principle possible. Hull's own language is often quasi-physiological. Although he does not presume to offer a neurophysiological theory of learning, he makes clear his belief that neurophysiology is the basis of a molecular explanation of molar events. It is only the nascent state of physiology which prevents the psychologist from going directly to molecular explanations (cf. N6.6).

It is, of course, one thing to issue promissory notes on reduction and quite another to square the accounts. For the present, all we can assess is the possibility of a reduction and what purpose, if any, a reductive program might serve. In his final formulation of his system (*A Behavior System*, 1952) Hull first presents seventeen postulates and as many corollaries. Assuming a glossary of terms and some rather poorly specified correspondence rules, he then utilizes the greater part of his monograph to deduce 132 theorems, each of which can be thought of as a behavioral hypothesis. A successful reduction of Hull's system would then mean that the lawlike statements concerning molar behavior, as set down in the theorems, would be deducible from, hence explainable by, a successful reduction of the postulates to the language of neurophysiology. As this statement stands, however, it makes no pretense of distinguishing significant from trivial reductions. A significant reduction, it must be emphasized, brings to a science explanatory enrichment which otherwise it would not have.

Suppose, for example, the simplest of behavioral sciences—one which is exhausted by a finite set of stimulus–response laws $R_i = f(S_j)$ without intervening concepts of any kind. If the language of this science contains only S and R terms, then any reduction of these terms to the language of neurophysiology would be trivial providing substitution of language is all that is achieved by the reduction. It would be quite a different matter, however, if mediating variables were introduced in the neurophysiological language such that the set of behavioral laws could be deduced from postulates not contained in the simple behavioral system. The behavioral laws would then be bound together in a way not found in the S–R behavioral science as such.

If we go a step further and introduce into the behavioral science intervening variables that are strictly interpretable (i.e., constructible) in stimulus and response terms (i.e., in the observation language), the situation is complicated but it is not altered in any significant way. Suppose, for example, that our laws are now of the form $R_i = f(S_j, IV_k)$ where any IV is itself a function of a set of stimulus variables. This might be the case if IV were a specification of motivation in terms of hours of food deprivation. Our behavioral function is a more complex one now, but it is still substantially an expression of S–R law without theoretical complications. The law now incorporates the facts of a maintenance schedule in the set of independent variables. And again, if we were to reduce all terms in the R, S, and IV language to neurophysiology, the reduction would be a trivial one, unless, of course, it carried with it some explanatory surplus not contained in a terminological transliteration, as such. This is simply a restatement of the argument in Chapter 5, in which a distinction was made between levels of explanation, i.e., between lawful explanation of individual events and theoretical explanation of the laws themselves. A reduction of the statements of one science to those of another is significant only if higher-order explanation is achieved by the reduction.

Proceeding now to Hull's postulates, we note that some deal with stimulus variables (postulates 1,2,3,6,7,10,11,12), some deal with response variables (postulates 1,3,14,15,) and some deal with mediating variables (postulates 3,4,5,6,7,8,9,10,11,12,13,14,15,16,17). The overlap here is considerable and a reductive roll-call over the postulates would not be particularly rewarding. What we should note is that all stimulus constructs are amenable to reduction whether the stimulus term refers to a segment of the environment or to intra-organismic functions. The physicalistic environmental language is, of course, common both to the psychological and physiological languages. And any description of a stimulus as an intra-organismic mediator is obviously reducible in principle to neurophysiology. A similar analysis holds for response terms, whether they refer to molar acts, response latencies, or response amplitudes. However, it is the mediating variables that are of particular interest. If they are in fact intervening variables, then like all logical constructions, their status is truth functional. Consequently, their reduction can be rather trivial. If, however, they are hypothetical constructs, carrying with them the implications of hypothesis about some mediating state not subject to a finite truth extension over a set of observables, then the question of neurophysiological reducibility is a pressing one. An important caution here! One must be careful to note the difference in our two senses of reducibility. He must distinguish between the constructual reducibility of the intervening variable as a logical construction and the theoretic reducibility of the hypothetical construct where existential foundations are to be secured in a lower order scientific discipline.

The major mediating variables of Hull's system are habit strength ($_sH_R$), reaction potential ($_sE_R$), inhibition (I_R, $_sI_R$), oscillation of reaction potential ($_sO_R$), and reaction threshold ($_sL_R$). To this list add the conditional factors of drive (D), stimulus intensity dynamism (V), and incentive motivation (K). Of these, habit strength and reaction potential play the most important roles in the chain of behavioral deductions. Now according to Postulate 4, habit strength is defined by an equation of the form

$$_sH_R = 1 - 10^{-aN},$$

where a is some empirically determined constant and N is the number of reinforcements from a base of zero reaction potential. Assuming that a reinforcement trial is observationally unambiguous, then $_sH_R$ is clearly an intervening variable. Its reduction would be trivial, as the matter stands. Reaction potential is a somewhat different matter. According to Postulate 8,

$$_sE_R = D \times V \times K \times {_sH_R},$$

where D, V, and K are determined by hours of deprivation, stimulus intensity, and quantity of incentive, respectively. Values of these latter variables are determined by observation. Therefore, $_sE_R$ would pass as an intervening variable if it carried no additional implications of existential substrata. However, it is not clear that $_sE_R$ is intended as a mere calculational convention. Postulates 14,15,16 also specify $_sE_R$ as functions of reaction latency (14), reaction amplitude (15), and number of trials to extinction (16). And other approaches have given different quantifications of $_sE_R$ in terms of starting latencies and running times (Zeaman, 1949), and in terms of reinforcements and trials to extinction (Yamaguchi, 1951). Thus, rather than a single definitional estimate of $_sE_R$, we have several convergent estimations of $_sE_R$ as if this reaction potential were a state of the organism to be inferred, observed, and measured. Although one may choose to play strict definitional and operational games, it is not clear that this is what is intended by Hull and by his students. From Hull's earlier postulation of habit strength (1943), one suspects that even $_sH_R$ is regarded as being something more than a convention. We sense that effects of reinforcement and trial repetition bring about changes in the structure of the organism which are what $_sH_R$ *intends* to measure. In other words, $_sH_R$ is not just a convenient invention, but is semantically tied to a state of the organism which we might better regard as a habit *structure* predisposing the increased probabilities of certain response patterns.

The ontological status of Hullian constructs has been the subject of conjecture and debate. In their classic differentiation between types of mediating variables, MacCorquodale and Meehl (1948) placed $_sH_R$ in the fold of intervening variables. Hull's 1952 revision of the postulates would appear to reinforce that opinion. On the other hand, Koch (1954) and Rozeboom (1956) would, by virtue of Hull's own presentiments, assign $_sH_R$ the status of an hypothetical construct—the surplus meaning, though not requiring neurophysiological content, certainly leaning in that direction. In spite of the authority of MacCorquodale and Meehl, the latter recourse seems the safer one. None of the mediating variables seems to stand as a pristine convention. When we introduce the inhibition variables (I_R, $_sI_R$) and the oscillation factor[2] ($_sO_R$), which are clearly more speculative, then there seems little point in holding out for the purely conventionalistic status of any of the mediating variables. No doubt it is safer to mean by the construct no more

---

[2] Together, these compose the Hullian analogues of the epicycles and equants of ancient astronomy.

than a set of definitive operations. In the early stages of theory construction, this strategy is likely to obviate unnecessary and fruitless arguments concerning ontology, which neurophysiology, in its present state, is in no position to arbitrate. But eventually the constructions come to mean more than a set of operations. That is to say, $_sH_R$ and $_sE_R$ have a different semantic status than has a logical construction (such as a "median response," or an "index of efficiency"). They point to something whose postulated ramifications are not exhausted by the set of values we can assign to a definitive equation. The 132 theorems of *A Behavior System* are given without proof. It is indeed doubtful whether they could be proven by the set of postulates and corollaries interpretable strictly as conventions.

What then is the reductive status of Hull's behavior system? We have skirted the answer, but the answer seems quite straightforward. Were all of the mediating variables to be considered intervening variables, then a reduction of Hull's behavioral descriptions would be possible by transliterating stimulus and response terms into equivalent sets of environmental and afferent and efferent statements. This being achieved, the reduction would, however, only be a trivial one. But if, as our own conjecture leads us to think, the mediating variables are hypothetical constructs with surplus meaning, then it seems that psychologically and methodologically the most fruitful recourse is that of reductivism. As Rozeboom (1956) argues, there is nothing logically compelling about the proposal to reduce hypothetical constructs to the neurophysiological substrata. However, he does not provide an alternative heuristic for the exploitation of the surplus meaning of a given construct. Pure pragmatics will not work, for invention itself is tied to preconception. To think otherwise is to think one can engage in the fruits of deductive argument without attending to and justifying the premises of the deductive system.

The difficulty in giving an out-and-out affirmative answer to the reductionist hypothesis is that, as it stands, Hull's behavior system is not sufficiently formalized to permit the direct application of the criteria of reduction. However, in an examination of Hull's theory we meet no logical barriers to reduction, and Hull's own linguistic biases would seem to place the genesis of the mediating variables in the microrecesses of neurophysiology (cf. N6.7).

DEFENSE OF REDUCTIONISM

It is now possible to pull together some diverse threads of the argument in behalf of reductionism. Some points of the preceding discussion will be restated. These will be followed by a statement of the criterion of reducibility for selecting among alternative theoretical constructions.

(1) Metaphysical reductionism implies that all questions as to the nature and status of mediating variables in psychology will be answered by reducing those variables to neurophysiology. If such mediators are indeed intervening variables, then that reduction can be trivial. However, if such mediators are hypothetical constructs with surplus meaning, then the existential status of such constructs is to be found in the reducing science. This thesis of reductionism does not entail that psychology should proceed immediately to neurophysiology any more than it entails that genetics should proceed immediately to biochemistry. Nor does it hold out the promise that reductions will be easily forthcoming, or that they will offer any particularly effective program or a plan for the development of the science in question. As shall be argued, acceptance of reductionism means to adopt a metaphysical position as to how certain questions arising over the tenability of alternative theoretical constructions are to be resolved.

(2) Reductionism does not entail our rejecting systemic developments of a secondary science in its own language and independently of the primary or reducing science. On the other hand, the difficulties of successful reduction should not be used as an argument against "premature" theory construction in the secondary science. One must keep in mind the promise of ultimate interpretations of theoretical terms in the language of the reducing science. In this context, it is appropriate to say that reduction is the source of some ontological direction.

(3) The argument for indifference, convention, or pragmatism as concerns the existential status of mediating variables is suspect. Mediators mediate between stimulus and response events, each of which is amenable to reductive analysis. This fact necessarily places mediation between two reducible environmental-organismic states. Consequently, as MacCorquodale and Meehl (1948) suggest, questions of the physical locale of the mediators become relevant. One's empirical commitments may be in jeopardy if he were to hold out for the purely conventional interpretation of a construct where, in fact, existential anchoring in functors of a higher-order science is possible (cf. N6.8). If, as several writers have intimated, the distinction between intervening variables and hypothetical constructs is a pseudo-issue (Marx, 1951; Bergmann, 1954; Madden, 1961), that is to say, if intervening variables also gain surplus meaning in their application, then their reduction would be neither trivial nor irrelevant. For then the prospect of reduction would provide the most fruitful heuristic to their amplification within the theory.

(4) As a final point, let us consider reducibility as a criterion for selecting among alternative theoretical constructions. In Chapter 5 several criteria were suggested for selecting among alternative scientific hypotheses. Among them was the criterion of reducibility. (a) First sub-

sume a hierarchy of sciences $T_j, \ldots, T_s \ldots, T_z$ such that any given science in the hierarohy contains all of the functors of the preceding science plus some set of functors not found in the preceding science (except possibly by means of reduction sentences). (b) For a given science, T_s, assume two or more alternative theories, $T_{s1}, T_{s2}, \ldots$ agreeing as to some finite set of predictions but differing as to their hypothetical terms $H_{1i}, \ldots, H_{2j}, \ldots$. Assume further that no set of experiments has led indirectly to the confirmation or disconfirmation of one over another of these hypotheses. The criterion of reducibility then asserts that that hypothesis which can be formally derived from the functors of the higher-order science is to be preferred to that hypothesis which cannot be so derived.[3] It is obvious that this criterion of reducibility is more easily stated than applied. Any successful reduction requires the formalization of both the primary and secondary sciences. Considering the state of personology, for example, there is little prospect of formalization sufficient to allow our reducing the constructs of personality to physiology. It is not surprising then that theories of personality carry with them the spirit of the option (Berenda, 1957), where conversion is likely to play a more significant role in selecting from among alternative constructions then any penetrative sense of realism. To be sure, the personologist has little reason to be impressed with the thesis of reductionism.

In learning theory the matter is somewhat different. The theories are often quasi-formal. The categories of stimulus–response and mediating variables predispose our thinking in terms of physical locus. Furthermore, theories of learning have much in common as to first principles. For the most part, they differ only as to how the response repertory is strengthened and secured. Consider the issue of reinforcement. This is where the formal systems of Hull, Guthrie, Tolman, for example, make their stand. When the language of reinforcement is stripped of its personalistic overtones (as if reinforcing agents were gremlins soldering circuits together) what is involved is a question of schematic layout. Is the input–output system sufficient unto itself to establish S–R connections by virtue of some mechanism of contiguity, or must we include some mechanism of reinforcement with possible feedback complications? And what is the role of drive in learning? There is good reason to believe that these issues (along with those of latent learning, presensory conditioning, exploratory behavior, and secondary reinforcement) will be resolved by more explicit models of neurophysiology rather than by more refined behavioral studies.

---

[3] The language of levels and orders is sometimes confusing. By *higher* orders and *higher* levels I shall mean the more inclusive generalization or explanation. Thus the primary science (the reducing science) is higher-order than the secondary science (the reduced science). Assuming reducibility for psychology then psychology is lower-order than physiology. And microphysics would presumably be the highest-order of the empirical sciences.

Doubtless motivational variables will prove significant, as even contiguity theorists will agree. But whether reinforcement itself warrants an agency of its own in the system, or whether it is a very general term to cover a myriad of selectivity processes, is a question likely only to receive its answer in neurophysiology (cf. N6.9).

NOTES

NOTE 6.1

In Hull's *A Behavior System* Postulate 4 defines habit strength initially in terms of the number of equally spaced reinforced trials. Thus for habit strength

$$_SH_R = 1 - 10^{-0.0305N},$$

where N is the total number of reinforcements. In Postulate 5 primary motivation or drive (D) is defined as a function of enhancing (D') and inanition (ϵ) components both of which are functions of hours of deprivation (h).

$$D = D' \times \epsilon$$

$$D' = 37.824 \times 10^{-27.496 \frac{1}{h}} + 4.001$$

$$\epsilon = 1 - 0.00001045 \, h^{2.486}$$

The exactness of the constants should not be disconcerting; as the definitions stand both habit strength and drive are logical constructions, that is, intervening variables. As concepts, their operational status is assured since N and h are both observational variables.

Skinner is somewhat less explicit but it is clear that he, too, favors operational interpretations of drive:

> In measuring strength of drive we are in reality only measuring strength of behavior. A complete account of the latter is to be obtained from an examination of the operations that are found to affect it. The 'drive' is a hypothetical state interpolated between operation and behavior and is not actually required in a descriptive system. The concept is useful, however, as a device for expressing the complex relation that obtains between various similarly effective operations and a group of co-varying forms of behavior. The properties assigned to the state are derived from the observations of these relations (Skinner, 1938, p. 368).

Again, in 1953 he writes:

> A drive need not be thought of as mental or physiological. The term is simply a convenient way of referring to the effects of deprivation and satiation and of other operations which alter the probability of behavior in more or less the same way (Skinner, 1953, p. 144).

Skinner makes it clear that drives are not internal stimuli or physiological states or any other substantive states not definable in terms of simple operations.

One finds that the mediating variables of Tolman's theory are also subject to simple reductive analysis. Tolman himself undertakes the operational analysis of demands (Tolman, 1937).

The job of defending the operational status of the intervening variables in several learning theories is often thankless. Although such variables are given operational interpretations they often emerge as possessing surplus meaning in use. This is apparent in the literature on the issue of intervening variables versus hypothetical constructs (Marx, 1951, 1963).

For an examination of the status of Hull's constructs, see Koch (1954).

NOTE 6.2

An ostensive definition is denotative and requires exemplification of what is defined. An explicit definition is one involving synonymity in which the thing defined is replaced by its equivalent set of defining properties. Logical constructions and operational definitions resemble explicit definitions. However, a distinction must be made between a defining set of properties, as such, and a set of operations performed on a set of observations. A measure of intelligence may be explicitly defined as a set of responses on a given test. But intelligence may be operationally defined in terms of the test response *and* the arithmetic operations performed on such test performances. In this case, intelligence as operationally defined would be akin to a logical construction without inferred elements. If by intelligence this is all we mean, or if all theoretical terms were like 'specific gravity' with its operational definition (the ratio weight/volume) then there would be no problem of meaning (Hempel, 1958). The theoretical intensions of such terms could be dispensed with. However, this would stultify theory construction. Not all theoretical terms can be defined in terms of an explicit set of observables or in terms of explicit operations performed on a set of observables. Rather, the whole operational enterprise calls for a dispositional setting. We must distinguish between explicit definitions and dispositional terms.

In the following discussion let us take C as some concept, S as a stimulus description, and R as a response description. We need to define C. An explicit definition here might be $Cx \equiv Rx$ def. That is to say, the concept C can be attributed to x if, and only if, x is also R. But this will not do, for the definition does not prescribe the conditions under which R is to occur. For example, a person may be considered of such and such level of intelligence if he knows the meaning of thirty out of a list of forty words. But by the above definition we would affirm Cx regardless of whether Rx because the subject x had R in his unrehearsed repertory, or because he had gotten hold of a clandestine copy of the list of words and had done some prior rehearsing. Even the most restricted operational definition requires a clear stipulation of the situational setting.

As a second effort let us try a dispositional definition of the form:

$$Cx \equiv (Sx \supset Rx).$$

That is to say, x has the theoretical property C if, and only if, it is the case that if x is S then x is also R. Thus, in the above example, S would specify the situational requirements of the test procedure. It is like the example "x is volatile if, and only if, it is the case that if x is exposed to air x loses mass." But this formulation, too, offers serious difficulties. By the definition of material implication $(S \supset R) \equiv \sim(S \cdot \sim R) \equiv [(S \cdot R) \vee (\sim S \cdot R) \vee (\sim S \cdot \sim R)]$. Note that assignment of C could then be justified whenever the test conditions were not imposed. Thus we could attribute C to x regardless of whether he was or was not tested. If tested then R must be true, but if not tested, then either R or $\sim R$.

Because of this difficulty Carnap has proposed an alternative explication of operational reductions which has found rather wide acceptance (cf. Hempel, 1958). By virtue of the "reduction pair"

$$S_1 \supset (R_1 \supset C)$$
$$S_2 \supset (R_2 \supset \sim C)$$

one is able to derive the bilateral reduction sentence for C, namely

$$Sx \supset (Cx \equiv Rx)$$

by equating S_2 to S_1 and R_2 to $\sim R_1$. Thus, for example, given an anxiety scale under specified conditions then a score above a given critical level means the person is assigned what we conceptualize as a critical anxiety factor.

The discussion of Carnapian reduction sentences is more complicated than I have shown. The simplified test conditionals, with $(S_2 = S_1)$ and $(R_2 = \sim R_1)$, need not hold for reduction pairs; in which case the reduction pairs may serve to define experimental conditions for assigning a new predicate, C, to objects in terms of the familiar experimental predicates S_1, S_2, R_1, R_2. In such a case, the truth of the reduction pair (equivalent to $\sim(S_1 R_1 \cdot S_2 R_2)$) is synthetic. However, as treated above the bilateral reduction sentence is conventional and analytic. This derives from the fact that the cut between R and $\sim R$ is in some sense arbitrary. But note that $Sx \supset (Cx \equiv Rx)$ is not equivalent to the explicit definition $SxRx \equiv Cx$. Logically, all that we can infer from an operational definition is what a measurement should be under given test conditions in order for the defined concept to apply. The implication for inferring Cx from Rx does not rule out other conjunctions of S_i and R_i. It is the very nature of operational definitions that they be open textured. Not only does the definitive biconditional hold, i.e.,

$$S_1 x \supset (Cx \equiv R_1 x)$$

but also

$$S_2 x \supset (Cx \equiv R_2 x)$$
$$\vdots \qquad \vdots$$
$$S_n x \supset (Cx \equiv R_n x)$$

where the range of the concept C covers many test result conditionals, and where $S_2, \ldots, S_n, \ldots$ and $R_2, \ldots, R_n, \ldots$ represent events different from those in the initial operational setting. It is the openness of this range which leads one to seek some higher-order binding factor over the range of application of *C*. Thus, for example, should *C* be an "anxiety factor," we might be led to extend the range of the factor by endowing it with presumptively existential properties which would enable us to deduce other sets of *S–R* values for appropriate biconditional reduction sentences. Initially, of course, *C* is measured operationally. But it is only partially interpreted. Its extension is then determined by empirical test of purportedly alternative operations. Thus, as Carnap suggests, electric current can be measured by a deflection of a magnetic needle, by a quantity of silver separated out of solution, by heat produced in a conductor, etc. Temperature can be measured by an expansion of mercury or by electrical resistance, etc. And anxiety might be measured by blood chemistry, by activity of the reticular arousal system, as well as by an anxiety scale. As I shall argue, the concept itself carries the inchoate conception of its own extension. Strict operational reduction of a concept does not exhaust its entire meaning.

For discussions of the issues mentioned here see Carnap (1936, 1937); Koch (1941); Feigl (1945); Hempel (1954, 1958); Pap (1949, 1962).

NOTE 6.3

The manifesto of operationism (or operationalism) has undoubtedly been P. W. Bridgman's *The Logic of Modern Physics* (1927). Although his thinking on operational definition dates from 1914, he makes no claim to originality. As the gospel crystallized into a dubious orthodoxy, Bridgman himself came to regret his role as expositor:

> I feel that I have created a Frankenstein which has certainly gotten away from me. I abhor the word *operationalism* or *operationism*, which seems to imply a dogma, or at least a thesis of some kind. The thing I have envisaged is too simple to be so dignified by so pretentious a name; rather, it is an attitude or point of view generated by continued practice of operational analysis (1954, 79, p. 224).

After two notable symposia (*Psychological Review*, 1945; *Scientific Monthly*, 1954), the dogmatic overtones of operationism tended to soften. Except for its logical interest, the subject eventually came to assume its proper role as a footnote to empirical procedure.

Etiologically, it is interesting that Bridgman's operationism was occasioned by the radical innovations introduced by the special theory of relativity. Newtonian concepts of absolute space and time had so prevailed that scientist and philosopher alike had come to take their empirical and absolute character for granted. However, speculations concerning events as measured from rapidly moving frames of reference necessitated our treating the idea of simultaneity as relativistic. Nor was Bridgman the only person to see the operational significance of the new physics. Eddington, in *Space, Time, and Gravitation* (1920), writes:

> Counting appears to be an absolute operation. But it seems to me that other physical measures are on a different footing. Any physical quantity, such as length, mass, force, etc., which is not pure number, can only be defined as the result arrived at by conducting a physical experiment ac-

cording to specified rules. So I cannot conceive of any "length" in nature independent of a definition of the way of measuring length. And, if there is, we may disregard it in physics, because it is beyond the range of experiment (p. 8).

The piece is spoken by the relativist in dialogue with an orthodox physicist and a mathematician. As one of the first people to expound on the philosophical significance of relativity, Eddington became a thorough-going operationist. But more uniquely, he elevated his pointer-reading operationism to the status of an idealistic ontology. His thinking, it is claimed, is neo-Kantian. Knowledge of the external world can only be mediated by consciousness and its operational play upon its sense data (Eddington, 1920, 1928, 1939).

Not all operationists will be embarrassed by this kinship to Kant. The contemporary "Italian operational school" draws its inspiration from Bridgman and from Hugo Dingler, the prolix neo-Kantian of the early part of the twentieth century (Ceccato, 1952). The argument from Dingler is interesting, for it brings operationism closer to metaphysics than votaries are prone to admit. The basis of Dingler's operationism is gnoseology, the problem of reification of the known out of the unknown. This was a matter of some mystery to the Greeks, for the unknown always provides the reservoir of potentiality. Dingler, however, was concerned with establishing the univocality of something's becoming known. He sought semantic constancy, as it were, by imposing a dictionary of operations on the knowing process. Thus univocality in the reification of the potential was the key idea in Dingler's operationism.

The Italian operationists tend to withdraw from these metaphysical commitments to the unknown. If the process of becoming aware of a reality "does not take place between a known and an unknown, it nevertheless takes place between a proposed definition and a semantical obligation." Although this process of operational reification translates into the unfortunate neologism "awarening" (*consapevolizzazione*) it designates an important epistemological attack—what one might call the operational invasion of the unknown. The contextual combination of apprisal and material or thing apprised through operation is called the "provenience" of the operational invasion. If we let the more metaphysical volatilia evaporate, what then remains is that substance of the operational predicament which has provided people such as Feigl (1945) and Hempel (1954) with material for their critiques of operationism. According to the latter, the operational invasion is always guided by something not fully conceptualized in the operational definition. Operationism must fulfill what Ceccato calls the semantical obligation.

We have discussed operationism without benefit of a definition of it. It is fitting that Bridgman be heard: "In general, we mean by any concept nothing more than a set of operations; *the concept is synonymous with the corresponding set of operations*" (1927, p. 5). However, it is just this strict equating of a concept to a set of operations which has proved the shortcoming of the dogma. Few, if any, theoretical concepts are synonymous with an explicit set of operations.

For some early espousals of operationism see McGeoch (1936, 1937), Tolman (1936, 1937), Boring (1936), Kantor (1938), S. S. Stevens (1935a, 1935b), Bergmann and Spence (1941), and C. C. Pratt (1939).

NOTE 6.4

The Newtonian synthesis of planetary laws and mechanics is one of the supreme achievements in the history of science. The saga is interesting not alone for Newton's creation of celestial mechanics but also for the example of Kepler's travails in arriving at the laws of planetary motion. Kepler was the phenomenologist, so to speak; Newton, the reductionist theory builder.

The story of Kepler is one of dogged but rewarding persistence. Formulation of his first two laws alone required in years the number of days he predicted the task would take. With respect to his "discovery" of both the first and third laws, he compares Truth to the lascivious maiden of Virgil "who surrenders unexpectedly to her pursuer when he has already given up hope" (Koestler, 1959). The first two laws derived from his efforts to describe the orbit of Mars—a task assigned to him by Tycho Brahe. As was known from antiquity, the revolutionary motion of planets in their orbits was not uniform; hence, the invention of epicycles and eccentrics such that appearances of nonuniform motion could be accounted for in terms of uniform motion in circular orbits. Despite his otherwise mystical inclinations, Kepler ruthlessly cast aside the old face-saving geometrical devices. In keeping unconsciously, at least, to the precept of parsimony, he tried to simplify assumptions as to the nature of both the orbit and planetary motion. This was difficult to do. The simplest of assumptions, a circular orbit and uniform motion, obviously would not suffice. Thus by combining principles of equal sweep in equal time with the assumption of the eccentric locus for the sun, and by trying first circular, then ovoid, and finally elliptical orbits, Kepler was able to arrive at the great planetary laws.

First law: The orbit of the planet is an ellipse with the sun located at one of its two foci.

Second law: The planet moves in nonuniform motion about the sun so that the radius of the planet with respect to the sun sweeps out equal areas in equal increments of time.

The third law came later, after extensive trial-and-error search for a cosmic principle interrelating all the planetary orbits.

Third law: The relation of the period of revolution of a planet to its mean orbital radius is such that the ratio of the square of the time to the cube of the radius is constant for all planets ($k = T^2/r^3$).

Kepler left planetary astronomy with three acceptable laws but no theory. Newton's reduction of the Keplerian laws derived from his own three laws of motion, the law of gravitation, and certain other basic assumptions. On the basis of such assumptions, Newton considered masses to attract one another; for the purpose of calculations, all mass was to be regarded as located at a center of gravity. Thus estimates concerning the diameter of the earth and the orbital radius of the moon could be utilized as the base for his computations concerning the mutual attraction of the two bodies.

Newton's laws of motion are as follows:

First law: The principle of inertia and conservation of motion.

Second law: The force acting upon a body is proportional to its change in momentum (*mv*), and determines the direction in which the change in momentum occurs. From this the familiar $F = ma$.

Third law: Conservation of action: action and reaction are opposite and equal.

Law of gravitation: Gravitational force between two objects is equal to the product of the masses of the two objects divided by the square of the distance separating their centers of gravity: $F = Gm_1m_2/r^2$, with G the gravitational constant being contingent upon units of mass, length, and time.

Newton could show that Kepler's first law was derivable from a gravitational force effective as the inverse of the square of the distance between the planet and the sun. Kepler's second law requires that an effective force must be directed toward the sun. The most graphic deduction is that of the continuous gravitational pull of the moon toward the earth as it maintains its constant tangential motion. A combination of the tangential (inertial) and gravitational forces results in the bodies following an elliptical orbit in periodic but nonuniform velocity. What is remarkable is that the system of celestial mechanics is sufficient to deduce hypotheses about the behavior of any planetary system—just as, for example, it is successfully used to predict (or explain) the behavior of Halley's comet.

A question we might wish to raise is this: Is the achievement of Newton a "reduction" or an "explanation"? Was there a prior theory for Newton to exploit? Debate would be fruitless. Actually there were poorly formed "theories" before Newton gave the world his *Principia*. Though no one took him seriously, Kepler himself was sure that the cosmic principle of the five regular solids would somehow allow these solids to hold all the orbits of the planets within their concentric shells. The phenomenological laws of the planetary universe were to be explained by Pythagoreanism. Newton did, of course, succeed in reducing the phenomenological laws of planetary behavior to the language of mechanics. In subjecting celestial phenomena to the language of mechanics, he did achieve both a reduction and an explanation. The reduction itself was the occasion for building a science of mechanics.

NOTE 6.5

Woodger, who is a pioneer in axiomatics for the life sciences (1929, 1937, 1952), is himself critical of reducing psychology to physiology. Neither of the two disciplines have been axiomatized, neither are particularly mature. With respect to reduction in general, he writes:

> Strictly speaking, we can only fruitfully discuss such relations between theories when both have been axiomatized, but, outside mathematics, this condition is never satisfied. Hence the futility of much of the discussion about whether theory $T_{(2)}$ is reducible to theory $T_{(1)}$ 'in principle.' Such questions cannot be settled by discussions of that kind but *only by actually carrying out the reduction,* and this is not done and cannot be done until the theories have been axiomatized (1952, p. 271).

Woodger, who is not at all reluctant to recommend anthropomorphism to us when we are speaking of man, prefers that we develop a person language for an interpersonal theory of behavior. We cannot wait upon the development of the primary discipline to which behavioral theory is to be reduced.

> I ask whether it is good empiricism and good science to postpone the study of persons until you have completed a behavior theory, founded on the study of white rats and robots, in the hope that you will then be able to deduce the statements descriptive of persons from the postulates at which you arrived from your experiments on rats? The behaviorist programme is a long-term policy. We do not know whether it will ever be completed. It would surely be foolish to reject a theory which is expressed in the person language and refuse to try to extend and improve it simply on the ground it cannot be translated into the physical language (1952, p. 309).

The most that could be achieved is for psychology to be interpreted in terms of physiology. But even that is prohibitively restrictive. According to Woodger, the theory of persons cannot wait upon the development of physiology; it must develop its own language and without concern for reduction.

Additional discussions of formal requirements of reduction can be found in Bergmann (1957) and in Kemeny and Oppenheim (1956). The latter is a discussion and extension of the Nagel–Woodger treatments.

NOTE 6.6

Hull's language has often been suggestive of a physiological bias (e.g., stimulus trace, afferent interaction, and his early discussion of drive in terms of tissue deprivations and needs). However, over the decade of his three theoretical books, he makes it clear that molar descriptions concern gross responses of the organism as apart from the molecular physiology. In the *Principles of Behavior* he wrote:

> It is conceivable that the elaboration of a systematic science of behavior at a molar level may aid in the development of an adequate neurophysiology and thus lead in the end to a truly molecular theory of behavior firmly based on physiology (1943, p. 20).

Almost a decade later he was to reaffirm that belief in the *Essentials of Behavior:*

> Now while this molar or non-physiological approach presumably permits a much less perfect behavioral science than will someday be possible with a full knowledge of neurophysiology, it does give us a great deal of understanding of behavior. . . . Meanwhile in the case these postulates stand up under logical utilization, they may serve as a suggestive lead to neurophysiologists in their empirical investigations, and ultimately to a higher integration of gross molar behavior and neurophysiology (1951, p. 6).

Here Hull alludes to a point that has been made by critics of classical reductionism (Feyerabend, 1962; Sellars, 1961; Feigl, 1961; Scriven, 1958). A reducing science is seldom so mature or so formalistically complete that a reduction is straightforwardly achievable. Rather the secondary science itself generalizes and modifies the concepts in the reducing science which are requisite for the reductive undertaking.

Other Hullians (Spence, 1956; Kendler, 1952) have emphasized the non-physiological basis of behavior theory. However, neither would preclude reductionism on logical grounds.

NOTE 6.7

Since formalization and axiomatization of the primary and the secondary science is propaedeutic to reduction, discussions of actual reduction are premature. Rather we should focus upon prospective reduction as the means of resolving theoretical issues, especially those concerning mediating processes. However, the task of defending reductionism on this prospective basis is simplified when the given theory of behavior has been the object of formal analysis. Hence attempts to formalize theories of learning are of considerable interest. Consider the following:

(1) Hull's postulational system is frequently offered as the example par excellence of formal behavior theory. Yet, its very lack of formal rigor has made it subject to hypercritical attacks on that account (Koch, 1954). However, in a little-referred-to paper of F. B. Fitch ond Gladys Barry (1950), the authors treat Hull's theory to a rigorous formal analysis. In spite of the brevity of the paper, the analysis is too long to give in detail; but the following points should give the flavor of the argument.

The complete formalization is composed of thirteen definitions and five axioms with their corollaries. The definitions cover the following terms, each of which plays a significant role in the postulates of Hull:

D1. Stimulus events.
D2. Response events.
D3. Time of occurrence or time stretch of such events.
D4. Initial time for dating onset of neural functioning.
D5. Tendency in a stimulus-response pair ($_SH_R$ at time t).
D6. Increment in tendency (acquisition).
D7. Stimulus similarity.
D8. Response similarity.
D9. Function for amount of drive.
D10. Goal gradient function (important in drive reduction).
D11. Function for effective drive reduction.
D12. Function for dependence of increment of tendency.
D13. Constant of proportionality between increment of tendency and effective drop in drive.

Although no consistent effort is made to tie these definitions to neurophysiological substrates, it is obvious that each can serve as a hypothesis for neurophysiological explorations. The axioms of the analysis cover the following items:

A1.   The state of habit strength at any given time.
A2.   Increment of habit strength as a function of stimulus similarity, response similarity, latency of response, and a function expressed in A3.
A3.   Effective drop in drive as an integrable function over time of goal gradient and average rate of drive reduction.
A4.1–A4.5.   The equation of increment of habit strength with partial derivatives for each of the independent variables as listed in A2.
A5.1–A5.6.   Goal gradient as function of drive reduction.

It is a comparatively simple matter to apply the criteria of reduction to this set of definitions and axioms. We can assume that the physicalistic language is common to both psychology and neurophysiology (hence all statements about the environment, time, space, etc., are admissible). The salient terms for reduction are then stimulus, response, and drive reduction. Since every stimulus and every response is a truth functional extension over afferent and efferent components, then drive reduction alone becomes the crucial concept. Thus, we may argue that a reduction of Hullian psychology is possible if drive can be describable in predicates admissible to the neurophysiological language. This latter condition can only be satisfied by empirical research. However, in light of recent advances concerning motivation and activation, achievement of the empirically reductive equivalences between drive and neurophysiological process seems quite possible. The promise of reductive achievement is perhaps not so remote as some critics have inclined to think (e.g., Bergmann, 1953).

(2) In a somewhat less ascetic vein, Voeks (1950) has undertaken the formalization of Guthrie's theory of learning. She proceeds from postulates and definitions to the deduction of a set of theorems, each of which expresses an hypothesis with behavioral implications. In brief the postulates (or principles) are as follows:

P1.   Principle of association.
P2.   Principle of postremity (a refinement on recency).
P3.   Principle of response probability (as a monotonically increasing function of number of stimulus cues).
P4.   Principle of a dynamic stimulus situation.

The definitions cover the following:

D1.   Stimulus.
D2.   Cue (an unconditioned or previously conditioned stimulus).
D3.   Response.
D4.   Conditioned response.
D5.   Indirect conditioned response to a stimulus pattern.
D6.   Postreme response.
D7.   Incompatible response.
D8.   Learning.

Because of the absence of mediating constructs (maintaining stimuli are not conspicuous in Voek's formalization), Guthrie's theory has not offered the challenge to reduction that Hull's theory has. Still the language of stimulus and response is certainly conducive to reduction, and simple conditioning and association models of learning, of all psychological models, have been most amenable to reductive analysis. As for response probability being a function of stimulus cue, this principle, essential both to the contiguity theory of Guthrie and to the statistical learning theory of Estes, is well modeled, so to speak, by the neurophysiological schematics of Milner (1957) and Rosenblatt (1958). Both the Mark II of Milner and the Perceptron of Rosenblatt account for a stochastic cueing process in terms of mediating cell assemblies which augment the probability of response.

To be sure, a Guthrian need not be concerned with neurophysiology, but there is nothing in the formal analysis of the principles and laws of learning which militates against a reductionist claim.

(3) A third major theory of learning to be treated to formalization is that of Tolman. Tolman's own presentations of his sign gestalt or expectancy theory were admittedly informal and "programmatic" (e.g., 1932, 1934, 1948). Moreover, because of his emphasis upon cognitive processes and purposive behavior, he himself has been accused of mentalism, of leaving his subjects "buried in thought" (Guthrie, 1935). With an avowed preference for a reinforcement principle, MacCorquodale and Meehl (1953, 1954) have attempted a formalization of expectancy theory. Noting among other things that the data language of Tolman and his students is ambiguous, that not all of their behavioral hypotheses can be derived from the expectancy construct, and that the language of expectancy has a mentalistic, intentional intonation, these writers prescribe a set of postulates which place the constructs of expectancy theory on firm behavioral and physicalistic foundations. The last item of their criticism is especially worthy of comment. As we shall see in the following chapter, the thesis of intentionality has frequently been offered as a barrier both to logical behaviorism and to reductionism. Since Brentano, it has been generally recognized that a mental act involves an element of "aboutness." Propositions expressing intentional events have a unique structure. There is the object of regard, judgment, thinking, etc., and there is the intentional act of regarding, judging, thinking, etc., which has a logical status different from that of the physical object. Strictly interpreted then, cognitive statements with intentional aspects are not themselves "truth functions of their components." To escape this predicament and to assure that all intentionalistic terms or descriptions are translatable into the data language, MacCorquodale and Meehl formulate postulates of expectancy in terms of stimulus and response.

A brief paraphrase of the postulates follows. What is missing from the condensation are the details of the characteristic curves of growth, strength increment, etc. The unit of analysis is the expectancy unit $(S_1R_1S_2)$ in which S_1 is the elicitor stimulus situation, R_1 is the response elicited, and S_2 is the expectandum or stimulus situation associated with goals and ends.

P1. *Mnemonization:* Growth of $(S_1R_1S_2)$ is a function of the valence of S_2 and the probability that S_2 follows from S_1R_1.

P2. *Extinction:* Expectancy strength of S_2 on S_1R_1 diminishes as a function of decrease in its probability on S_1R_1 from some prior rate.

P3.   *Primary generalization:* Other elicitors (S^*) of R_1 and S_2 events will receive expectancy strength from ($S_1R_1S_2$) as a function of the similarity between S^* and S_1.

P4.   *Inference:* The temporal contiguity of S_2S^* given an expectancy ($S_1R_1S_2$) yields an increment of strength to a new expectancy ($S_1R_1S^*$).

P5.   *Generalized inference:* If S^*S_2 occur in temporal contiguity, wherein S_2 is inferrable from S'_2 in the expectancy of $S_1R_1S'_2$, then that contiguity will produce an increment of strength in ($S_1R_1S^*$).

P6.   *Secondary cathexis:* Contiguity of S^* and S_2 when S^* has valence produces an increment of strength in the absolute valence of S_2 (analogous to secondary reinforcement).

P7.   *Induced elicitor cathexis:* Acquisition of valence by an expectandum S_2 induces valence in the elicitor S_1.

P8.   *Confirmed elicitor cathexis:* Confirmation of an expectancy when S_2 has a valence produces an increment in the cathexis of S_1 (reinforcement of S_1).

P9.   *Valence:* The valence of a stimulus S^* is a multiplicative function of the need D and the cathexis C^*.

P10. *Need strength:* Need strength is a temporal function of deprivation since a prior satiation.

P11. *Cathexis:* Cathexis of S^* is an increasing function of the number of contiguities of it and the consummatory response.

P12. *Activation:* Reaction potential $_SE_R$ of response R_1 in presence of S_1 is a multiplicative function of the strength of ($S_1R_1S_2$) and the valence of S_2.

Some important terms remain undefined (e.g., consummatory response), but care is taken by the authors to define stimulus and response as classes of afferent and efferent events. Note should be taken that MacCorquodale and Meehl present their set of postulates only as a provisional and "nonsufficient" attempt at formalization. However, it is significant that they are able to deduce confirmed hypotheses from the domain of latent learning, and that they bring together certain principles of reinforcement and expectancy theories.

The authors' own preference (1954) is for a system of implicit definitions wherein the meanings of the constructs are uniquely contingent upon the whole system of postulates and grow, so to speak, with the accretions to the system. Although no attempt is made at reduction itself (the language of physiology "will be fine when we can get it") they prefer hypothetical constructs, with their openness of meaning, over allegedly "direct, operational definitions." "Stimulus" and "response" are terms in the peripheral language to be sure; but "mnemonization," "inference," and "cathexis," are terms for the centralistic locale. And so, also, for the language of strengthening, increment, and extinction. Responding to an article by Kendler (1952) (in which he argues that the issue of what is learned is a pseudo-issue, and that all we seek in our constructions is to amplify upon lawful behavioral relationships), MacCorquodale and Meehl (1953) declare it both fruitful and empirically legitimate to speculate on the mediating process. In fact, such speculation is regarded as essential in the long run. No one denies that the brain and nervous system mediate behavioral process. We may speak as if our constructs are no more than strict logical constructions out of the data language, but such constructs become reified if for no other reason than that the empiricist is more comfortable in palpable than in abstractive locales. Since reductive and nonreductive psychologists admit the need for mediating variables, the question of physical locus is relevant. If it were presumed not, it would be like asserting that the request for the existential credentials of mediating constructs is inappropriate where, in fact, such credentials are in principle obtainable.

In summary, formalization facilitates reductive analysis. Formalization brings into sharp relief the constructs mediating the ontologically basic language of stimulus and response. In the reductive framework, such constructs become the hypothesis of neurophysiology. Making good on the promise of reductionism, however slow that process may be, will eventually decide which constructs will stand and how they will be modified.

NOTE 6.8

In this context it is interesting to consider what the conventionalistic tactics of the parapsychologist might be. Should he argue strictly from observables, as the extrasensory psychologist often does, than any mediators would be fair pragmatic support of a theory that accounts for the paranormal behaviors. What is distressing here is the denial by many parapsychologists that one can seek a neurophysiological reduction of paranormal behavior. Yet such reductionism is just what some radical behaviorists consider as irrelevant. It is perhaps ironic that Skinner, a nonreductionist and a critic of extrasensory experiments (1948), cannot base his critique of parapsychology upon the reductionist's claim that the physical locale for the stimulus–response rubric be an intact neurophysiological continuum.

NOTE 6.9

The last decade has seen a growing interest in building models for the deduction of behavioral phenomena. Deutsch (1960), for example, gives a schematic model that is compatible with Hull and the principle of reinforcement and that is amenable to reduction. In fact, Deutsch visualizes the psychologist as blocking out in schematic form hypotheses for the neurophysiologist to explore.

> The psychologist can, by inference from the behavior of the system, suggest hypotheses which the physiologist, helped by knowing what types of phenomena to look for, can then confirm by direct observation. On the other hand, the physiologist's observations, the significance of which may be obscure to him, can suggest to the psychologists the type of hypotheses which could account for certain behavior, and this he can go on to test by making behavioral predictions. In this way the psychologist and the

physiologist can work together, the psychologist relieved of the necessity of physiological speculation and the neurophysiologist presented with actual hypotheses he can test (Deutsch, 1960, p. 173).

According to him, then, his schematic should provide the neurophysiologist with testable hypotheses concerning structure and function. Details of the model are provided in Figure 6.1. The mechanics of this basic behavioral

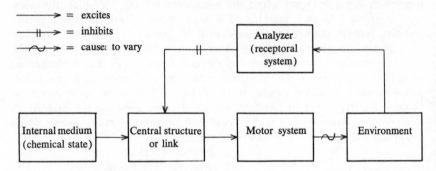

Figure 6.1   Diagram to illustrate suggested mechanism of need (from J. A. Deutsch, *The Structural Basis of Behavior*. Cambridge: Cambridge University Press, 1960).

unit or link can best be presented in Deutsch's own words:

> The system which has been postulated can be described in five propositions. There are five elements in it, related to each other in three different ways. The elements will be called an analyzer (a receptoral system), a link, a motor (or effector) organization, an environment, a feature of the internal environment. The three kinds of relation are activating; switching-off; causing to vary. The elements are related to form the unit in the following way:
> 1. The primary link is set into activity by a feature of the internal environment.
> 2. When the primary link is active it indirectly activates the motor organization.
> 3. The activity in the motor organization causes the environment to vary.
> 4. A particular variation in the environment activates the analyzer.
> 5. The activated analyzer switches off the link. Most of these relations will not be all or none, but more or less in nature (1960, pp. 33–34).

Note that this "need"-oriented system provides no place for a construct of need as such. The internal (subcortical) activating system is itself sensitive to various kinds of physiological deficits. Motor activity (behavioral hypotheses, as it were) continues until a particular response and environmental variation evokes stimulus input (the analyzer) which in turn effects cessation of the activating link. Any sequential act will involve a series of units such as in Figure 6.1, each with its link. The underlying deficit serves as an activator of the sequential set of links until it too is eventually terminated by the analyzer of some consummatory response. But the activity of each link is terminated by the elicitation of its own analyzer; thus the cessation of one link allows activation of the next link in the series and those two links will become connected. Thus far, the linkage series is explanatory of any unlearned sequence of behavior (e.g., it coincides nicely with Tinbergen's sequential analysis of instinct; 1951). Additional principles are required for explaining contiguity and frequency effects in learning. Deutsch finds that he can derive hypotheses concerning the phenomena of reinforcement, latent learning, exploration, extinction, self-stimulation (see Gallistel, 1964) without hypostatizing drive and need. At each point he is conscious of the possibility of translating his schematic into neurophysiological hypotheses.

Deutsch's model is only one among many which draw support from recent discoveries concerning the activating and alerting functions of the subcortical reticular system. Berlyne's theory of exploratory behavior (1960) presents a conjectural exploitation of the limited data of arousal. Subcortical nuclei both facilitate and inhibit activity of the cortex. Thus they serve both to alert the cortex for processing specific sensory inputs and to inhibit other areas that might offer cortical competition. In combination they mediate the selectivity of attention and efficient response. There is, however, an optimal state of arousal. Overarousal may result in fixations and compulsive behavior; underarousal may result in disorientation. Both states in their extremity result in relatively inefficient behavior. Drive states are activators; in other words, they serve to stimulate the arousal state. In presence of such drive, the "consummatory behavior," itself, results in deactivation. Intensive and novel stimuli also serve to activate and to arouse. One might think then that boredom and the absence of stimulation would mean low arousal and that curiosity is the manifestation of a search for arousal (Hebb), but Berlyne disagrees. Rather, he suggests, boredom means high arousal and high activation level. Under the circumstances, novel stimulation is sought. To some extent competing arousals will inhibit one another. But what is more important is that the increased arousal due to curiosity in an explorable situation is relieved (i.e., diminished) by exploration, by familiarization, and by recognition. In affective terms, arousal is pleasurable up to a certain level; beyond the optimal level, it becomes unpleasant and instigates behaviors directed, in the end, toward reducing arousal. Berlyne has some interesting speculations to present concerning behavior in the face of uncertainty, but where his system is most fruitful is in the deduction of the learning that takes place in the absence of ostensible reinforcements.

Perhaps the best known of the behavior models to incorporate hypotheses of arousal is that of Hebb (1949, 1955). Its most distinctive innovation is that of postulating mechanisms for establishing order, stability, and habit out of assemblages of randomly organized components. Instead of presenting complex sets of prepotent reflex structures (there may be these, of course), the cortex offers myriads of randomly firing associative and processing cells which adventitiously become associated with specific sensory inputs. Association takes place between the input mosaic and some particular set of processing components that happen to be firing at the moment of input. Input is, of course, projected to specific areas of the cortex, but just what cells participate in processing a perceptual configuration are selected according to the coincidence of input and the random firing of the processing cells. This "cell assembly," so to speak, is built up as a processing manifold through cell modification and growth. Such processing manifolds can either be transient or lasting. Associative processes of stimulus and stimulus and of stimulus and response are implemented by phase sequences in which contiguously active cell assemblies are connected at the level of neural function.

The original model was hardly more than a prolegomenon to a future system. Certain objections arose in conjunction with Hebb's limited neural postulates. For example, learning would occur much too rapidly, and there would apparently be no deterrent to a cataclysmic recruitment of cell firing. Drawing upon the works of Eccles (1953), Lorente de Nó (1949), and others, Milner (1957) modified the cell assembly mechanism so as to overcome these objections. Furthermore he proposed specific subcortical arousal mechanisms to accommodate motivational and learning effects. To Hebb's original set of neural postulates (temporal summation, synaptic strengthening, refractoriness, neural fatigue), Milner added postulates of collaterally induced inhibition and cell priming. Establishment and strengthening of cell assemblages is occasioned not only by the coincidences of cell firings but also by the fact that the firing of any long axone neurone induces inhibitory effects at the synapses of adjacent inactive cells. Collateral branchings of such long axone cells fire short axone cells which in turn inhibit synaptic transmission of adjacent transmitters. Cell assemblies thus become self-protective and self-sustaining under steady input. Once the assemblies are secured their phase sequences are established, as Hebb had postulated.

In addition, Milner was more explicit as to the role of the subcortical (reticular) arousal system. The postulate of priming states that any subthreshold stimulation of a cell leaves that cell primed for subsequent firing. Thus, one assembly primed by previously active assemblies can be excited by fractional complements of the original stimulus (witness, for example, the effectiveness of cues and redintegration in learning). But priming also renders the cortical cells (i.e., those associatively linked to active cell assemblies) susceptible to arousal. Let the arousal centers become active either from cortical input or by receptors sensitive to deficit; these centers in turn activate the cortex so as to increase the rate of random firing of the cortical cells. However, because some cells are primed they are more likely to be firing at the incidence of a stimulus input than any random sampling of cells. Associative strengthening is thereby predisposed.

Motivational level affects learning in two ways: (1) by eliciting cortical activity and response, and (2) subsequently by affecting the rate of learning. The effects are not independent of one another. Since arousal varies with motivation level, more cortical cells will be active and available for the coincident firing underlying the formation and association of the cell assemblies. Moreover, the effects of reinforcement, reward, and satiation are such as momentarily to reduce the level of arousal. This in turn decreases the availability of cells and cell assemblies for the associative processes essential to learning.

None of the mentioned systems presents actual physiological models of learning processes. That is, none deals with a point-by-point, process-by-process, mapping of neuroanatomical units. At most they block in hypothetical components which serve as the blue prints for conceptual nervous systems. It is for the neurophysiologist to implement the function of components with his own explorations and findings. Nevertheless, the above theories do differ in a significant way from learning theories such as that of Hull, Tolman, and Guthrie. The hypothetical constructs refer to possible microstructures of the mediators and are not alone conjecturable from molar behavioral events.

Speculations in modeling conceptual nervous systems are extensive. They vary from studies of cybernetics and automata to actual neurophysiological models. F. H. George (1961) presents a fairly comprehensive review of the literature of cybernetics and adjacent disciplines. With respect to brain functions, D. A. Sholl (1956) offers a very readable survey of some of the statistical aspects of cerebral organization. There are two notable symposia on brain functions and integrative processes: Delafresnaye (1954) and Jeffress (1951), and another symposium edited by Delafresnaye (1961) on brain mechanisms and learning.

More elaborate conceptual nervous systems are to be found in Rosenblatt (1958); Pribram (1960); and Galanter, Miller, and Pribram (1960). One should, of course, not overlook the classic works of Hebb (1949, 1955).

Advances in biochemistry already suggest that reduction can be carried a step further. Presently one finds impressive hypotheses on how stimulus inputs may modulate changes in the structure of DNA and RNA molecules of nerve cells such that unique structure of the molecules may code the response potentials of the cell or may affect the resonance properties of cell response (Landauer, 1964). Reviews relating biochemistry to memory and learning are to be found in Morrell (1961), John (1961), Thomas (1962), and Gaito and Zavala (1964).

The intention here is not to give a survey of the literature in psychobiology but only to indicate that it is a fairly rich one. Speculations concerning future reductions of psychology are not as idle as they have appeared to some. The advances are perhaps sufficient to make the criterion of reducibility a useful one for evaluating the theoretical terms of psychology.

CHAPTER 7

Reductionism: II

IN SPITE of the dramatic developments in the domain of psychobiology, reductionism has not been a particularly popular doctrine within psychology itself. Occasionally calls come for psychologists to formulate their explanatory systems in neurophysiology (e.g., MacCorquodale and Meehl, 1948; Krech, 1950; Hebb, 1955), but for the most part, the psychophysiology is done by physiologists, engineers, and biophysicists rather than psychologists. On the contrary, psychologists have frequently demurred as concerns the value of neurologizing. One can, of course, understand the objections to a premature neurophysiology; it is likely to interfere with explicit treatment of data and lawful description of behavior (cf. N7.1). Yet the objections continue when the arguments on grounds of prematurity no longer seem quite so trenchant.

For the psychologist objections to reductionism can be grouped into two categories: methodological and phenomenological. The former of these includes policies and procedural commitments as to the subject matter and theory of psychology. As such, no crucial logical issues prohibitive of reduction are involved. The issue of the logical impossibility of reductionism is, however, raised with respect to the phenomenological aspects of psychology. Here, the personalistic and cognitive languages purportedly offer difficulties not encountered in a purely physicalistic language. We will not be concerned here with objections based solely on the preference for remaining in the behavioral language on grounds that much remains to be done of a descriptive and exploratory nature. One cannot quarrel with such a decision. As Sellars (1956) and Bergmann (1957) have pointed out, reductionism as an article of faith in the absence of a well-structured secondary science (psychology) is a trivial thesis. At this stage of the science much remains to be done in the behavioral language as such. Hull, Tolman, and Spence all might agree to some such statement of the situation. None objects to the ultimate possibility of neurophysiological explanations. And, though individually preferring the behavioral language, none has made the disavowal of reductionism a commanding statement in his scientific credo—even though their respective procedural preferences may have been interpreted as such.

At the outset it should be noted that the point of view expressed in this chapter is that there are no logical barriers, and perhaps no technological ones, to reductionism in psychology and that all explanations of behavior can in principle be reduced to the language of neurophysiology.

METHODOLOGICAL OBJECTIONS

In general, when the qualifier "methodological" is found in the philosophy of science it has been used to designate a point of view calling for firm procedural commitments. Though such commitments are not logically entailed and may often arise only for the lack of metaphysical support for one over another procedure, they are binding all the same. They do indeed become part of a working credo. As a rule, then, methodological decisions are made when issues are raised for which no straightforward answers are forthcoming. Such was the case, for example, when Lashley (1923) sought to disallow consciousness as a suitable subject matter for psychology. With respect to a methodological (nonreductive) behaviorism, the argument is somewhat analogous. Reliance upon neurophysiology is unwarranted, untested, or too restrictive. Under the circumstances, a strict operational behaviorism is considered essential to psychology. Intervening variables with strict behavioral interpretability are preferred to hypothetical constructs. This, the nature of our "hypothetical" terms, seems to be the focal issue and the one to which we want eventually to turn. But first, some preliminaries.

Reductionism and Psychology

When the psychologist speaks of reduction he means, of course, the reduction of psychology to physiology, or more precisely, to neurophysiology. If he is unfamiliar with the formal requirements for reduction, as he is likely to be, he is inclined to espouse some article of faith such as "no psychosis without neurosis," only substituting "behavior" for "psychosis" as more befits the proper subject matter of psychology. Whether any science in its history has exemplified the paradigm of formal reduction is for the present immaterial. Neither the language of psychology nor that of physiology is so rigorously developed that conjointly they permit the reduction of the statements of one science into the statements of the other. Nor is there any immediate prospect of this being achieved. What we do have are some rather impressionistic, at best, schematic accounts of how the concepts of one science can be related to those of the other.

Note that I say related and not reduced. This is simply a precaution to avoid the implication that the reducing science in this case is either a finished or a mature science standing independently of the reduced science. Both neurophysiology and psychology are relatively immature sciences. Their relationship has been a symbiotic one. The concepts of one science have been instrumental to the development of the concepts of the other. Rather than a neurophysiology offering a tidy system of finished concepts for the deduction of certain laws of psychology, we find one in which the concepts are subjected to substantial revisions in order that they may be adopted as an explanatory basis of psychology. Nowhere, perhaps, is this more clear than in the study of memory functions. Early neurophysiology was reflex oriented. The functional unit of the central nervous system was the reflex arc, with the accompanying processes of synaptic growth and neurobiotaxis. These conceptions fit well into the traditions of associationism, and in time they became the neurophysiological model for Thorndikean stimuli–response psychology. But the subsequent investigations of people like Bartlett, Lashley, Köhler, and Hebb soon made it obvious that the functional unit of memory had to be more complex than the reflex arc. Consequently, we find conceptions of reverberating circuits emerging to complicate the synaptic picture. Similar examples can be found in the area of perception. The phenomena of afterimages, of perceptual constancies, of perceptual generalization have served both to stimulate and to guide neurophysiologists in their work. Contrariwise recent work on the subcortical centers of the brain, particularly the reticular formation, has led to the rediscovery of consciousness and the language of awareness (Delafresnaye, 1954).

Two Types of Reduction

One needs, however, to look more closely at the meaning of reductionism for the psychologist. I have said that for the most part reductionism means the reduction of psychology to neurophysiology. But this is a restricted usage; for one could speak of the reduction of theoretical terms without necessarily implying that the theoretical terms are reduced to terms in the neurophysiological language. In the philosophical literature, one finds reductionism discussed in at least two contexts. In the context of what in the last chapter was called constructual reduction, one speaks of reducing theoretical terms to a set of observation statements, or, for the phenomenalist, to a set of statements about sense data. This is reductionism as discussed by the phenomenalists, by the physicalists, by the logical atomists, and critically by people like Quine (1953) and Barker (1957). In the second context, that of theoretic reduction, one speaks of reducing one theory to another. Such would be the case in reducing psychology to neurophysiology, or in reducing genetics to biochemistry. This is the treatment of reductionism that appears to predominate in the philosophy of science (e.g., Nagel, 1949, 1961; Woodger, 1952; Kemeny and Oppenheim, 1956). It should be apparent that the two treatments of reductionism are not mutually exclusive. On the other hand, they do not mutually entail one another. This is quite clear in the reductive accounts of psychology. One can, for example, be a strict reductionist so far as concerns his theoretical terms, yet not believe that it is either necessary or desirable that psychology make reductive use of neurophysiology. Such a view is explicitly defended by B. F. Skinner (1938, 1950) and by Spence (1956). There are other psychologists who defend psychology as a neurophysiologically reducible discipline yet would suggest that the theoretical concepts be treated as inferred entities rather than as logical constructions deriving from strict behavioral data reduction. MacCorquodale and Meehl (1948) and Hebb (1949) defend this type of argument, as do perhaps most psychologists who believe in the neurophysiological foundations of psychology. At first glance, this appears paradoxical. People who are reductionist in the constructual sense may be nonreductionist in the theoretic sense. Witness, for example, Skinner and Tolman. On the other hand, people who are reductionist in the theoretic sense may not be strictly so in the constructual sense. There is no logical difficulty here, however, and any sense of paradox disappears when we examine the possibility of reducing the theoretical constructs of systems such as those of Skinner or Tolman to neurophysiological terms. The preference of, say, a Skinnerian for a radical nonphysiological behaviorism is just that, a preference. Indeed there is nothing to prevent him from reducing either his observational or his theoretical terms to an inclusive language of neurophysiology (i.e., to the physical language and the language of neurophysiology, as such).

Hypothetical Concepts and Reductionism

There have been several occasions to refer to the distinction between intervening variables and hypothetical constructs, as proposed by Mac-Corquodale and Meehl (1948). Whether this distinction holds for the physical sciences may be open to some debate; but doubtless it has proved useful in psychology for distinguishing those people who want stringent operational reductions with no element of surmise from those who wish to include the element of surmise as a promise of constructual reification. For example, in the systems by Skinner and Tolman, different as they are, the variables mediating between stimulus and response are really translations of statements of observable events. That is to say, they are anchored either to the stimulus complex of events or to the response complex. Regardless of which anchorage, the translation is achieved at no cost of empirical uncertainty. There is no open texture implicit in the translation, no surplus of meaning which appeals either to the fictionalists or to the reductionists opting for the promise of a more explicit translation of their theoretical terms.

Our concern here should be to recognize that psychologies that insist upon using intervening variables as mediating between stimulus and response are readily adaptable to reductive translations ("psychologies" rather than "theories," for in this context Skinner appears to be correct in his insisting that stimulus–response psychology, which utilizes only intervening variables as its theoretical terms, can be lawful but it is not theoretical). (Cf. N7.2.)

The Case for Reductionism

Now the radical behaviorist prescribes just those conditions for behavioral analysis which have led philosophers such as Bergmann (1954) to assert the triviality of the reductive thesis. In other words, the radical behaviorist prescribes a linguistic range which assures the possibility of neurophysiological reduction. Bergmann does not spell out the argument, but it is a simple matter to do so. Since neuronal activity is an all-or-none affair, it is amenable to analysis within the truth functional paradigm of logical atomism. Note that the inclusive physiological language includes statements about the physical world as well as those concerning the properties and activities of organic systems. The physiological language will, of course, contain statements of laws and of theoretical terms, but that need not concern us here. It will be sufficient to show that any statement admissible to radical behaviorism is translatable into a statement in the neurophysiological language.

Let us first consider response. We may define response as any anatomical displacement occurring over some specified increment of time. (It is doubtful that any treatment of response would lead to the rejection of this broad definition.) In turn we may then define organismic behavior as some complex of responses. We may then justify neurophysiological reduction by the following argument. Every anatomical displacement is mediated by the motor-efferent system of the organism. Thus each possible response and each behavior is describable as a molecular proposition whose truth value is a function of the truth conditions of each and every atomic proposition corresponding with each and every motor unit in the organismic system. Each response is specified at any given instant of time when we know which motor units are contracting at what instant of time. Since response is defined as occurring over some increment of time, then some particular response will be equivalent to a molecular proposition which sums over the neuronal instants for the increment of response time. In general, behaviors are not so anatomically refined as responses. But the crudeness of behavioral descriptions such as that of bar pressing, turning toward a goal, etc., offers no difficulty. For, in what is a one–many relation of responses to behavior, any given behavior can be represented by a class of many molecular propositions each expressing concatenations of responses.

Thus so long as behavior is the appropriate subject matter of psychology, all response states and behavioral descriptions are expressible in the language of neurophysiology. However, one notes that stimuli are also involved. But this is not problematic. Descriptions of the physical stimulus are coadmissible to our two languages (e.g., to psychology and physiology). We need only describe the stimulus as an afferent function of the organism. Since every possible stimulus is some kind of input and every input is coded in terms of afferent activity (ruling out extrasensory inputs), then every possible state of stimulation is expressible as a truth function concerning the response of each and every afferent cell. In principle, then, both stimulus and response are reducible to neurophysiological states.

Note that nothing has been said of mediating variables. All that has been asserted is that the observables, the data of behavior, of stimulus–response, and of the ecological setting, are expressible in the neurophysiological language. What can we now say of the mediating variables? If such are intervening variables, that is to say, if they are logical constructions, then there is no element of such variables which is not reducible to the inclusive language of neurophysiology. On the other hand, if the mediating variables are hypothetical constructs, then regardless of what may be their inferred neurophysiological status they cannot be strictly reduced to a set of statements in the neurophysiological language. That is, there is an unspecified set of predicates which schematize the open texture or the heuristic possibilities of the construct. An expectation may be that research will lead us to a closing up of the texture of the construct, but the state of neurophysiological knowledge being what it is for the present, all that can be offered is a promise. But the radical behaviorist's proscription of all hypothetical constructs ensures the possibility of complete neurophysiological reduction! There is just a touch of irony here. For in what passes as learning theory, Skinner and Tolman have been among the most persistent opponents of neurologizing psychology. Yet their equally persistent espousal of intervening variables over hypothetical constructs assures us that their own "theories" of psychology are reducible to neurophysiology.

The first point to be made then is that radical behaviorism (under which include Tolman as well as Skinner) has no argument against reducing psychology to neurophysiology other than that of a vocabulary preference. Indeed the insistence upon intervening variables, operational definitions, and the observational language guarantees the reduction of psychology against either logical or technological difficulties.

But now what of open-textured theories in which the theoretical terms are only partially interpreted? It has been argued effectively that theories which utilize only intervening variables, which insist upon the strict operational reduction of their theoretical terms, are heuristically sterile. Innovations, other than *ad hoc* ones to accommodate deviant events, are apt to be wanting. Moreover, the level of explanation provided by laws without theoretical synthesis is lower than that provided by a synthetic theory. That much is granted by behavioral theoreticians. But, on the other hand, it is the despair over reducing the inventions of theoretical psychology to neurophysiology which has led some people to embrace instrumentalism, or rather to take instrumentalism and turn it into the boast of fictionalism. Let us consider a sampling of opinion here.

Berenda (1957) has made a plea for peace among personologists on the ground that all personality theories enjoy equal veridical status providing, of course, all account for behavior. His plea was made to clinical psychologists, and the need for modifying aberrant behavior being as pressing as it is, perhaps the gambit of pragmatism is understandable.

Setting his argument on such background statements as one "must give up the preconception that physics is engaged in revealing the ultimate nature of some real objective world behind the world of phenomena," and "theories do not give us pictures or laws of an absolute reality but (as John Dewey emphasized) are merely the tools or instruments created by brilliant minds to deal more or less adequately with some selected aspects of observable phenomena," Berenda goes on to assert:

> A scientific system need not try to provide us with a *unique* theory of phenomena, nor need its abstract concepts be visualizable in terms of concrete or mechanistic imagery, nor need the theory be quantitative. More than one theory of personality or of therapy could be used by the clinician, and possibly the abstract terminology of various theories (all "verified") could be shown to be equivalent. Which of such theories the clinician uses may be a matter of personal preference, congenial to his own temperament. We can only seek to construct some self-consistent system of abstractions or concepts that, as simply as possible, logically organizes a given area of phenomena in the field of human behavior. More than one such system is possible (1957, p. 727).

This is a clear and unguarded statement of an instrumentalistic position. For reasons stated in Chapter 6, exception must be taken to the language of "temperament" and "personal preference."

But let us now turn to the area of learning theory, not so pressed, as it were, by the demands of behavioral crises. Consider the following quotations. Responding to the question of "What is learned?" Kendler writes:

> I am convinced that the selection of any theoretical model, be it physiological or phenomenological, or for that matter, physical, mechanical or statistical, is in the last analysis a decision having *no truth character*.

That is, in spite of the fact that the choice of a model may, and usually does, influence both experimentation and theorizing, *the choice itself* cannot be evaluated as being right or wrong. It is a matter purely of personal taste (1952, p. 276; Kendler's italics).

Then speaking of the temptation to reify constructs, he writes:

This reification in turn is due to the failure to distinguish sharply and consistently between the operational meaning of intervening variables and the intuitive properties ascribed to these concepts. If we conceive the intervening variables as being an economical device by which experimental variables are ordered in relation to behavior variables, then this confusion will not arise. The basic difference between such intervening variables as "habit" and "cognitive map" can be specified only in terms of their stated relationships to the observed variables, not in terms of the connotations they arouse (p. 276).

And writing specifically to the question of reductionism, Kessen and Kimble assert:

Our version of the purely psychological psychologist is the scientist who erects his theory and develops his concepts so the deduced theorems can be confirmed or disproved by observations of behavior. This we demand of him *and nothing more*. The symbols he uses for theoretical manipulation may have any flavor he likes—neurological, physical, sociological, aesthetic—but such a psychologist is not required to specify locus or 'real' nature in his theory so long as concepts mediate the prediction of behavior. . . . Nor is the pure psychologist inhibited in the range of constructs he may choose. He can invent concepts to the limit of his ingenuity and vocabulary. . . . We must repeat that the mere claim that a theory is neurological does precisely nothing to give it greater authority than a "purely psychological" approach (1952, p. 264).

Now it is interesting that both Kendler and Kessen and Kimble have adopted the metaphor of taste, as if the anterooms to the laboratory are to become scientific kitchens. There is substantial defense of Kendler's essay. As a spokesman for Hullian theory, he makes a plea for operational reduction of theoretical terms. Realization of this program would result in the conditional refinements of the S–R laws, but not in a theory in the philosophical sense. A putative theory including only completely interpreted terms and including no provisions for reduction to a more basic science could provide no explanation of the laws of behavior. Indeed, no particular explanatory purpose is served by translating behavioral laws into the language of neurophysiology unless the laws as translated are then deducible from a set of postulates in the neurophysiological language. Kendler is not clear as to what he wants of his theory. At times he appears to require that it have some higher-level explanatory power—in which case he would have to augment his theory with hypothetical constructs. And in that case, the critique on behalf of reductionism would be germane.

For Kessen and Kimble the case is more clear-cut. They are thinking of theories whose theoretical terms, sentences, and transformation rules permit the deduction of behavioral laws. Why then their emphasis upon the extreme pragmatic approach? It is true, as they intimate, that one does not validate the theoretical antecedents in a confirmatory experiment. However, one does not generally argue that since a true hypothesis implies all antecedents, then all antecedents are equally plausible. It is also true that the abstract nature of models in microphysics and the impalpable character of some of the theoretical terms lend themselves to conventionalistic considerations. In physics there are both logical and technological factors complicating the experimental accessibility of theoretical entities (cf. N7.3). But this is not the case in psychology where the theoretical terms designate such constructs as motivation, habit, memory. There are, as yet, no clearly stipulated logical strictures upon tying the hypotheticals directly to a dictionary. Thus when psychologists argue the example of physics as to the abstract character of the hypotheticals, they do so without specifying how it is that the example of psychology is like that of physics. Fictionalism, even at the despair of reifying hypothetical constructs, seems cavalier. That the psychologist should introduce his hypothetical constructs as convenient fictions when neither logic nor technology would preclude his formulating them within the scope of neurophysiology would be to renege on his empirical commitments.

There is, however, a more serious objection to an uncritical instrumentalism. It concerns questions of the psychology of invention. How do we, in fact, undertake the invention and renovation of our theoretical concepts? What are the crutches of insight into their open texture? One might answer, "Models." But let us be more specific.

In order to find answers to the questions of invention, we must labor the distinction between intervening variables and hypothetical constructs. Previously it was suggested that a strict interpretation of an intervening variable restricts its generalizability. For example, in Skinner's operant conditioning, the variable of motivation level enables us to select an appropriate law of extinction. But the law incorporating the variable is not itself generalizable except through an empirical search. The point can be made clearer, perhaps, if we consider a treatment of intelligence, Q. Let Q be an intervening variable mediating between stimulus and response. Its status as an intervening variable is assured by our defining it operationally either by explicit definition or by reduction sentences. In either case, the measure of Q is a matter of test performance, and a strict interpretation of Q is such that if the test conditions and a given level of Q then by implication we infer a given level of performance (i.e., $SxQx \supset Rx$ from $Sx \supset (Qx \equiv Rx)$). But, of course, not even the most radical of empiricists wants to be so restricted in the application of Q to the test performance. Rather he seeks to generalize his predictions to a class of S–R laws contingent upon Q. That is, he seeks the class of generalizations $\{(x)(S_i x Q x \supset R_j x)\}$, where i and j range over all appropriate values of S and R, including, of course, those necessary for defining Q. But then how does he establish this expanded class of generalizations? Either his search is random or it is guided by the endowment of Q with surplus meaning. With but rare exceptions, it proves to be the latter alternative. It is the surplus meaning of Q which serves as the basis for explaining why i and j have the range they do. For example, if Q meant *only* what it measures on test performance, then any generalizability would be adventitious. On the other hand, suppose that Q designates a set of properties of the central nervous system. By postulating what these properties are, not only would we be able to deduce the test behavior but also the range of stimulus–response relations for which Q serves as mediator. Moreover, our freedom to postulate indicates that that range itself is left open (cf. N7.6).

This much of the analysis is straightforward and finds expression in most critiques of operationism. But as this analysis stands, it is not critical of instrumentalism as such. Difficulties arise only when we consider the relative heuristic potentialities of different kinds of hypothetical terms. Presumably instrumentalism, with an unlimited field for speculation, lacks principles of inherent guidance which we expect from a reductive discipline. How, in fact, do we modify our theoretical terms? Surely our conceptual improvisations are not merely matters of aesthetics or taste. More than likely, heuristic potentiality is latent within the theoretical term itself. It is the language of the science itself which prompts the model and, in turn, the family of hypotheses which that model provides. The reason for this is not hard to find. In psychology, for example, the language of perceptual and behavioral description has from its inception been interlarded with the language of physiology. Witness the formative work of Helmholtz, Fechner, Müller, and Wundt. Thus the direction of explanation is all but mandatory. Psychology's linguistic involvements being what they are, neurophysiology then serves as the basis of its microstructure.[1]

Because of these linguistic predilections, the argument in behalf of aesthetic enterprise seems suspect. The built-in guidance is missing. One

---

[1] J. R. Kantor points this out effectively and disapprovingly in his *Problems of Physiological Psychology* (1947). In this work, he rejects tradition and calls for the introduction of a new vocabulary of interbehavioral descriptions. Whether such a vocabulary escapes the traditional S–R language is subject to doubt. However, his argument that our present language makes neurophysiological reduction unavoidable is convincing.

cannot enhance what he sentimentally calls the "elegance" of his theory by aesthetic innovations except that such contrivances are somehow simplifying and basic. So long as one considers models that are not purely mathematical (and that, it appears, is what Kessen and Kimble have in mind), the model ought to possess reasonable analogy. That is, a theory would suffer less from the strains of improvisation, and would be less susceptible to becoming a quaint paragraph in the history of the subject, if it should seek reduction in another theory that is more basic in the sense that the latter theory includes a formalization of terms and concepts appropriated by the former. Observe here psychology's appropriation of the language of stimulus–response itself, of 'inputs' and 'outputs,' of 'afferents' and 'efferents,' of 'sensory' and 'motor.' No stimulus–response psychology, no behaviorism does without these analogues. Some of the confusion over defining stimulus and behavior could be obviated by a reduction of these terms to the components that are neurophysiological and to those that entail statements concerning the social and physical environments. The plea for aesthetic license, on the other hand, is reminiscent of the episode with epicycles. The analogues within psychology are drive and inhibition. One can adduce almost any kind of behavior with these two mediating constructs, just as one can manufacture almost any celestial motion with some appropriate machinery of epicycles and eccentrics. Indeed, many S–R psychologies incorporate inhibition and facilitation into their theoretical structures. But these are also concepts in neurophysiology with substantial observational interpretation (cf. N7.4). Since for the psychologist there is a proven analogy involved here, and since he is not engaged arbitrarily in appropriating vocabulary, he is exposing himself to subsequent embarrassment if he does not take pains to bind his terms to their usage in the primary science.

PHENOMENOLOGICAL OBJECTIONS

Thus far we have contended only with arguments that maintain that reductionism is unwarranted, or untested, or restrictive. Calling for procedural agreements, these contentions take a pragmatic turn, but they are not compelling. Turning to a different line of attack, what about arguments that would rule out reductionism on logical grounds? All such arguments can be classified as "phenomenological." Furthermore, they can be separated into those which involve psychological problems of meaning and those which are purely phenomenalistic. The former of these two classes of argument can be further divided according to their embracing either behavioral or mentalistic phenomenology. Thus, in outline, the argument considers:

(1) Phenomenological objection:
    a. for behavioral phenomenology
    b. for intentionalistic phenomenology
(2) Phenomenalism and the mental language

Each of these items will be considered in turn.

Behavioral Phenomenology

Behavioral phenomenology (Koffka, MacLeod, Snygg and Combs, Krech and Crutchfield, Tolman, Brunswik, Lewin) is based on the premise that the individual's response to his environment reflects a unique cognitive structuring of his behavioral world. Accordingly, the world, which we can undertake to describe objectively, has for the individual a unique meaning determined by his values, attitudes, memory, as well as by the structural functions of his sensory-perceptual apparatus. Thus behavioral descriptions entail descriptions of the environment, but it is a personalized social environment. An accurate behavioral description must therefore report on the functional interaction between the person and his ecology. From this point of view, it has been argued that a reduction of psychology to physiology is impossible on the grounds that phenomenological descriptions require a nomenclature for which the language of neurophysiology offers no translation. It is not just the absence of vocabulary that offers a problem; presumably there is a logical barrier to our translating functional world-organism descriptions into the physicalistic language of physiology (Jessor, 1958).

Now this appears to be an incorrect presumption. Descriptions of the physical environment can, of course, always be included within the set of initial and boundary conditions which are stated for the neurophysiological description. There is no point of logic why statements describing the behavioral (psychological) environment cannot also be included in the set of all statements to be reduced to neurophysiology. The difference is one of reference, not of logic as Jessor, for example, has maintained. For neurophysiology, statements about the extradermal physical environment are found in the set of statements about initial conditions (e.g., statements of the specific physical energies capable of eliciting the sensory response), whereas the statements about the psychological environment either are inferred from behavior or are taken to be those of constructs implicitly reified as neurophysiological processes. We may conjecture with Krech (1950) that the only adequate explanation of behavioral phenomenology will be that which offers a neurophysiological reduction of the cognitive structure; to be explicit, that which explains the functional relationship between the proximal and distal stimuli. The fact that one set of environmental statements involves extradermal descriptions and the other set of environmental statements involves intradermal descriptions may constitute a difference of reference, but it does not constitute a point of logic against the possibility of reductionism (cf. N7.5).

What is needed, and what with but rare exceptions is missing from phenomenological accounts of behavior, is some set of schemata for describing that diversity of S–R relations which ascribe to a particular organism its apparent uniqueness. In its place, we often substitute highly personalized postulates of the cognitive agent that are suggestive of a ghost in the chain of hypotheticals. However, Mario Bunge (1963, 1964) has constructed a set of schemata for the concrete representation of S–R systems within a phenomenological rubric. Assuming that stimuli are either constant, sudden, or periodic, and assuming that the transmitting system containing such unspecified hypothetical subsystems as memory, heredity, etc., is either perfect, amplifying, or damping, he is able to derive dependent integral equations (Bergmann's "process functions") descriptive of unique response classes. Furthermore, complex organisms can be represented as multichannel transmitters, with the application of scattering matrix theory yielding the response equations. It is interesting that Bunge calls his approach "phenomenological." His black boxes give concrete descriptions of responses without specifying the structure of the box itself. And it is interesting also that he calls his own schematization "superficial," useful perhaps in behavioral science "where mechanisms are not sought either because of an anachronistic methodological conviction, or because the grapes are still sour" (1963, p. 357). Needless to say, his black-box analysis of phenomenology does not run into any logical difficulties in describing the data of input and output. All that is missing are the details of the black box, and those details neurophysiology could presumably provide.

Intentionalistic Phenomenology

There is another side to phenomenology, the mentalistic one. It turns upon the distinction between intentional and nonintentional events. An intentional event is a mental act involving a mental content. What sets it off from nonintentional events or objects is the fact that it is ontologically imbedded in a context of active aboutness. A thought is a thought *about* something, a belief is a belief *about* something, a fear is a fear *of* something, etc. The logical status of such acts is unique. The meaning of an intentional event is neither conventional nor factual. It contains both the mental content of the intended experience and the thinking, believing, or hoping about it. Thus in order to seek, establish, or know the referents of intentional terms, we must enter the realm of privileged access. Needless to say, the contexts of aboutness do not surround nonintentional events. Physical objects, for example, are sufficient unto themselves.

This thesis is more poignantly stated for the case of an intentional act. The latter is a mental activity culminating in a decision which at the behavioral level is the occasion for some behavior selected from a set of behavioral options. In the language of intention, then, this activity underlies the motive for the particular decision. But the actual behavior reflecting that decision requires a different type of description, and as such, is reducible to physicalistic terms. On the other hand, the phrase 'wanting to go to the movie' designates an intentional act in which the wanting is *about* going to the movie but which itself is not an objectively describable act. The two languages are quite different. One is mentalistic and intentional, the other is physicalistic and nonintentional, with neither a logical nor an empirical bridge between the two. If one now wishes to maintain that psychology should concern itself with motivational explanation in the intentional language, and that this would distinguish it logically from the physical sciences, then, to be sure, the idea of reduction would be incompatible with our understanding of psychology and physiology (Peters, 1958; Winch, 1958).

This argument is not convincing. Doubtless, Brentano's distinction between intentional and nonintentional events is a trenchant one. It helps to elaborate mentalistic doctrine. But just as in other arguments for the uniqueness of mental events, acknowledgment of such events does not preclude the development of a science in which the difficulties of reduction across kinds are circumvented. Brodbeck (1963), for example, has argued that intentional meanings can, for reductive purposes, be treated as equivalent to psychological meanings. In behavioral phenomenology these latter meanings are given dispositional interpretations. An object O means P to S if S behaves in such and such a way. According to her, then, the intentional meanings of mental events are reflected in decisions, and such decisions are psychologically interesting only if they are accompanied by responses appropriate to the decision. Thus intentional meanings are also given dispositional interpretations. However, it is necessary to remember that behavioral dispositions are not causally connected with intentions. Causation belongs alone to the physical language. There is, therefore, a conventional commitment to be found in the decision to treat intentional meanings as dispositional. But it would seem that this is a reasonable commitment, at least as reasonable as postulates of parallelism. The clues to intentional meaning are such as wanting and believing. These are least refractory when we treat them as dispositions to act.

As in other mentalistic arguments this one testifying to the uniqueness of intentional events asks too much of reductive science. It condemns efforts at scientific explanation on grounds that we cannot provide a logical basis for the transmutation of the "mental" into the "physical," and vice versa. However, the issues suggested here are more easily pursued in terms of the raw data and contents of mental experience. How are we to handle the mind–body problem within the reductive framework?

The "Mental" and the "Physical"

No attempt will be made here to review in any systematic way the many tactics for dealing with the mind–body problem. One might, for example, adopt the tactic of methodological behaviorism. Then without further ado he could dispense with the mental language and proceed to his behavioral analyses. There should, however, be some reasoned defense of his Procrustean bias. It is not sufficient to point out that introspectionism and phenomenology have led to sterile preoccupations with hypotheses about publicly unverifiable inner experiences, as the early behaviorists were inclined to do. There is always the question as to whether some significant thing is left out of the account of experience by our censoring it of its offensive mentalistic predicates.

The problem was attacked by the empiricists themselves at a more sophisticated level than that undertaken by the behaviorists. Questions such as "Is there a mental language?" "If so, to what does the mental language refer?" "What are the unique features of a mental language?" have to be answered. (It is significant that mentalistic language has never been successfully suppressed either in psychology or psychoneurology.) For a while the English analysts were preoccupied with problems of "other minds." For example, in a long series of papers (*Other Minds,* 1952), Wisdom argued that there is a feature about reports of private experience, the immediacy of one's own sense data, and self-analysis that is different from statements in the physical language. One cannot point to what he experiences as his own sense data in the way he can point to physical objects. When observer A speaks of his own experience, the language has a different semantic structure than it does when he calls observer B's attention to the data, say, of behavior. Nevertheless, one cannot deny significance to the mental language on that account.

This issue was followed by two others: the problem of a private language and questions concerning the significance of any so-called mental language. In his posthumous *Philosophical Investigations* (1953), Wittgenstein asks if any reliable means exists for learning a private language; i.e., a semantically rigorous language about the data of one's consciousness. Noting that learning a language involves "referring-to" in which the reference must be reliably held over a time span, Wittgenstein concludes that one cannot refer to, say, a particular pain in the way he can refer to the objects in a cupboard. There is no temporally sustained check on correct usage. In his *Concept of Mind* (1949), Ryle, on the other hand, questions even the intentions of the so-called mental language. Analyzing a number of traditional mentalistic statements (concerning will, emotion, etc.,) he concludes that they are really disposition-like statements whose correct analysis reveals them to designate behavioral events. Thus Ryle maintains that mental language only pretends to a special status, and that adequate translations in the behavioral language are substitutable for the mental statements.

Now none of these critical treatments of the mental (or private reference) language in any way represents an effective denial of mental events.[2] We need hardly try to say what a mental event is. It is simply given. What Tolman has called the raw feels of experience are indubitable. The important questions are: Can a significant mental language be developed? And can the predicates of such a language be incorporated into the language of psychology through reductive reference?

Identical Reference Hypothesis

In the discussion that follows our attention shall be confined to the hypothesis of the identical reference of sets of mental and physical events. Such an hypothesis has an inherent plausibility to psychologists and physiologists. It has been held explicitly by Mach (1897), by W. Köhler (1947), Place (1956), Smart (1959, 1963), but especially by Feigl (1958). Simply stated, it asserts that there is a point of common reference for mental and the corresponding physical events and the description of such compresent events converges upon that point of reference. It shall be assumed, one, that no proscriptively monistic solution of the mind–body problem is acceptable, and two, that the contemporary languages of psychology and physiology give a certain relevance to questions of mind–body reduction which early behaviorists found it convenient to deny. We shall want first in the discussion to examine the question of what constitutes an adequate explanation of mental events; and second, through a consideration of Feigl's ideas we shall want to examine questions concerning the adequacy of a mental language. Remarks which follow express the belief that the reduction of the mental to the physical is contingent upon our treating mental terms as dispositional.

First, then, what constitutes an explanation of mental events? If one considers this question a meaningful one, he is likely to respond with some of the familiar statements on the mind–body problem. He may espouse theses of epiphenomenalism, or psychophysical parallelism, or even interactionism. But such theses are merely relational in character; apparently they do not present formal explanations of mental events, as such. On the other hand, he may recognize in the question a request for deducing

[2] In a review of *The Concept of Mind*, Hanson (1952) mentions that Ryle's analysis is one of what we mean by statements in the putative mental language and is not an examination of what, if anything, there is for a possible mental language to refer to. Quite a different matter from that of metaphysical behaviorism.

statements about mental events from some set of statements which are, in an explanatory hierarchy, judged to be more basic.[3] Thus he may proceed in one of two ways. One, he may seek to deduce statements about mental events from the application of relevant psychophysical and psychoneurological laws. But, even though this may meet the minimal formal requirements of explanation, it is not likely to prove very satisfactory. I, for example, unmollified by my Cartesian training, may be looking for someone to explain how it is that consciousness, the redness of the rose, pain, redolence, and the taste of honey, can be produced by the responses of congeries of nerve cells. It is the failure in just this "meaningful" quest that has prompted neurologists to proclaim ignorance as to why neural terminus or specific energies should spell the difference, say, between seeing red and feeling that peculiar piquance of a sneeze. In these circumstances I am not likely to be satisfied with the information that the striate cortex and the reticular formation have roles to play. Black boxes do not provide the kind of explanations I might seem to want.

Two, our respondent may offer us a theoretical model and a higher level of explanation. Consider now a model of a neuronal network which on the basis of its assumptions shows that output excitation is proportional to the log of its input excitation. From such a model we could deduce the Weber–Fechner law on the relation between sensation and physical stimuli. Or consider an ingenious mechanical analogue suggested by Howells (1954). He found that ordinary laboratory scales discriminate just detectable differences among weights according to the Weber ratio, $k = \Delta w/w;$ i.e., the constant ratio between the increment of detectably different weight and a base weight. Thus, he could construct a friction model for the perceptual discrimination of weights. In either case, the theory might enable us to deduce the Fechnerian laws of psychophysics. Does the successful deduction of psychophysical laws then provide us with an explanation of consciousness? Formally, yes, if by consciousness we mean a person's reporting his subjective judgments. But again this may not satisfy the querist. What he wants to know is how any set of physical events, bioelectrical, biochemical, or mechanical, can produce the raw data of consciousness. Nothing less than the details of transmutation apparently will satisfy him.

In all of this our intransigent querist appears to be asking the impossible. No so-called explanation satisfying the logical requirement of explanation is going to satisfy him. He is mixing his categories. Ryle was not the first to call our attention to category mistakes and ghosts in the machine (cf. N7.7). In an article published in 1933 and prophetically

---

[3] One cannot rule out the attempt to explain mental events in purely mentalistic terms, but the prospect is unlikely; for if one retains his allegiance to the idiom of phenomenalism, he is not likely to regard the raw data of awareness as requiring explanation.

titled "The Ghostly Tradition and Descriptive Categories of Psychology," H. B. English attributed difficulties in the mind–body problem to the fact that psychological events and physiological events are abstractions of a fundamental process occurring in an anatomical locus. Like Mach before him, he argued that one cannot explain how two constructions of the same process interact or how they reduce one to the other. The request for such explanations is apparently a meaningless one.

Here, it would appear wise to join the skeptics. To ask of an explanation of mental phenomena that it be other than a formal one (e.g., a deduction from a psychophysical law) is to commit a category mistake. It is almost, but not quite, like asking the phenomenalist to explain what is given and indubitable by means of logical constructions (physiological terms) which are themselves based upon those givens. Still, there is a sense in which dual descriptions of the same process may satisfy our demands for an explanation. Mental concepts are ambiguous. Therefore, if we adopt an hypothesis of the identity of reference, and if we achieve a systematic development of the concepts of neurophysiology then we can, in a way, achieve an understanding of our mental concepts.

Feigl has doubtless been the most persistent advocate of this identity hypothesis (1950, 1958, 1961). According to him, qualitatively different sources of evidence converge upon the same fact. Thus he contends "that the designata of the mentalistic language are identical with the descripta of the behavioristic language and both are identical with the designata of the neurophysiological language." He goes on to say that "the factual reference of some of the terms in each of these different languages (or vocabularies) may be the same, while only their evidential bases differ" (1950, p. 623).

The factual reference is the world event. The evidential bases for this event are expressed in our introspective reports, and in our behavioral and neurophysiological descriptions. The three descriptions, being compresent to the event, are not deducible from one another but share a common variance with the event through manifest intercorrelations. Therefore, it is the establishment and confirmation of such correlations that accomplishes the reduction of psychology to physiology. There are two assumptions to be met here. One, what Feigl calls the systemic identities must be empirically ascertained; and two, the mental language must be sufficiently pure and sufficiently precise so that it brings to the systemic analysis the unique contents which we attribute to mental events. Otherwise, we would not be in contact with the problem of mind and consciousness. Meeting the first assumption is contingent upon meeting the second; so it is to the latter that we should direct our attention.

Now reductionism is possible within this schema if for every relevant event E there are subsets of descriptions in the mental, the behavioral, and the neurophysiological languages that can be intercorrelated. In this context the language of behavior and that of neurophysiology have not been problematic in the way that the language of pure phenomena has been. It is not a question of whether there are raw-feels (the methodological behaviorist does not dispute this) but rather a question of whether what can be asserted in the mental language can be said less equivocally (or inferred) within the behavioral and neurophysiological languages. I say, "less equivocally" because there is question as to the meaning of purely phenomenal statements.

This is not the place to review the arduous explorations of "other minds" and "private languages." However, it is essential to seek some commitment as to what kinds of statements are to be included in the mental language. What, if any, is the contribution of raw-feel statements to the compresent descriptions of the referent–event? The answer to this question is usually, "None!"—that is to say, manageable statements in the mental language are regarded as being translatable into the more semantically precise statements in the behavioral language.

To explore what may, or may not be, an obvious point, let us look at a simple experiment in the study of tolerance of pain. The experimental subject in the presence of a group of his peers is subjected to electric shock. From an initial subliminal intensity, the voltage is increased until the shock becomes "unbearable." According to Feigl, the complete description of this event-complex would involve statements from the mental, behavioral, and neurophysiological languages, and, of course, from the physical language. Again, only the statements in the mental language will be problematic.

Provisionally, we may grant raw-feels without our necessarily acknowledging that we can talk meaningfully about them. In order to describe them let us say that from the initial absence of feeling there emerges the phenomenal sequence, "a pleasant tickling, a prickling, an unpleasant vibrato, a jolting, an unbearable convulsive-like seizure of the member." The fact that we have mixed phenomenal and behavioral descriptions is unfortunate. But what other linguistic recourse is there? Perhaps we should invent a terminology. We could use words such as "tickle," "prickle," "stickle," etc., but this is not the problem. The question is, after we have invented the terminology, can it have any significance other than that deriving from its contaminative translation into the behavioral language?

Initially it should be made clear that by a mental language which suppresses behavioral reports, reference is not being made to the language of psychophysics. Statements of psychophysical relations are reports of discriminations and judgments made in the presence of physical stimuli. They can be given a strict operational interpretation, in which case they would make no reference to the raw-feels with which we are presently concerned (Bergmann and Spence, 1944; Stevens, 1939). But what of "prickles" and "stickles"? Are they comparable in any way? For example, are they matters of degree, or are they pointillist variates in the multifarious set of raw-feels? It is tempting to say that pains, as such, are not matters of degree. A convulsive jolt is just as unique and *interesting* in its raw-feel way as a tickle. What makes one pleasant and the other unbearable are the behavioral and physiological co-respondencies. If we could succeed at pure introspection with an accompanying suppression of the behavioral and physiological concomitants, we might achieve that mythical demeanor of the purified existentialist, oblivious to everything but the sublime kaleidoscope of qualia. But, of course, we cannot suppress the behavioral and physiological variables, otherwise we would have different qualia, and *a fortiori* different events.

The difficulty arises from our trying to establish qualitative relations among our raw-feels. It is not a case of "this pain next to that pain" but of "Is this pain greater (more painful) than that pain?" What is the meaning of, "This pain is unbearable, the other is not"? And what of the statement, "S_1 can stand more pain than S_2 can"? It is not difficult for us to translate these statements into the behavioral and neurophysiological languages. Pain is "unbearable" when specified verbal and withdrawal responses occur, and when the significant complex of nociceptive reflexes occurs. On the other hand, it is much more difficult for us to translate these statements into a purely mental language. And I suspect that it is not just a case of our being tongue-tied because of the behavioral contamination of our language. It may be that the person does not know and cannot identify the purely phenomenal state of unbearable pain. He can writhe *with* pain, withdraw *from* painful stimuli, and even cry out for the anaesthetic *because of* pain, but the putative fact of that unbearable pain is implied by the behavior and reflexive response of the organism, not by the raw-feel as such.

This is familiar behavioristic terrain. However, it is important to emphasize that dispositional analyses of mental terms do not obviate the semantic pretensions such terms have for relating to possibly genuine nondispositional mental contents. In other words, there may be something more to the translation of a mental term than the set of its dispositional predicates. But what that something more is, is not a subject matter for science; indeed, it cannot be described at all.

Feigl's analysis fails us then in the way contemporary psychology fails us; it cannot say what cannot be said. Disappointment arises over the fact that the promise of a "true" psychophysics or "true" psychophysiology reduces to a behavioral-physics or a behavioral-physiology wherein the behavior is that which occurs in the context of a person's attending to his own awareness. Such disappointment is inevitable, but then one cannot very well complain that a science has limitations on the grounds it fails to do what cannot be done. Just as psychology earlier at Titchener's behest was unable to avoid the stimulus-error, so now at the mentalists' behest it cannot avoid the response-error. Sperry (1952), for example, has made a very good case for treating perception as a perceptual-motor complex, in which the two components are as inseparable as stimulus and stimulus object. (See also Langfeld, 1931; MacKay, 1956; Broadbent, 1958.) Psychologically, the argument is all but clinched by the facts of motor feedback. Perception involves sensory input, a scansion function, motor response, and an afferent feedback. Not only is a perception of some object complex, but it contains information not found in the primary or the secondary qualities of the object.

In way of summary, let us look in on a serious poker game about to reach a climactic moment. Our hero has overcommitted himself, and the stakes are high. It is too costly for him to stay and too costly for him to get out. Moreover, he holds three cards of a royal flush. He discards, draws two cards, and peeks! Behold, he has filled out his royal flush! Now! He must contain his joy. His winning is assured. He must draw out the bets. He cannot smile; he cannot frown; he cannot blink, blanch, or blush. Far better now if he were to show no signs at all. Pulse and blood pressure? He must control these, too. His opponents are sensitive detectors. They watch the pupils of his eyes, the color of his cheeks, the artery along the temple. Safest then to suspend all propensities. What then of our player's feelings? There are those who would contend that our player would have no feeling at all, no exuberance, no joy, none of the exaltation which comes to the poker table on wings of the sure-thing principle. But then, feelings cannot be ruled out, not on logical grounds at least. How, then, would he, and how would we, describe those feelings?

Suppose at this moment of our subject's expressionless transport, we were to pluck him from the table and take him into the laboratory. Since expression is now denied him, we can as well dispense with all his motor apparatus, all his efferents, save, perhaps, those of speech. We must allow him to speak to us of his feelings. Nor need we deprive him of all his sensory inputs, for we need to interrogate him. "What is your joy like now?" we ask. "Has there been any change? Is it just like the joy you feel when you dance for it, clap your hands and swoon?" Suppose our subject, X, answers, "There has been no change." Then, of course, we understand him, for we can substitute within our psychophysical descriptions the dispositional predicates appropriate to that joy. Moreover, we understand his feeling by analogy, for 'joy now' designates one of those feelings which is accompanied by the class of behaviors we label 'joyful.' But suppose he says, "No, joy is not the same; there is some ineluctable remainder that is pure feeling." Can he help make the meaning of this residual feeling clear to us? I think not; we have been deprived of the source of analogy. Will some kind of cerebrograph help? Again, the answer is negative. There is no suitable analogy, for the brain recording which we get from him is like no other picture with which we are familiar. The efferent system is dormant. We can test our own use of feeling-words by matching behavioral descriptions and cerebrograms; therein the source of Feigl's psychophysical correlations. However, no such testing can occur where behavioral descriptions are denied and the cerebrograms necessarily are disparate.

As a matter of concern, then, we may ask: what contribution does the mental language make to the elucidation of the compresent event? If it carries nothing but the burden of behavioral paraphrase, why then insist upon the mentalistic dimensions of the event? Now, it is obvious that identity theorists such as Feigl want to acknowledge the unique content of consciousness itself. Mental content is not merely embedded in the disposition to act. Dispositions are not at all the mental content itself. There is a psychic residue, as it were, that participates in the event. Physiology, behavior, and mental content are inseparable. Together their components comprise the event.

What troubles the reflective behaviorist here is the absence of any specification as to what the contribution of the mental language might be. What can a nondispositional language add to the description of a person's experiencing and responding. It is not that our psychologist would deny consciousness. Even radical behaviorists have given up quoting William James (1904) out of context. Nor is it just that the semantics of mental statements are problematic in the way methodological behaviorists have found them to be (Lashley, 1923). Rather it is also the case that statements about mental contents fail to add useful information to the description of the compresent event. What is significant are the facts of sensory discrimination as such, not the unique qualities of mental contents. We could replace some present set of primary qualities with an entirely different set, and it would, I surmise, not make a jot of difference. That is to say, it is inconsequential, if not accidental, that we see the chromaticized world through the conscious media of blue, green, red, and yellow rather than, say, sweet, sour, bitter, and salty. This could presume to be a radical thesis. What it suggests is that speculations about cerebroscopes and the contents of other minds are quite beside the point. One person's red could be another person's salt and there would be no detectable perceptual difference. Both persons would see the world as they do see it—I am tempted to say, as the world is. For what is important are (1) the structure and sensitivity of the receptor and (2) the central processing of input into invariant perceptual patterns. So long as there are structures, i.e., cell aggregates to process the input, they would be sufficient to effect a perceptual structure (cf. N7.8). The particular code of conscious qualia may be intrinsically interesting, but it is secondary to the fact that some code should exist (cf. N7.9).

NOTES

NOTE 7.1

To take a sampling of opinion over the years: J. B. Watson writes, "We need in psychology all the available facts neurologists can give us, but we can very well leave out of consideration those ingenious puzzle pictures that compose the action of the central nervous system with a series of pipes and valves, sponges, electric switchboards, and the like" (1929, p. 19). He then goes on to assert that "physiologist qua physiologist" operates at the molecular level and is not concerned with behavior. It is for the psychologist to define his own problems, techniques, and language at the molar level.

Concerning human learning McGeoch writes:

It seems futile to define learning in terms of hypothetical factors such as neural charges, tensions, or the logical properties of total fields. These factors may conceivably aid interpretation, but they do not at present define learning. A definition must keep as clear as possible of theory and as close as possible to the facts, and to the conditions and operations by which they are obtained. A definition which can be given no specific meaning in terms of performable operations is not a satisfactory experimentalist's definition. An operational definition is implied in what critical experimenters do and write. It is implied here in saying that by learning is meant the phenomena of the learning curves and of the learning experiments in general (1936, p. 110).

Doubtless Spence speaks for a large group of contemporary psychologists, when, in comparing his own formulations to those of Hull, he writes:

A second matter in which Hull and I differed, although the difference was one of degree, was the extent to which, after defining a hypothetical intervening variable in purely quantitative terms as a mathematical function of some experimental variable, further neurophysiological specifications should be made. Hull was particularly prone to add further specifications suggesting the possible locus, structure, or functioning in the nervous system of these constructs. His justification always was that such conjectures provided experimental hints to physiologically oriented psychologists interested in making such coordinations of our knowledge.

Now my interest in the integration of knowledge from different fields would, I think, make me one of the last to deny the potential value of such attempts. However, I would insist that the added physiological concepts introduced by the psychologist should be significant ones, by which I mean they should be concepts that appear in the network of physiological laws. Unless such is the case, one does little more than add a physiological name. Moreover, there is no little danger that such physiological notions will mislead or at least distract from the significant aspects of the mathematical portion of the theory. Indeed there is probably no better instance of this than that provided by Hull's concept of habit strength (H). After defining habit strength as a mathematical function of the present stimulus and antecedent environmental conditions, Hull then identifies it further with the notion of a receptor–effector connection in the nervous system (Hull, 1943).

Just what the *beneficial* "surplus meanings" accrued to the mathematical concept of habit as a result of this added physiological connotation has never been made clear to me. That it did provide for additional meanings is amply shown by the extent to which critics used them to characterize the whole story as based on an outmoded conception of the nervous system, or, worse still, to deride it as a mechanistic, telephone-switchboard theory of behavior. . . . Let me hasten to add here that I am not advocating that behavior scientists eschew all physiological concepts. That all behavior has physiological correlates seems as certain to me as anything I know. Hence, I should not hesitate to employ fruitful physiological concepts whenever I thought they might help. At the present state of development they are not, in my opinion, very useful (1956, p. 55).

NOTE 7.2

This point bears upon the heuristic potentialities of theoretical behaviorism as against those of the radical behaviorisms of Skinner and Tolman. Consider Skinner's treatment of motivation and reinforcement which, in theoretical systems such as that of Hull and Deutsch (1960), are mediating variables. For Skinner, reinforcement is a response-anchored variable reducible to changes in the rate of response with respect to time. Motivation is a stimulus-anchored variable reducible to manipulations and changes of the subject's environment. Thus hunger motivation is completely describable in terms of deprivation schedule. What there is to be said about the subject's hunger is exhausted by an explicit statement of its food intake, eating habits, weight status, etc. Consider first, the role of motivation as a mediating variable. A strict S–R psychology would be one for which there is a set of S–R laws such that for the appropriate stimulus conditions one could predict the subsequent response. One explanation of this behavior would then be in the familiar form of *modus ponens*, which from Sx and $(x)(Sx \supset Rx)$ one concludes Rx. Suppose, however, we are now to include mediating variables that are anchored at the stimulus end. What we are achieving by this refinement is a more limiting specification of the stimulus variables. Although Skinner would like to emphasize the mediating variables and utilize objects in the physical world merely as stimulus cues, the whole physical stimulus–deprivation schedule complex composes the stimulus description. We do not have a theoretical description of behavior here; we have only a lawful one. Skinner is quite justified in his antitheoretical bias. Indeed he has no need for theory. Any manipulation of motivational factors results simply in his prescribing different laws for different stimulus conditions. There is, for example, no recognized need for explaining *why* the probability of a response increases with increased motivation. (Such an explanation might derive, for example, from a deduction of the events at the neurophysiological level.) That it does occur is a sufficient explanation of the events. One can, I think, evaluate Skinner's treatment of primary and secondary reinforcement in the same way. All explanation is of the type wherein the behavior is deduced as an application of a law. The range of behaviors explainable is, of course, confined to the range of empirically derived laws.

NOTE 7.3

As is well known, the study of microphenomena in quantum physics has evoked puzzles and predicaments not encountered in classical deterministic mechanics. One cannot study the microstructure of the atom without using a probe to elicit information concerning such structure. With particles as small as the electron, any detector, even one as small as the photon, has sufficient energy to affect the state of the electron. If we pinpoint the electron with high energy, short-wavelength "illumination," we give it such a kick that we alter its momentum in a significant way. On the other hand, if we mitigate this effect by reducing the energy and increasing the wavelength of the illuminative probe, we can conceivably get an accurate measure of the momentum of the electron but because of the minuteness of the electron relative to the wavelength of the light source, the illuminative agent is diffracted so as to leave the "picture" record of the position of the electron uncertain. Such is the predicament of the uncertainty principle as visualized in the Gedanken experiment.

The derivation of the uncertainty relationships can be demonstrated by reference to Figure 7.1.

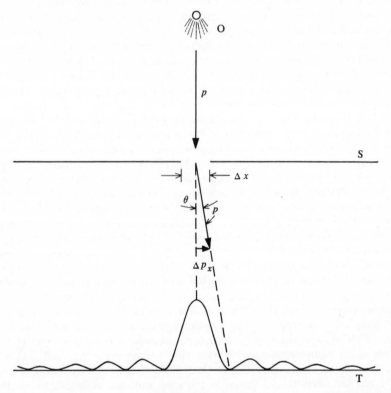

Figure 7.1   Illustration of the uncertainty of momentum for a particle which has passed through a single slit (from R. T. Weidner and R. L. Sells. *Elementary Modern Physics*. Boston, Allyn & Bacon, 1960).

In this set-up, T is a scintillation screen, S is a screen with slit comparable in dimensions to those of a diffraction grating, and O is the source of illumination. Now visualize a source at O, emitting electrons with momentum, p. The curve at T is the probability density of the electron shower arriving at T and indicates the nature of the diffraction pattern. The momentum, p, is a function of the wavelength of the electron, $p = h/\lambda$, (with λ, the wavelength, and h, Planck's constant). The uncertainty of the momentum in the x direction is then expressed by

$$\Delta p_x \geq p \sin \theta. \tag{1}$$

According to the diffraction pattern, θ, the angle giving the first nodal point on the probability density, is

$$\sin \theta = \pm \frac{\lambda}{\Delta x}. \tag{2}$$

Substituting for p and $\sin \theta$ in (1), we then get the uncertainty relation

$$\Delta p_x \Delta x \geq h, \tag{3}$$

namely, the product of the uncertainties of the momentum and position components is at least as great as Planck's constant. Note that we can decrease Δp_x, the uncertainty in momentum, by increasing Δx, since $\sin \theta$ in (2) is an inverse function of Δx. But we can only know p with certainty by taking Δx infinitely large. Hence, the familiar difficulty; should we determine the momentum of a particle with certainty, we would be completely uncertain as to the position (since it could be anywhere within Δx). And, *mutatis mutandis*, similarly for position and momentum (cf. Weidner and Sells, 1960, pp. 150–157).

Now the interesting thing here is that the premises upon which the argument is based permit no exceptions. Granting such premises, and many others that constitute the foundations of classical quantum mechanics, von Neumann (1932) has offered a proof that the system within its formal framework provides no exception to the uncertainty principle.

What is the significance of this for the psychologist? Arguing from the effect of the probe and the principle of complementarity, Bohr himself sees an analogy for psychology (Bohr, 1950). One cannot probe the brain without altering, or even destroying, the functioning tissue. Perhaps so, but it does not follow that we need probe every cell of the nervous system in order to get the prerequisite information. Recent microtechniques in electrode plants are exquisitely refined and are sufficient for us to gain information concerning the functioning of single cells. The neurologist can infer from his limited observations to complex functions. There are no logical barriers to his explicit inference. But this *is* the case in the quantum effects. It is not only technically impossible, it is logically inconsistent to make statements about a determinate system of microstructures with completely specified positions and momenta. This is so at least so far as quantum mechanics now formally stands.

This last sentence must be added because that formal system of quantum mechanics is being challenged. The issues are too complex to go into here, but doubtless they present one of the most significant problems in all of contemporary philosophy of science. The attack upon the indeterministic foundations of quantum physics is led by the physicists Bohm and Vigier and by the philosopher Feyerabend. Discussion of the issues by these three people can be found in Körner (editor), *Observation and Interpretation in the Philosophy of Physics.* The so-called Copenhagen Interpretation of the implicit character of indeterminancy is held in effect by von Neumann, by Bohr, Heisenberg, Born, and Dirac, and by the philosopher Hanson (1958, 1963). Papers and discussion by Feyerabend and Hanson can also be found in Feigl and Maxwell (editors), *Current Issues in the Philosophy of Science.*

NOTE 7.4

In this context it is worth pausing over the concept of inhibition. Inhibition is explicitly defined within Hull's S–R psychology. And it finds implicit expression in the psychoanalytic concepts of repression and the superego. In neither case does it reduce to neurophysiology. But note what Kessen and Kimble (1952) have to say in this context. Responding to an argument of Krech in behalf of a field theory of brain function, they express the popular pragmatic riposte ". . . the concept of the superego has as sound possibilities for the integration of behavior as the concept of brain fields or dynamic systems." I think not, and for the reason that the concept of inhibition as inherited from neurophysiology carries with it greater generalizability than is found in its unique contextual interpretation in psychodynamics. This comment applies both to Hull and to psychoanalysis but let us confine our attention to the concept of the superego.

According to psychoanalytic theory, the superego is a theoretical construct from which we deduce that certain classes of response are inhibited; that is, the superego stands as a kind of mediator or filter through which certain responses are processed while others are blocked. There is no effort here to interpret the hypothetical construct in neurophysiological terms, rather the properties intended by the construct are translated into the control system incorporating the introjected rules and values of the person's world. From this and other theoretical assumptions we can deduce that an anxiety state will implement certain inhibitory blockages of what otherwise might be an habitual or a rational response. The story is familiar, and indeed, very satisfying to people who wish to dramatize those personalized samplings of behavior we call maladjustment. But it is not difficult to find a more generalizable treatment of inhibition within the precincts of neurophysiology. Consider, for example, a Hebblike model of brain function in which responses are mediated by means of cell assemblies. In its nonactivated state, the system may exhibit sporadic firing of its components in which the units of synaptic inhibition are summative and the response random. Any input into the system effects a synchrony of neuronal response within the assembly and the assembly in turn instruments the response. Thus the assembly is a process element in the S–R system. Now synchronization of the neuronal responses results in a summative increase in inhibitory potential, in other words, in an increase of the threshold for subsequent response. Allowing for both synaptic and neuronal recovery, we can deduce normal function under periods of sustained input. But what if the input reaches a chronic state, such as it does in states of anxiety. Then it is not difficult to see that the inhibitory resistance reaches a critical level wherein the so-called normal processing of response is itself inhibited. From this neurophysiological model not only can we deduce the dramatic disruptions of behavior that we find in some psychopathology but we can also predict behaviors not initially predictable by psychoanalytic theory. For example, any sustained input, say attention inordinately enforced, will result in the inhibition of response. This is a hypothesis that has been confirmed in experiments on mental fatigue (Karsten, 1928), periodic blocking in sustained routine tasks (Bills, 1931; Broadbent, 1958), and can account for various types of panic inhibitions (Hebb, 1959). Hebb's treatment of a more elaborate theory enables him to deduce behavioral disorganization under conditions of sensory deprivation.

The point of this note should be obvious. It is a kind of testimonial on behalf of neurophysiological reduction. One could, of course, opt for more; say, for a logic of discovery. But that does not seem to be forthcoming (Hanson, 1958). As it is, the language of psychology is rooted in that of physiology. It offers us terms of stimulus–response, sensation–perception, emotion, and intelligence, all of which carry a mixed pedigree in psychology and physiology. One can, of course, appropriate any language he chooses for his theoretical terms. Both repression and mental fatigue might be suggested by the facts and hypotheses of neural inhibition, and the neurophysiological hypotheses serve only as a manner of speaking and nothing else. But without a genuine reductive support, an integration of the two concepts under a common construct might very well be missing. That is to say, if a formal reduction were not applied, the two theoretical terms would remain isolated without the significant reductive bridge. The substance of the foregoing argument is that reductionism is preferable to instrumentalism. It could as well be phrased in terms of the existential status of theoretical concepts but this is not required. Psychology carries with it systemic bias, and because of this it will find its most fruitful source of hypotheses within the reducing science.

NOTE 7.5

It is not clear to me why a preference for phenomenological descriptions should be conceived as the basis for a logical objection to reductionism. Although, to be sure, the Gestalt psychologists distinguished clearly between physical and behavioral languages, they did not regard the languages as being logically incompatible. Witness the importance given to Wertheimer's doctrine of isomorphism. Even Koffka (1935, p. 61), perhaps the least physiologically minded member of the Gestalt triumvirate, could accept physiology as the locale for mediation between the behavioral and geographic environments.

Now if one is to establish the logical incompatibility of two languages, he must show that biconditional translations are impossible by virtue of the limitations implicit in the domains of the two languages, e.g., as between the language of one science and that of the putative reducer. However, one must be careful to distinguish between limitations due to the incipient state of a language and those that are matters of logic. For example, suppose we were to have a science of consciousness and were to note the emergence of a new, unique property of experience, such as seeing infrared. According to the emergentist's case against hypothetico-deductive explanation (Broad, 1925), one cannot deduce the new experience from what he knows of physiology; hence, the new experience is uniquely nonreducible. But only at that time! Nothing precludes enrichment of the language of physiology sufficient to give reductive cover to the emergent phenomena.

However, the purpose of this aside is to take note of a more serious possibility of logical incompatibility as between scientific languages. If we visualize the neurophysiological mechanism as functionally describable in the language of the computer system, e.g., a digital system, then certain theorems relating to completeness and computability within computer systems turn up difficulties for reducing certain problem-solving behaviors of human computers to the language of mechanical computers. The argument turns on one of the most significant of the theorems proved by Gödel. In paraphrase: assuming some formal (computer) system L to be consistent, then that system is necessarily incomplete; more specifically, there is some proposition in L such that it can be shown to be true (by our resorting to a metasystem) but which cannot be proved in L. It is the parenthetical phrase "by our resorting to a metasystem" that is particularly significant. Gödel, a human computer of the highest excellence, has the option of an ingenious recourse which is denied the extant computer, bound as the latter presumably is by its formal language, L. That is, Gödel was able to prove the incompleteness of his primary computer logic by going outside that logic. And this the computer cannot do.

It is this getting outside one's logical system in order to assess the system itself that would appear to be denied any explicitly constructible computer system. This, at least, is the argument of Nagel and Newman (1958) who were among the first to communicate the significance of Gödel's work to the nonspecialist. In this (what Smart (1963) calls "the argument from Gödel") they have been supported by Kemeny (1959), J. R. Lucas (1961), and Bronowski (1966), among others. But there has been a strong counterargument stemming from important work on the character of computability within conceivable computer systems (see, for example, Putnam, 1960; Scriven, 1960; George, 1961; Smart, 1963). It *is* conceivable that we can build a computer that will prove Gödel's theorem of incompleteness. Thus the machine can be said to simulate Gödel. But not quite. What Gödel revealed is that *any* system L (however we may complicate it by adding axioms and supplementary logics) will be incomplete. That is to say, we may establish a new system L', including L *and* the metasystem, sufficient to prove the incompleteness of L. And we may build a computer to implement that L' (thus simulating Gödel). However, that extant computer will not function to determine its own incompleteness. This counterargument poses something of a paradox. Although on a complete set of instructions (as given in Gödel's proof) we can build a computer to compute a given result (i.e., Gödel's theorem), we cannot at the same time build a computer that can apply that significant result to itself. To be more concise, although we can build a computer to simulate *any* given act of ratiocination of which the human computer is capable, we cannot build a computer that will simulate *all* acts of which the human computer is capable.

The argument can be poignantly stated as the problem of simulation. Are there any behaviors of organisms which are nonsimulable? If indeed there are nonsimulable behaviors and if we assume that, functionally, neurophysiology is a computer language, then it should follow that some behavior, some aspect of psychology, is not reducible to neurophysiology.

It should be helpful here to introduce the idea of a Turing machine as a vehicle for talking about machines, their capabilities and limitations. (See Turing, 1937; George, 1961; Kemeny, 1954; Putnam, 1960; Hawkins, 1964; and for technical accounts, Kleene, 1952 and Davis, 1958.) A Turing machine is a conceptual (rather than hardware) machine with the following components. There is a tape, possibly of infinite length, which is divided into squares. There is also a scanner that can inspect some given square at some instant of time in the machine's operation. In addition the machine possesses a writing element such that it can either write a symbol from a finite alphabet on the tape, or it can erase any symbol in the square that is being scanned. Furthermore, the machine contains a driving element that can effect one of the following options: it can move the tape one square to the right of the square presently scanned, it can move the tape one square to the left, or it can leave the tape as is, any option being implemented upon its receiving instructions from the machine program. This, in effect, instructs the machine as to which square the machine should scan. Finally, there is a machine program which is instrumented by a finite set of internal configurations (logical states) such that the scanned symbol *and* the internal configuration form a couplet which dictates the next operation of the machine. A Turing machine is then fully described by a machine table for which every couplet of scanned symbol and internal configuration, there results an instruction as to tape scansion and printing. A machine table thus determines a set of "instantaneous descriptions" (a description of the tape and some internal configuration at a given time) such that from its initial state the machine continues to run through a sequence of instantaneous states with one of two eventualities: either the machine reaches a stopping state, in which case there is no continuing instruction, or the machine runs forever. Should the machine, on the former eventuality, reach a terminal instantaneous description, then a solution to the computer problem is reached, and it can be read from the finite record of the tape. Should no such terminal state be conceivable, then the problem which the machine undertakes to compute is unsolvable.

Proofs within the theory of Turing machines belong to the technology of metalogic. However, the following results are to be noted. (1) A problem of computation is computable (provable) if one can prove that the machine eventually will reach a terminal state; otherwise it is noncomputable. (2) Any algorithm of computation, any systematic proof, can be programmed into some Turing machine. (3) Any given Turing machine can be incorporated into a universal Turing machine; thus any problem that can be computed by some machine can be computed by a universal Turing machine. And (4), in support of Gödel, it can be shown that for some simple Turing machine there is a halting problem (i.e., the problem as to whether a terminal state will be reached) which itself is unsolvable.

Von Neumann (1951) has pointed out the significance of the universal Turing machine. Such a machine, incorporating a finite set of instructions, can compute any problem for which the computational procedure can be made explicit. Another related and (to the issue of reductionism) significant proposition is that due to McCulloch and Pitts (1943). They establish that any logical function, any computation that can be described in a finite set of words, can be realized by a system of neural networks functioning on digital lines.

The substance of the arguments of Turing, von Neumann, and McCulloch and Pitts is that if one can describe completely the processes and linkages of a problem-solving behavior, then it is possible, at least in principle, to build a machine that can simulate that behavior. Let us now see how the argument from Gödel fares.

We now formulate the argument along somewhat different lines which are more amenable to the issue of simulation as such. Is there any behavior of which the human computer is capable which cannot be simulated? The consensus seems to be: "Not if we can fully describe the actual computation." Visualize now a game, in which the human computer H is to compute against a putative simulator S. The purpose of the game is for S to simulate H and for H to outwit S such that on the basis of telephonic response cues, H is to provide an intelligent observer a cue which clearly distinguishes his response from that of S. (This is a version of Turing's game of imitation; Turing, 1950.)

Should S properly simulate H, then presumably the observer would not be able to distinguish the two. We may as a matter of definition say that S simulates H if and only if on equivalent sets of inputs we obtain equivalent sets of output from H and S. By equivalent sets we mean that for a set of statements $\{E_H\}$ describing the input for H there is a biconditional translation into the set of statements $\{E_S\}$ describing the input for S. Thus

$$\{E_H\} \equiv \{E_S\}$$

symbolizes the input equivalence. Similarly for the response or output sets,

$$\{R_H\} \equiv \{R_S\}.$$

Then we define equivalence such that H and S are equivalent if and only if

$$\left\langle \{E_H\}, H \right\rangle \rightarrow \{R_H\}$$

$$\left\langle \{E_S\}, S \right\rangle \rightarrow \{R_S\}$$

and $\{E_H\} \equiv \{E_S\}$ and $\{R_H\} \equiv \{R_S\}.$

Now, generally, S simulates H if two requirements are met: (1) *substitution*, and (2) *inclusion*. Substitution implies that wherever $<\{E_H\}, H>$ occurs as an occasion to predict some $\{R_H\}$, we can *substitute* some $<\{E_S\}, S>$ $\rightarrow \{R_S\}$ and infer $\{R_H\}$ from $\{R_S\}$. Inclusion stipulates that there is no set $\{R_H\}$ such that we cannot establish $\{R_S\}$ by translation (substitution), nor subsequently is there any $\{R_H\}$ without an equivalent $\{R_S\}$.

We now propose the game of the *mischievous self*. The behavior to be described belongs to the class of all behaviors and hence is a behavior to be simulated. Our human computer H assumes there is some machine S such that S simulates H; it is then the purpose of H to outwit S. Now H easily outwits S by the strategy of being mischievous. H builds a machine, M_S, which is a replica of S. He assumes M_S will indicate to him, H, what he ought to do. But then he, H, will do something else—thus assuring invalidation of any computation by M_S.

One's initial response is that H is taking an unfair advantage of S and M_S through introducing a time lag. And, to be sure, H is. But note that H's *behavior is among the class of all behaviors to be simulated.*

One alternative for us, now, is to impose our requirements of equivalence upon the argument. When H insists on a time lag before committing himself to the mischievous response he is, in fact, supplementing $\{E_H\}$ with $\{E_{\Delta H}\}$; that is, he is acting at time $t_0 + \Delta t$ rather than at t_0. Thus we have

$$\left\langle \{E_H, E_{\Delta H}\}, H \right\rangle \rightarrow R_H$$

$$\left\langle \{E_{M_S}\}, M_S \right\rangle \rightarrow R_{M_S}.$$

Since the inputs are now not equivalent, then $\{R_H\}$ and $\{R_{M_S}\}$ understandably are not equivalent. A better simulation triple would then be $<\{E_{M_S}, E_{\Delta M_S}\}, M_S>$ where $\{E_{\Delta M_S}\} \equiv \{E_{\Delta H}\}$. However reasonable this tactic appears to be, it will not work. H now takes his cue from the new simulator and then again imposing the time lag, he does something nonequivalent to what M_S computes. The game now becomes regressive with the following schema:

$$H_0, R_{H_0} \longleftrightarrow M_0, R_{M_0}$$
$$H_1, R_{H_1} \longleftrightarrow M_1, R_{M_1}$$
$$\vdots \qquad\qquad \vdots$$
$$H_{n-1}, R_{H_{n-1}} \longleftrightarrow M_{n-1}, R_{M_{n-1}}$$
$$H_n, R_{H_n}$$

Here H_i, R_{H_i} is a couplet indicating that the human computer H at stage i makes the response R_{H_i}. Each horizontal double arrow establishes the putative simulation of H by M_S. The diagonal arrow indicates the actual play, as it were, i.e., the programmed state and response of the mischievous H.

Now you may not like the rules of the game. You may indeed demand that H and M_S respond simultaneously. (It is not clear this would save simulation against the mischief, since H may, prior to any time t_j, ascertain what M_S would compute at t_j.) However, the rules are explicit. Any H can follow them; and for any M_S, the response of M_S can be controverted no matter how faithful a simulator we attempt to construct. Accepting this paradigm for the game, we cannot build the simulator which H cannot controvert. The result of this game is that H's behavior cannot be simulated by any simulator, M_S, *which we seek to enter in H's game.*

(Suppose we were to enter H's nervous system as M_S; H would still controvert it. Although we may grant "no psychosis without neurosis," H can, because of the time lag, do something different at $t_0 + \Delta t$ than he does at t_0.)

There is, however, a better alternative. We can attempt to simulate the above game such that now we have S interacting with M_S, where S is the simulator of H and M_S is the putative simulator of S. Moreover since S and M_S are both machines, we can make one the replica of the other. Now this is a rather more interesting situation. And again the game develops:

$$S_0, R_{S_0} \longleftrightarrow M_{S_0}, R_{M_{S_0}}$$
$$S_1, R_{S_1} \longleftrightarrow M_{S_1}, R_{M_{S_1}}$$
$$\vdots \qquad \qquad \vdots$$
$$S_{n-1}, R_{S_{n-1}} \longleftrightarrow M_{S_{n-1}}, R_{M_{S_{n-1}}}$$
$$S_n, R_n$$

Here S simulates H's behavior in the previous game. S plays the mischievous game against its replica, and the play of S cannot be simulated by any M_S that *we enter in this game.*

Thus it would appear there is something of a paradox in simulation. The rules of this mischievous game stipulate those conditions which render it impossible that any *extant* simulator can simulate the behavior of the mischievous self. On the other hand, it is possible to conceive a mechanical simulator, S, that can simulate the behavior of the mischievous self.

In my opinion this "paradox" is not incompatible with the results of the theory of Turing machines. Although it is possible to imagine a game in which H can outwit the machine which would simulate him, once we detail the game, then we can simulate *that* game. We can indeed simulate the game of the mischievous self, the game of outwitting, of controverting, the best-conceived simulator. It would appear that there is no logical barrier to the kind of simulation which is implicit in reductionism.

There is, however, a melancholy afterthought. Suppose we put a boundary on our computer resources; for example, on the tape resource of a Turing machine or on the program resource of any computer. Then we may visualize the ultimate machine S_z and its putative simulator M_{S_z}. The play of the game for S_z then regresses to

$$S_{z-1}, R_{S_{z-1}} \longleftrightarrow M_{S_{z-1}}, R_{M_{S_{z-1}}}$$
$$S_z, R_{S_z} \longleftrightarrow M_{S_z}, R_{M_{S_z}}$$
$$S_z, R_{S_z} \longleftrightarrow M_{S_z}, R_{M_{S_z}}$$
$$\vdots \qquad \qquad \vdots$$

and M_{S_z} now simulates S_z. In a word, S_z cannot contradict itself. But for H the situation is conceivably different:

$$H_{z-1}, R_{H_{z-1}} \longleftrightarrow M_{z-1}, R_{M_{z-1}}$$

$$H_z, R_{H_z} \longleftrightarrow M_z, R_{M_z}$$

$$H_{z+1}, R_{H_{z+1}} \longleftrightarrow M_z, R_{M_z}$$

$$H_{z+1}, R_{H_{z+1}}$$

And there is *no* point at which H cannot controvert its putative simulator.

I am not at all sure that the argument for the boundedness of computer resources is an allowable one. However, for the moment, I find it enticing to consider the possibility that in the long run it is the machine that turns up moral. Ultimately the machine must do what it ought to do. To man alone, we assign the possibility of caprice.

NOTE 7.6

The argument in behalf of reductive guidance is akin to what Rozeboom (1961) has called "ontological induction." He gives a rigorous formulation to some of the issues adumbrated in the text. However, the gist of his argument can be given here in less formal exposition.

Just as according to the Russellian theory of types we have particulars, classes of particulars, classes of classes of particulars, and so on, so in empirical science we have laws, laws about laws, laws about laws about laws, and so on. Beginning with laws as empirically ascertained, we proceed to theories (which, in a sense, are laws about laws), to reductions (which are, in a sense, laws about theories), etc. The problem for ontological induction is that of proceeding from lower-order hypotheses to higher-order ones.

The question of ontological induction is one of how we proceed, say, from simple laws of behavior to the synthesis of a set of laws all belonging to a family of laws according to the synthetic principle. A strict allegiance to the empiricistic principle would mean that the synthesis of a law of laws would be haphazard. Indeed, if the radical empiricist is as serious about eschewing theory as he claims, then he cannot in conscience direct his experimentation via the synthetic principle implicit in ontological induction. For example, after having obtained a law of extinction, he could not systematically explore the higher-order relation of extinction and schedule of reinforcement, except that experience or a hunch leads him to anticipate some relevant interdependence. But, whether it is the comparative naïveté of experience or a neurophysiological model is logically irrelevant. The fact is, a premise operates to guide the search for new relationships.

Now the search for information is seldom random. Even if accidental experience is the source of hypothesis, one finds himself leaning toward one source rather than toward another. It is this epistemic leaning, so to speak, which becomes the instrument of ontological induction. Consider the case of the relation of extinction to schedule of reinforcement. A simple law of extinction may describe the response function from the point of terminal reinforcement. Why then, from the statement of this law as formulated upon a schedule of regular reinforcement, should we proceed to explore the effects of partial reinforcement upon extinction? The accidents of discovery, serendipity, may play a role, but more than likely our hypotheses about the processes of reinforcement afford us a basis for generalizing to related phenomena. A theory of partial reinforcement which systematically integrates extinction over the entire range of reinforcement schedules (e.g., Deutsch, 1960) may come along after the facts are in. This is quite often the case. But the collation of related laws itself reflects a principle of implicit systematic bias which only a theory can render explicit.

Following a hierarchy of types of laws, Rozeboom starts with some sample dispositional concepts and proceeds to structural variables (the parameters of a dependent-independent variable function) and then to still higher-order variables of structural covariation. Each level represents an ontological jump. Each tells us something of the "structure" of events. It is, however, the higher level of integration that is ontologically more interesting. Here we seek the element of communality among laws and their structural variables. By virtue of the covariation of one set of structural variables (say, that of reinforcement) with another set (say, that of extinction) we seek the principle of communality. Thus by a triangulation of the communal variables, we arrive at hypotheses signifying a higher-order structure.

NOTE 7.7

Ryle attacks the concept of mind analytically as mistaken doctrine. The doctrine follows the mentalist tradition of placing a "ghost in the machine." The mistake, a category mistake, deals with confusing statements belonging to different logical types. Ryle first notes that the "official doctrine" incorporates "Descartes' myth," namely, a dualism of mental and physical. One is "inner"; the other "outer." Even as metaphors they allude to distinctly different classes of things. Each has its own laws, its own existence status.

> But the actual transactions between the episodes of the private history and those of the public history remain mysterious, since by definition they can belong to neither series. They could not be reported among the happenings described in a person's autobiography of his inner life, but nor could they be reported among those described in someone else's biography of that person's overt career. They can be inspected neither by introspection nor by laboratory experiment. They are the theoretical shuttle-cocks which are forever being bandied from the physiologist back to the psychologist and from the psychologist back to the physiologist (1949, pp. 12–13).

And moreover, the conundrum is carried forth to infest the contemporary problems in psychology and philosophy.

Secondly, Ryle points to what he labels 'category mistakes.' Category mistakes are made by people who treat concepts belonging to different logical types as if they belong to the same logical type. He demonstrates this mistake by a number of forest-for-the-trees type confusions. For example, a person can see the buildings, offices, and members of a university but he cannot see the university as such; or the foreigner can see the members of a cricket team, and even (what is more amazing) understand the rules of the game, but he cannot see the element of team spirit. It is the old problem of wanting to assign to a logical construction the same kind of existential status that one assigns to objects upon which the logical construction is based—like saying there is the response of subject A, the response of subject B, the response of subject C, *and* the average response of the three.

Ryle then maintains that variants of the myth of Descartes, and the materialist and idealist counterstrategies for dissipating the myth by monistic reductions, are all examples of category mistakes. All assume that the predicates assigned to mind and those assigned to matter are of the same logical type. Since, Ryle maintains, the two classes of predicates belong to different types, then the doctrine of interaction and reduction are pseudo-doctrines occasioned by linguistic confusion. One can attempt a language of sense data, he can also (as Russell does) speak of logical constructions which are operational extensions of those sense data; but he cannot speak of causal relations, or of any relations but logical ones, between the two without indulging in a category mistake.

NOTE 7.8

One might ask, "What does it mean to say that there is a psychic residuum that is not reducible to a dispositional language, that there are raw-feels, redness now, pain, sour, and putridness that have subsistent qualities not in any way translatable into dispositional terms?" This is an interesting question. For although we think we understand it when it is asked (i.e., we think we understand the intention of the question), we fail utterly to conceive what might constitute its adequate answer. We have all played games with fictive cerebroscopes ("Your red may be like my green"), but even these fantasies fail to convince. For, if we were to switch brains around, we would not alter the extent of public agreement; and if we were to use the peephole of the cerebroscope just to have a peek and compare, we could not circumvent the logical difficulty of the peeking observer's looking at S's sensorium through the mediation of his own nervous system and sensorium, whereas S himself has but direct access to that same sensorium.

These are interesting puzzles, and it is surprising more thought has not been given to their difficulties and possible outcomes. Psychologists, for example, can provide us with some relevant though perhaps less dramatic analogy from the laboratory of perception. Stratton (1897), I. Kohlér (1955, 1962), and J. G. Taylor (1962), among others, have carried out experiments on inverting, reversing, and otherwise distorting visual fields. What is remarkable is how adaptable the perceptual system is. After a period of disorientation, and readjustment, the perceptual calculator reconverts the data back into a stable, familiar perceptual surround. It is as if we were to affix some kind of

color converters to the eyes such that every hue is converted to its complementary hue. After some initial discomfort over seeing the grass as red and
the sky as yellow, we would in time adjust to seeing normal turf and the usual
pleasant skies. Whether we would ever see the red as green is a question
difficult to answer. But no doubt a person with such converters would learn
anew to recognize "green" grass and his "blue" skies; and in time he would
learn to adjust his vocabulary such that his red is green, his yellow is blue.

Aha, but now we may remove the converters. Our subject is confused
again. Green, our actual green, does not look green to him. It is at this moment
that it is of interest to speculate about how the world is in the eyes of another.
But only in passing, it would appear. From the experiments on inverted vision
we would expect that the readjustment to normal vision comes about rapidly
and the subject again sees the world as others see it.

Inverting devices need not be peripheral to the nervous system. Suppose
some demon inserted such devices at the portals of the sensorium. Then indeed
my red might be like your green. But only a test would show this, and because learning to see is a protracted process and because we all adjust to a
public language of perception no such test is possible. What I wish to maintain
here is that conceivably we could have inverted vision as between two observers but we would never know it. Moreover, if there were inverted vision—
or even inverted modalities—it could not make any practicable difference in
our perception. For that reason I would suggest that the debates over other-
minds, private access, and the impossibility of private language are, with the
exception of placing logical restrictions upon some types of discourse, largely
gratuitous.

The issue can be carried even further. Suppose you learn that in an
autopsy on Mr. S, his brain had been hooked up in an unusual manner. The
optic tracts were found to terminate in an area normally reserved for taste,
whereas the gustatory tracts ended in the occipital center. By the usual anatomical inference Mr. S should have tasted with his eyes and seen with his
tongue. Let us see. Was the autopsy performed because, while living, Mr. S
showed aberrant perception, or simply because his body had been bequeathed
to medical school for the routine cadaverous dissections? I commit myself by
suggesting it was the latter case; which is to say, that it came purely as a sur-
prise that the brain of S had been wired incorrectly. Since this case is a hypothetical one, let us bring Mr. S back to life and submit him to the ritual of
a Gedanken experiment. First, the following facts. Mr. S has normal 20–20
vision. He is not color blind, has excellent depth perception, and in every way
has shown normal vision. In addition he appears to have normal gustation.
He can discriminate salty, sweet, sour, and bitter, is reported to have a fine
palate for vintage wine, and suffers the usual palatary deficit when afflicted
with a head cold. Second, let us assume Mr. S actually "tastes" his way down
the labyrinthian paths he takes and actually "visualizes" his way through the
arts of savory. I say assume, because it would really make no difference how
Mr. S, or any of us, is hooked up providing sufficient cerebral cells are allotted
to the task of processing sensory input. The crux of this argument is: not only
is it not important to question whether one man's red is like another man's
green, but it is equally unimportant that one man's vision might be like another

man's taste. That this should be the case is suggested by the following experiment.

Mr. S is placed in a reclining chair at the side of our study table. He is given a pencil and requested to draw what appears to him when his left eye is open and his right eye closed. Mr. S is a skilled draftsman and what emerges is a sketch very much like that which Ernst Mach drew for his book *Analysis of Sensations*. It shows the frame of the eye, the side of the nose, the vest, trousers, shoes, and off into the detail of the room. And he does this, mind you, with the sense modality—our sense modality—of taste. Mr. S sees as well as you or I. But where our rods give rise to achromatic figure and ground, his give rise to a figure-ground complex of, let us say, salty tastes. Where our cones give rise to the spectrum of the rainbow, his give rise to a similar rainbow—or should I say the same rainbow—in a sensory complex of bitter, sweet, salty and sour. He can thread a needle and he can walk a tight-rope, such is the fineness of his discrimination. Every movement before his eyes plays upon his retina, the shifting patterning of figure upon ground, the constancies, the chromatic complexes: all of these are processed to become his visual images in terms of sweet and sour, bitter and salty. And no one, I submit, could ever tell the difference.

This fantasy has several implications that appear to be compatible with some contemporary speculations upon brain functioning. One, it may make little difference where the sensory tract ends within the cerebral cortex, providing there are sufficient cells to process information and providing the scansion functions of the diencephalon are not disrupted. Two, a significant factor in perceptual discrimination is the peripheral apparatus with its specific responsivities to different types of stimuli. And three, learning is indispensible for establishing the "public" foundations of the experienced world.

The first point appears to be supported by the recent statistically flavored speculations in neurophysiology and neuroanatomy (e.g., Pitts and McCulloch, 1947; Hebb, 1949; Milner, 1957; Rosenblatt, 1958; Sholl, 1956; Uttley, 1954; Hayek, 1952). Neither the doctrines of specific energies nor specific connections seem particularly significant for the neural processes in perceptual organization. Rather we have equipotential systems with random interconnections and initial randomness of function. With experience and its sensory impress, facilitative and inhibitory growth processes occur to create the anatomical units of perception (e.g., of equivalence classes, pattern templates, recognition classes, etc.). Thus plasticity of structure and function is stressed rather than specificity and inflexibility. There is, of course, some specificity of structure. The receptors have their unique structures and the sensory modalities have their specific projection areas; but returning to the world of fiction, if a switching of sensory tracks were to be achieved in the prenatal organization, and were we somehow to compensate for differences in cell availability in the respective projection areas, then it might very well be that a tasting viewer would see the world as any other viewer does. Behaviorally at least we might very well be unable to detect the difference.

The second point stresses the importance of the peripheral apparatus. It is the structure of the eye, its resolving power and complexity of the input matrix which is significant, as much if not more than the particular aspect of the sensory quality, as such. The eye of the tasting viewer performs like the eye of any other viewer. It responds differentially to chromatic and achromatic stimulation. It has the same distribution of rods and cones, the same thresholds, the same convergence toward common optic pathways. The only difference is that the input data are decoded in dimensions of taste rather than what we are prone to preempt for vision. Mr. S as tasting-viewer (and viewing-taster), just as any other viewer, experiences the world that the peripheral sensory apparatus (with sufficient central processing units) makes possible. It is the structure of experience which is important not the content. Alternatively, for Mr. S it makes little difference what qualities accompany taste. So long as food substances in solution differentially evoke the gustatory nerves, that and differential processing at the cortical level implement the gustatory aspects of taste. It is purely accidental, and immaterial, that lemonade tastes sour and a little bit sweet rather than, say, yellow and a little bit blue.

Finally, the third implication stresses the significance of learning. The work of Senden (1932) and Riesen (1947) has shown that vision comes slowly to the newly seeing subject. The puzzle Molyneux proposed to Locke has been answered. Not only can the subject who gains his sight after congenital blindness not distinguish the cube from the sphere, he even has to learn to see what it is he is supposed to judge. The infant does not see a world of objects and detail when it opens its eyes. The world emerges only very slowly, partly by association with other sensory inputs, partly by the complex of integrations behind constancy phenomena, but not the least of all, by the public context in which he learns what is to be an object and how it shall be symbolized.

What has been given here is just the outline of highly speculative aberrations. One would indeed have to know more about these tasting-viewers. But two hypotheses emerge from these speculations which I find it hard to resist. One, it would be impossible to detect such aberrant perceivers as tasting-viewers (a riposte to all that has been fantasied?). And two, since cerebroscopic inspection appears technically impossible and since experiments on inverted vision indicate that discrepancies in perceived context are not lasting and occur primarily at the moment of inversion, those protracted deliberations on private access and the content of other minds seem to be singularly pointless. Insofar as individuals make compatible perceptual judgments, they see the same world. By "sameness" I mean there is no evidence that perceptual processing results in the reification of discrepant worlds under standard conditions of observation. However, there is stronger suggestion of "sameness" than that we obtain simply from perceptual agreements. It is tied to the facts of peripheral stimulation. What is important is the fact that the eye, as the complex receptor it is, is responsive to differences in wavelength and intensity of light. The relevant facts are the number, distribution, and response characteristics of the rods and cones. The facts of neuronal summation and convergence of the tracts may also be significant. But what is not particularly significant are those unique qualities of experience which emerge in the perceptual processing. Should any one of us through intervention of a perceptual demon suddenly become a tasting-viewer, we should no doubt suffer some temporary disorganization, but in a relatively short time the perceived world would come back into focus and "look" pretty much as it always had. The facts of sameness of the world thus derive from the attributes and dimensions of the physical stimuli and from the response characteristics of the particular receptors. The world would be different to different observers only if it presented different faces to each of them. This might be the case if light varied in wavelength for observer S_j but not for observer S_k. It might also be the case if S_j had the normal complement of rods and cones but S_k had only rods. In the latter case S_k would only be a partial detector. But even then, the two would agree as to the facts mediated by the rods. And they would not disagree as to color. It would only be that S_k is blind to some characteristics of the stimulus to which S_j responds.

Consider now a nation of tasting-viewers, viewing-tasters, smelling-touchers, touching-smellers. (Our case would be simplified if there were as many primary tactual qualities as there are olfactory qualities but this condition is not necessary.) They could be from another planet, if you wish, but it would obviate some irrelevant matters if we were to keep them here on earth, looking in all respects like the rest of us except for certain anatomical details of their brains. We may ask: will such a group have a different picture of the world? Will they make a different construction of the world based on a different set of properties? Only a moment's reflection prompts a "no" answer to both questions. How would they visualize the world? In three dimensions, of course. Doubtless, they would embrace coordinate geometry and differential equations; and doubtless they would consider "vision" the most important of the descriptive senses. Newtonian mechanics would be as real as it would be to "normal" viewers. Mass, force, acceleration, momentum, all of these would derive from their conceptualizing the data of sensory input. That an object "smells" solid and "smells" heavy, as it were, is quite immaterial to the fact that the object is perceived as being solid and as being heavy. Thus perception results from the fact that the sensory apparatus is responsive to certain properties of the physical world. So long as the individual can discriminate among his sensory cues to the extent he does as a normal perceiver, then it makes no difference as to how (as to content or qualia) those sensory data are processed. The chiaroscuro in nuance of saltiness will be the "same" as it is in black and white. That is to say, there will be no conceivable difference in the complex descriptions as given by tasting-viewer and normal viewer. The physical descriptions will be invariant. They will be invariant so long as we maintain sensory differentiation and discriminability. Thus, it is essential that we have qualities and degrees among the sensory components of perceptual content. But how these qualities differ, or what they are, or that they should be as they are, are not questions of concern for science. Nor, I suspect, should they be of concern to philosophy.

In resumé then, the hypothesis of the irrelevance of the unique contents of perception leads me to the following conclusions: (1) assertions concerning the private, unique, and irreducible character of conscious events are meaningless in that neither they nor their contradictions (e.g., your red may not be my red) have conceivable consequences either for science or for ordinary language. (2) The distinction between primary and secondary qualities of experience is largely irrelevant. Quality differentiation among stimuli is the

perceptual counterpart of sensory detectability of the physical stimulus variables. That such stimulus variables are detected is important; the uniqueness of
the perceptual quality in sensory decoding is not. (3) The nondispositional
properties of perception, the residue of consciousness, is but an artifact of
discrimination. Things that are physically different are judged to be different,
just as the figure is different from the ground. What is significant is that
a differentiation is made, and not that it should be blue against green rather
than sweet against salty. A color or a taste is not something one describes.
And a tasting-viewer points as well as a "normal" viewer. That is all he needs
to do and really all he understands about the uniqueness of what he sees!

NOTE 7.9

Bibliographic addendum: Skinner's antitheoretical, antireductive bias finds expression in his Presidential address to the Midwestern Psychological Association (1950). For a critical assessment of this point of view, see Feigl
(1951), and Scriven (1956).

Bergmann (1953, 1954, 1957) also expresses objections to reductionism on methodological grounds. He distinguishes between process laws
with significant historical variables (as in psychology) and process laws without
them (as in physics). Although the form of the equations expressing the
laws may differ (integro-differential as against differential equations), this
need not constitute an objection to reductionism as such.

Woodger (1929), who has made one of the classic statements on the
formal requirements of reductionism, objects to reductionism in biology on
grounds that mechanical principles cannot adequately explain hierarchies of
levels of organization in living organisms. He objects to reductionism in psychology on the grounds that the person language of psychology with its
cognitive, affective, personalistic overtones cannot be translated into the language of some higher-order disciplines.

REFERENCES

ALLPORT, F. H. *Social psychology*. Boston: Houghton Mifflin, 1924.

ALLPORT, G. W. *Personality, a psychological interpretation*. New York: Henry Holt, 1937.

ALLPORT, G. W. Personalistic psychology as a science: a reply. *Psychol. Rev.*, 1946, **53**, 132–135.

APOSTEL, L. Toward a formal study of models in the non-formal sciences. *Synthese*, 1960, **12**, 125–161. Also in H. Freudenthal (Ed.), *The concept and role of the model in mathematics and natural and social sciences*. Dordrecht: D. Reidel, 1961.

ARBUTHNOT, J. An argument for Divine Providence taken from the constant regularity observed in the births of both sexes. *Philos. Trans. Roy. Soc.*, 1710, **27**, 186–190.

ASHBY, W. R. *Design for a brain*. London: Chapman & Hall, 1952.

ASHBY, W. R. Induction, prediction, and decision-making in cybernetic systems. In H. E. Kyburg (Ed.), *Induction: some current issues*. Middletown: Wesleyan University Press, 1963.

ATKINSON, R. C. *See* Suppes and Atkinson, 1960.

ATTNEAVE, F. *Applications of information theory in psychology*. New York: Holt-Dryden, 1959.

ATTNEAVE, F. Perception and related areas. In S. Koch (Ed.), *Psychology, a study of a science*, Vol. 4. New York: McGraw-Hill, 1962.

AYER, A. J. Demonstration of the impossibility of metaphysics. *Mind*, 1934, **43**, 335–345.

BACON, F. *Novum organum*. (orig. 1621) Oxford: Oxford University Press, 1889.

BARRY, G. *See* Fitch and Barry, 1950.

BEAMENT, J. W. L. (Ed.). *Models and analogues in biology*. Cambridge: Cambridge University Press, 1960.

BECK, W. W. Constructs and inferred entities. *Philos. Sci.*, 1950, **17**, 74–86.

BERENDA, C. W. Is clinical psychology a science? *Amer. Psychol.*, 1957, **12**, 725–729.

BERGMANN, G. The logic of psychological concepts. *Philos. Sci.*, 1951, **18**, 93–110.

BERGMANN, G. Theoretical psychology. *Annu. Rev. Psychol.,* 1953, **4,** 435–458.

BERGMANN, G. Reduction. In J. T. Wilson and others. *Current trends in psychology and the other behavioral sciences.* Pittsburgh: University of Pittsburgh Press, 1954.

BERGMANN, G. *Philosophy of science.* Madison: University of Wisconsin Press, 1957.

BERGMANN, G. Physics and ontology. *Philos. Sci.,* 1961, **28,** 1–14.

BERGMANN, G. and SPENCE, K. W. Operationism and theory in psychology. *Psychol. Rev.,* 1941, **48,** 1–14.

BERGMANN, G. and SPENCE, K. W. The logic of psychophysical measurement. *Psychol. Rev.,* 1944, **51,** 1–24.

BERGMANN, G. The logic of psychological concepts. *Philos. Sci.,* 1951, **18,** 93–110.

BERGSON, H. *Creative evolution.* (tr. A. Mitchell) New York: Henry Holt, 1911.

BERGSON, H. *An introduction to metaphysics.* London: Macmillan, 1913.

BERKELEY, G. *Selections.* (M. W. Calkins, Ed.) New York: Scribner, 1929.

BERLYNE, D. E. *Conflict, arousal, and curiosity.* New York: McGraw-Hill, 1960.

BEVERIDGE, W. I. B. *The art of scientific investigation.* London: Heinemann, 1950.

BILLS, A. G. Blocking: a new principle in mental fatigue. *Amer. J. Psychol.,* 1931, **43,** 230–245.

BLACK, M. *Language and philosophy.* Ithaca: Cornell University Press, 1949.

BLACK, M. *Models and metaphors.* Ithaca: Cornell University Press, 1962.

BOHR, N. Discussion with Einstein. In P. A. Schilpp (Ed.), *Albert Einstein, philosopher-scientist.* New York: Tudor, 1949. (Reprinted New York: Harper Torchbook, Harper & Row, 1959.)

BOHR, N. On the notions of causality and complementarity. *Science,* 1950, **111,** 51–54.

BOOLE, G. *An investigation of the laws of thought.* New York: Dover, 1854.

BORING, E. G. Temporal perception and operationism. *Amer. J. Psychol.,* 1936, **48,** 519–522.

BRAGG, W. H. and BRAGG, W. L. *X-rays and crystal structure.* London: G. Bell, 1925.

BRAIN, W. R. *Mind, perception, and science.* Oxford: Blackwell, 1951.

BRAIN, W. R. Physiological basis of consciousness. *Brain,* 1958, **81,** 426–455.

BRAITHWAITE, R. B. *Scientific explanation.* Cambridge: Cambridge University Press, 1953.

BRAITHWAITE, R. B. Models in empirical science. In E. Nagel, P. Suppes, and A. Tarski (Eds.), *Logic, methodology, and philosophy of science.* Stanford: Stanford University Press, 1962.

BRIDGMAN, P. W. *The logic of modern physics.* New York: Macmillan, 1927.

BRIDGMAN, P. W. Some general principles of operational values. *Psychol. Rev.,* 1945, **52,** 246–249.

BRIDGEMAN, P. W. Remarks on the present state of operationism. *Sci. Mon.,* 1954, **79,** 224–226.

BROAD, C. D. *Mind and its place in nature.* London: Kegan Paul, 1925.

BROADBENT, D. *Perception and communication.* New York: Pergammon Press, 1958.

BRODBECK, MAY. Explanation, prediction and 'imperfect' knowledge. In H. Feigl and G. Maxwell (Eds.), *Minnesota studies in the philosophy of science,* Vol. III. Minneapolis: University of Minnesota Press, 1962.

BRODBECK, MAY. Meaning and action. *Philos. Sci.,* 1963, **30,** 309–324.

BRONOWSKI, J. The logic of mind. *Amer. Sci.,* 1966. **54,** 1–14.

BRUNSWIK, E. Distal focusing of perception: size-constancy in a representative sample of situations. *Psychol. Monogr.,* 1944, **56,** No. 254.

BUCK, R. C. Reflexive predictions. *Philos. Sci.,* 1963, **30,** 359–369.

BUNGE, M. A general black box theory. *Philos. Sci.,* 1963, **30,** 346–358.

BUNGE, M. Phenomenological theories. In M. Bunge (Ed.), *The critical approach to science and philosophy.* Glencoe: Free Press, 1964.

BUSH, R. R. and MOSTELLER, F. *Stochastic models for learning.* New York: Wiley, 1955.

CAMPBELL, N. R. *Physics, the elements.* Cambridge: Cambridge University Press, 1920. Also published as *Foundations of science.* New York: Dover, 1957.

CAMPBELL, N. R. *What is science?* (orig. 1921) New York: Dover, 1952.

CARNAP, R. *Der logische Aufbau der Welt.* Berlin: Weltkreis-Verlag, 1928.

CARNAP, R. Testability and meaning: I, II. *Philos. Sci.,* 1936, **3,** 419–471; 1937, **4,** 1–40.

CARNAP, R. *The logical syntax of language.* London: Kegan Paul, 1937.

CARNAP, R. The methodological character of theoretical concepts. In H. Feigl and M. Scriven (Eds.), *Minnesota studies in the philosophy of science,* Vol. I. Minneapolis: University of Minnesota Press, 1956.

CECCATO, S. Contra Dingler, pro Dingler. *Methodos,* 1952, **4,** 266–290.

CHURCH, A. A note on the Entscheidungs-problem. *J. symbol. Log.,* 1936, **1,** 40–41; 101–102.

COMBS, A. W. *See* Snygg and Combs, 1949, 1959.

COTTON, J. W. On making predictions from Hull's theory. *Psychol. Rev.,* 1955, **62,** 303–314.

CRAIG, W. Replacement of auxiliary expressions. *Philos. Rev.,* 1956, **65,** 38–55.

CRAIK, K. J. W. *The nature of explanation.* Cambridge: Cambridge University Press, 1943.

CRONBACH, L. J. and MEEHL, P. E. Construct validity in psychological tests. *Psychol. Bull.,* 1955, **53,** 281–302.

CRUTCHFIELD, R. S. *See* Krech and Crutchfield, 1947.

DAVIS, M. *Computability and unsolvability.* New York: McGraw-Hill, 1958.

DELAFRESNAYE, J. F. (Ed.), *Brain mechanisms and consciousness.* Oxford: Blackwell, 1954.

DELAFRESNAYE, J. F. (Ed.), *Brain mechanisms and learning.* Oxford: Blackwell, 1961.

DEUTSCH, J. A. *The structural basis of behavior.* Chicago: University of Chicago Press, 1960.

DIRAC, P. A. M. *The principles of quantum mechanics* (3rd ed.). London: Oxford University Press, 1947.

DUFFY, E. *Activation and behavior.* New York: Wiley, 1962.

DUHEM, P. *The aim and structure of physical theory.* (1914, 2nd ed., tr. P. P. Weiner). Princeton: Princeton University Press, 1954. Also New York: Atheneum, 1962.

DUNOÜY, L. *Human destiny.* New York: Longmans, 1947.

ECCLES, J. L. *The neurological basis of mind.* Oxford: Oxford University Press, 1953.

EDDINGTON, A. *Space, time, and gravitation.* Cambridge: Cambridge University Press, 1920.

EDDINGTON, A. *The nature of the physical world.* Cambridge: Cambridge University Press, 1928.

EDDINGTON, A. *The philosophy of physical science.* Cambridge: Cambridge University Press, 1939.

EINSTEIN, A. *The origin of the general theory of relativity.* Glasgow: Jackson Wylie, 1933.

ESTES, W. K. The statistical approach to learning theory. In S. Koch (Ed.), *Psychology: a study of a science,* Vol. 2. New York: McGraw-Hill, 1959.

ESTES, W. K. Toward a statistical learning theory. *Psychol. Rev.,* 1950, **57,** 94–107.

ESTES, W. K. and others. *Modern learning theory.* New York: Appleton-Century-Crofts, 1954.

ESTES, W. K. and SUPPES, P. C. Foundations of linear models. In R. R. Bush and W. K. Estes (Eds.), *Studies in mathematical learning theory.* Stanford: Stanford University Press, 1959.

FEIGL, H. Operationism and scientific method. *Psychol. Rev.,* 1945, **52,** 250–259.

FEIGL, H. Some remarks on the meaning of scientific explanation. In H. Feigl and W. Sellars (Eds.), *Readings in philosophical analysis.* New York: Appleton-Century-Crofts, 1949.

FEIGL, H. Existential hypotheses. *Philos. Sci.,* 1950, **17,** 35–62.

FEIGL, H. Principles and problems of theory construction in psychology. In W. Dennis (Ed.), *Current trends in psychological theory.* Pittsburgh: University of Pittsburgh Press, 1951.

FEIGL, H. The mind-body problem in the development of logical empiricism. *Rev. Int. Philosophie,* 1950. In H. Feigl and M. Brodbeck (Eds.),

Readings in the philosophy of science. New York: Appleton-Century-Crofts, 1953.

FEIGL, H. The 'mental' and the 'physical.' In H. Feigl and G. Maxwell (Eds.), *Minnesota studies in the philosophy of science,* Vol. II. Minneapolis: University of Minnesota Press, 1958.

FEIGL, H. Reduction of psychology to neurophysiology. Paper read to AAAS meetings, Denver, December, 1961.

FEIGL, H. and MAXWELL, G. (Eds.), *Current issues in the philosophy of science.* New York: Holt, Rinehart and Winston, 1961.

FEYERABEND, P. K. On the quantum theory of measurement. In S. Körner (Ed.), *Observation and interpretation in the philosophy of physics.* New York: Dover, 1957.

FEYERABEND, P. K. An attempt at a realistic interpretation of experience. *Proc. Arist. Soc.,* 1958, **58**, 141–170.

FEYERABEND, P. K. Complementarity. *Proc. Arist. Soc. Suppl.,* 1958, **32**, 75–104.

FEYERABEND, P. K. Niels Bohr's interpretation of the quantum theory. In H. Feigl and G. Maxwell (Eds.), *Current issues in the philosophy of science.* New York: Holt, Rinehart and Winston, 1961.

FEYERABEND, P. K. Explanation, reduction and empiricism. In H. Feigl and G. Maxwell (Eds.), *Minnesota studies in the philosophy of science,* Vol. III. Minneapolis: University of Minnesota Press, 1962.

FEYERABEND, P. K. Problems of microphysics. In R. G. Colodny (Ed.), *Frontiers of science and philosophy.* Pittsburgh: University of Pittsburgh Press, 1962.

FEYERABEND, P. K. Realism and instrumentalism. In M. Bunge (Ed.), *The critical approach to science and philosophy.* Glencoe: Free Press, 1964.

FITCH, F. B. and BARRY G. Towards a formalization of Hull's behavior theory. *Philos, Sci.,* 1950, **17**, 260–265.

FREUDENTHAL, H. (Ed.), *The concept and the role of model in mathematics and natural and social sciences.* Dordrecht: D. Reidel, 1961.

GAITO, J. and ZAVALA, A. Neurochemistry and learning. *Psychol. Bull.,* 1964, **61**, 45–62.

GALANTER, E. *See* Miller, Galanter, and Pribram, 1960.

GALLISTEL, C. R. Electrical self-stimulation and its theoretical implications. *Psychol. Bull.,* 1964, **61**, 23–34.

GARNER, W. R. A Technique and a scale for loudness measurement. *J. acoust. Soc. Amer.,* 1954, **26**, 73–88.

GEORGE, F. H. Logical constructs and psychological theory. *Psychol. Rev.,* 1953, **60**, 1–6.

GEORGE, F. H. Inductive machines and the problem of learning. *Cybernetica,* 1959, **2**, 109–126.

GEORGE, F. H. Models in cybernetics. In J. W. L. Beament (Ed.), *Models and analogues in biology.* Cambridge: Cambridge University Press, 1960.

GEORGE, F. H. *The brain as a computer.* New York: Pergammon Press, 1961.

GIBSON, J. J. The concept of stimulus in psychology. *Amer. Psychol.,* 1960, **15,** 694–703.

GINSBERG, A. Hypothetical constructs and intervening variables. *Psychol. Rev.,* 1954, **61,** 119–131.

GÖDEL, K. *On formally undecidable propositions of Principia Mathematica and related systems.* (tr. B. Meltzer; intro. R. B. Braithwaite; orig. 1931) London: Oliver Boyd, 1962.

GOUDGE, T. A. Causal explanation in natural history. *Br. J. Philos. Sci.,* 1958, **9,** 194–202.

GREGORY, R. L. On physical model explanations in psychology. *Br. J. Philos. Sci.,* 1953, **4,** 192–197.

GREGORY, R. L. The brain as an engineering problem. In W. H. Thorpe and O. L. Zangwill (Eds.), *Current problems in animal behavior.* Cambridge: Cambridge University Press, 1961.

GUTHRIE, E. R. *The psychology of learning.* New York: Harper, 1935.

GUTHRIE, E. R. Association by contiguity. In S. Koch (Ed.), *Psychology: a study of a science,* Vol. 2. New York: McGraw-Hill, 1959.

HADAMARD, J. *The psychology of invention in the mathematical field.* London: Oxford University Press, 1945.

HANSON, N. R. Professor Ryle's Mind. *Philos. Quart.,* 1952, **2,** 246–248.

HANSON, N. R. *Patterns of discovery.* Cambridge: Cambridge University Press, 1958.

HANSON, N. R. Five cautions for the Copenhagen interpretation's critics. *Philos. Sci.,* 1959, **26,** 325–337.

HANSON, N. R. On the symmetry between explanation and prediction. *Philos. Rev.,* 1959, **68,** 349–358.

HANSON, N. R. The Copenhagen interpretation of quantum theory. *Amer. J. Physics,* 1959, **27,** 1–19. Abridged in A. Danto and S. Morgenbesser, (Eds.), *Philosophy of science.* New York: Meridian Books, 1960.

HANSON, N. R. The dematerialization of matter. *Philos. Sci.,* 1962, **29,** 27–38.

HANSON, N. R. *The concept of the positron.* Cambridge: Cambridge University Press, 1963.

HAWKINS, D. *The language of nature.* San Francisco: Freeman, 1964.

HAYEK, F. A. *The sensory order.* London: Routledge, 1952.

HEBB, D. O. *The organization of behavior.* New York: Wiley, 1949.

HEBB, D. O. The role of neurological ideas in psychology. *J. Person.,* 1951, **20,** 39–55.

HEBB, D. O. Drives and the C. N. S. (Conceptual Nervous System). *Psychol. Rev.,* 1955, **62,** 243–254.

HEBB, D. O. *A textbook of psychology.* Philadelphia: Saunders, 1958.

HEBB, D. O. A neurophysiological theory. In S. Koch (Ed.), *Psychology: a study of a science,* Vol. 1. New York: McGraw-Hill, 1959.

HEBB, D. O. Intelligence, brain function, and the theory of mind. *Brain,* 1959, **82,** 260–275.

HEMPEL, C. G. The function of general laws in history. *J. Philos.*, 1942, **39,** 35–48.

HEMPEL, C. G. General systems theory and the unity of science. *Human Biol.,* 1951, **23,** 313–322.

HEMPEL, C. G. A logical appraisal of operationism. *Sci. Mon.,* 1954, **79,** 215–220.

HEMPEL, C. G. The theoretician's dilemma. In H. Feigl, M. Scriven, and G. Maxwell (Eds.), *Minnesota studies in the philosophy of science,* Vol. II. Minneapolis: University of Minnesota Press, 1958.

HEMPEL, C. G. Deductive-nomological versus statistical explanations. In H. Feigl and G. Maxwell (Eds.), *Minnesota studies in the philosophy of science,* Vol. III. Minneapolis: University of Minnesota Press, 1962.

HEMPEL, C. G. Explanation and prediction by covering laws. In B. H. Baumrin (Ed.), *Philosophy of science: the Delaware seminar,* Vol. I. New York: Wiley, 1963.

HEMPEL, C. G. and OPPENHEIM, P. Studies in the logic of explanation. *Philos. Sci.,* 1948, **15,** 134–175. Reprinted in H. Feigl and M. Brodbeck (Eds.), *Readings in the philosophy of science.* New York: Appleton-Century-Crofts, 1953.

HENDRICK, I. *Facts and theories of psychoanalysis.* New York: Knopf, 1934.

HENLE, P. The status of emergence. *J. Philos.,* 1942, **39,** 486–493.

HERBART, J. H. *Letters and lectures on education.* (tr. H. M. and E. Felkin) London: S. Sonneschein, 1898.

HERBART, J. H. *The application of psychology to the science of education.* (tr. B. C. Mulliner) London: S. Sonneschein, 1898.

HERON, W. H. The pathology of boredom. *Scientific American,* January, 1957, **199,** 52–56.

HESSE, MARY B. Models in physics. *Br. J. Philos. Sci.* 1953, **4,** 98–214.

HESSE, MARY B. *Forces and fields.* London: Nelson, 1961.

HESSE, MARY B. *Models and analogies in science.* London: Sheed, 1963.

HESSE, MARY B. A new look at scientific explanation. *Rev. Metaphys.,* 1963, **17,** 98–108.

HEYER, A. W. *See* Osgood and Heyer, 1951.

HINDE, R. A. Energy models of motivation. In J. W. L. Beament (Ed.), *Models and analogues in biology.* Cambridge: Cambridge University Press, 1960.

HOCHBERG, H. Intervening variables, hypothetical constructs and metaphysics. In H. Feigl and G. Maxwell (Eds.), *Current issues in the philosophy of science.* New York: Holt, Rinehart and Winston, 1961.

HOSPERS, J. On explanation. *J. Philos.,* 1946, **43,** 337–346.

HOWELLS, T. H. Is Weber's law reducible to the physical coefficient of friction. *J. gen. Psychol.,* 1954, **50,** 249–260.

HULL, C. L. *Principles of behavior.* New York: Appleton-Century-Crofts, 1943.

HULL, C. L. *Essentials of behavior.* New Haven: Yale University Press, 1951.

HULL, C. L. *A behavior system.* New Haven: Yale University Press, 1952.

HUME, D. *A treatise of human nature.* (Ed. L. A. Selby-Bigge; orig. 1739). Oxford: Clarendon Press, 1888.

HUTTEN, L. H. On the principle of action by contact. *Br. J. Philos. Sci.,* 1951, **2,** 45–51.

HUTTEN, L. H. The role of models in physics. *Br. J. Philos. Sci.,* 1954, **4,** 284–301.

JAMES, W. Does "consciousness" exist? *J. Philos.,* 1904, **1,** 477–491.

JAMES, R. W. *X-Ray crystallography.* (4th ed.) New York: Wiley, 1950.

JEFFRESS, L. A. (Ed.), *Cerebral mechanisms in behavior.* New York: Wiley, 1951.

JESSOR, R. The problem of reductionism in psychology. *Psychol. Rev.,* 1958, **65,** 170–178.

JOHN, E. R. High nervous functions, brain functions and learning. *Annu. Rev. Physiol.,* 1961, **23,** 451–484.

KANT, I. *Critique of pure reason.* (tr. N. Kemp Smith) London: Macmillan, 1963.

KANTOR, J. R. The operational principle in the physical and psychological sciences. *Psychol. Rec.,* 1938, **2,** 1–32.

KANTOR, J. R. *Problems of physiological psychology.* Bloomington: Principia Press, 1947.

KAPLAN, A. *The new world of philosophy.* New York: Random House, 1961.

KAPLAN, A. *The conduct of inquiry.* San Francisco: Chandler, 1964.

KARSTEN, A. Psychische Sättigung. *Psychol. Forsch.,* 1928, **10,** 142–254.

KATSOFF, L. O. Observation and interpretation in science. *Philos. Rev.,* 1947, **56,** 682–689.

KATSOFF, L. O. The role of hypothesis in scientific investigation. *Mind,* 1949, **58,** 222–227.

KATSOFF, L. O. Facts, phenomena, and frames of reference. *Psychol. Rev.,* 1953, **60,** 40–44.

KAUFMANN, F. The logical rules of scientific procedure. *Philos. Phenom. Res.,* 1942, **2,** 457–471.

KEMENY, J. G. Man viewed as a machine. *Sci. Amer.,* 1955, **192,** 58–67.

KEMENY, J. and OPPENHEIM, P. On reduction. *Philos. Studies,* 1956, **7,** 6–19.

KEMENY, J. G. *A philosopher looks at science.* Princeton: Van Nostrand, 1959.

KENDLER, H. K. "What is learned?"—a theoretical blind alley. *Psychol. Rev.,* 1952, **59,** 269–277.

KESSEN, W. and KIMBLE, G. A. "Dynamic systems" and theory construction. *Psychol. Rev.,* 1952, **59,** 263–267.

KIMBLE, G. A. *See* Kessen and Kimble, 1952.

KLEENE, S. C. *Introduction to metamathematics.* New York: Van Nostrand, 1952.

KLEIN, D. B. Scientific understanding in psychology. *Psychol. Rev.,* 1932, **39,** 552–569.

KNEALE, W. *Probability and induction.* London: Oxford University Press, 1949.

Koch, S., The logical character of the concept of motivation: I, II. *Psychol. Rev.*, 1941, **48**, 15–38, 127–154.

Koch, S., Clark L. Hull. In W. K. Estes and others. *Modern learning theory.* New York: Appleton-Century-Crofts, 1954.

Koch, S. (Ed.), *Psychology: a study of a science*, Vol. 1. New York: McGraw-Hill, 1959.

Koestler, A. *The sleepwalkers.* New York: Macmillan, 1959.

Koffka, K. *Principles of Gestalt psychology.* New York: Harcourt, Brace, 1935.

Kohler, I. Experiments with prolonged optical distortions. *Acta Psychol.*, 1955, **11**, 176–178.

Kohler, I. Experiments with goggles. *Scientific American*, 1926, **206**, 62–72.

Köhler, W. *Gestalt psychology.* New York: Liveright, 1947.

Kolmogorov, A. N. *Foundations of the theory of probability.* (tr. N. Morrison, 2nd ed.; orig. 1933) New York: Chelsea, 1956.

Körner, S. (Ed.), *Observation and interpretation in the philosophy of physics.* New York: Dover, 1957.

Körner, S. Deductive unification and idealization. *Br. J. Philos. Sci.*, 1964, **14**, 274–284.

Kotarbińska, Janina. The controversy: deductivism versus inductivism. In E. Nagel, P. Suppes, and A. Tarski (Eds.), *Logic, methodology, and philosophy of science.* Stanford: Stanford University Press, 1962.

Krech, D. Notes toward a psychological theory. *J. Person.*, 1949, **19**, 66–87.

Krech, D. Dynamic systems as open neurological systems. *Psychol. Rev.*, 1950, **57**, 345–361.

Krech, D. Dynamic systems, psychological fields and hypothetical constructs. *Psychol. Rev.*, 1950, **57**, 783–790.

Krech, D. and Crutchfield, R. S. *Theory and problems of social psychology.* New York: McGraw-Hill, 1947.

Lachman, R. The model in theory construction. *Psychol. Rev.*, 1960, **67**, 113–129.

Landauer, T. K. Two hypotheses concerning the biochemical basis of memory. *Psychol. Rev.*, 1964, **71**, 167–179.

Langfeld, H. S. A response interpretation of consciousness. *Psychol. Rev.*, 1931, **38**, 87–108.

Lashley, K. S. The behavioristic interpretation of consciousness, I, II. *Psychol. Rev.*, 1923, **30**, 237–272; 329–353.

Lewin, K. *A dynamic theory of personality.* New York: McGraw-Hill, 1935.

Lewin, K. *Principles of topological psychology.* New York: McGraw-Hill, 1936.

Lewis, C. I. A pragmatic conception of the a priori. *J. Philos.*, 1923. In H. Feigl and W. Sellars (Eds.), *Readings in philosophical analysis.* New York: Appleton-Century-Crofts, 1949.

Lewis, C. I. *Mind and the world order.* (orig. 1929) New York: Dover, 1956.

LINDZEY, G. Hypothetical constructs, conventional constructs and the use of physiological data in psychological theory. *Psychiatry,* 1953, **16,** 27–33.

LOCKE, J. *An essay concerning human understanding.* (orig. 1690; abr. and edit. by A. S. Pringle-Pattison) Oxford: Clarendon Press, 1924.

LORENTE DE NO', R. Cerebral cortex: architecture. In J. F. Fulton, *Physiology of the nervous system.* (3rd ed.) New York: Oxford University Press, 1949.

LUCE, R. D. *Individual choice behavior.* New York: Wiley, 1959.

MACCORQUODALE, K. and MEEHL, P. E. On a distinction between hypothetical constructs and intervening variables. *Psychol. Rev.,* 1948, **55,** 95–107.

MACCORQUODALE K. and MEEHL, P. E. Preliminary suggestions as to formalization of expectancy theory. *Psychol. Rev.,* 1953, **60,** 50–63.

MACCORQUODALE, K. and MEEHL, P. E. Edward C. Tolman. In W. K. Estes and others, *Modern learning theory.* New York: Appleton-Century-Crofts, 1954.

MCCULLOCH, W. S. and PITTS, W. A logical calculus of ideas imminent in nervous activity. *Bull. Math. Biophys.,* 1943, **5,** 111–133.

MCCULLOCH, W. S. *See* Pitts and McCulloch, 1947.

MCDOUGALL, W. *Introduction to social psychology.* London: Methuen, 1908.

MCGEOCH, J. A. The vertical dimensions of mind. *Psychol. Rev.,* 1936, **43,** 107–129.

MCGEOCH, J. A. A critique of operational definition. *Psychol. Bull.,* 1937, **34,** 703–704.

MACKAY, D. M. The epistemological problem of automata. In C. W. Shannon and J. McCarthy (Eds.), *Automata Studies.* Princeton: Princeton University Press, 1956.

MACLEOD, R. B. The phenomenological approach to social psychology. *Psychol. Rev.,* 1947, **54,** 193–210.

MACH, E. *The analysis of sensations.* (orig. 1897) La Salle: Open Court, 1914.

MADDEN, E. H. Definition and reduction. *Philos. Sci.,* 1961, **28,** 390–405.

MARGENAU, H. *The nature of physical reality.* New York: McGraw-Hill, 1950.

MARSHALL, W. H. and TALBOT, S. A. Recent evidence for neural mechanisms in vision leading to a general theory of visual acuity. In H. Klüver (Ed.), *Visual mechanisms.* Lancaster: Cattell, 1942.

MARX, M. H. Intervening variable or hypothetical construct? *Psychol. Rev.,* 1951, **58,** 235–247.

MARX, M. The general nature of theory construction. In M. Marx (Ed.), *Psychological theory.* New York: Macmillan, 1951. Revised in M. Marx (Ed.), *Theories in contemporary psychology.* New York: Macmillan, 1963.

MAXWELL, G. The ontological status of theoretical entities. In H. Feigl and G. Maxwell (Eds.), *Minnesota studies in the philosophy of science,* Vol. III. Minneapolis: University of Minnesota Press, 1962.

MAXWELL, G. Theories, frameworks, and ontology. *Philos. Sci.,* 1962, **29,** 132–138.

MAYO, B. The existence of theoretical entities. *Penguin Science News,* 1954, **32,** 7–18.

MAZE, J. R. Do intervening variables intervene? *Psychol. Rev.,* 1954, **61,** 226–231.

MEEHL, P. E. On the circularity of the Law of Effect. *Psychol. Bull.,* 1950, **47,** 52–75.

MEEHL, P. E. *Clinical versus statistical prediction.* Minneapolis: University of Minnesota Press, 1954.

MEEHL, P. E. *See* MacCorquodale and Meehl, 1948; 1953; 1954.

MEEHL, P. E. *See* Cronbach and Meehl, 1955.

MEISSNER, W. W. Non-constructual aspects of psychological constructs. *Psychol. Rev.,* 1958, **65,** 143–150.

MERTON, R. K. *Social theory and social structure.* Glencoe: Free Press, 1957.

MICHOTTE, A. E. *The perception of causality.* New York: Basic Books, 1963.

MILLS, J. S. *A system of logic.* London: Longmans, 1884.

MILLER, G. A., GALANTER, E. and PRIBRAM, K. H. *Plans and the structure of behavior.* New York: Henry Holt, 1960.

MILNER, P. M. The cell assembly: Mark II. *Psychol. Rev.,* 1957, **64,** 242–252.

MONTGOMERY, K. C. An experimental investigation of reactive inhibition and conditioned inhibition, *J. exp. Psychol.,* 1951, **41,** 39–51.

MORGAN, C. L. Physiological theory of drive. In S. Koch (Ed.), *Psychology: a study of a science,* Vol. 1. New York: McGraw-Hill, 1959.

MORRELL, F. Electrophysiological contributions to the neural basis of learning. *Physiol. Rev.,* 1961, **41,** 442–494.

MOSTELLER, F. *See* Bush and Mosteller, 1955.

MUENZINGER, K. F. Vicarious trial and error at a choice point, I: a general survey of its relation to learning. *J. genet. Psychol.,* 1938, **53,** 75–86.

MUENZINGER, K. F. *Psychology: the science of behavior.* New York: Harper & Row, 1942.

MURPHY, G. *See* Schafer and Murphy, 1943.

NAGEL, E. The meaning of reduction in the natural sciences. In R. C. Stauffer (Ed.), *Science and civilization.* Madison: University of Wisconsin Press, 1949.

NAGEL, E. Some issues in the logic of historical analysis. *Sci. Mon.,* 1952, **74,** 162–169. Also in H. Feigl and M. Brodbeck (Eds.), *Readings in the philosophy of science.* New York: Appleton-Century-Crofts, 1953.

NAGEL, E. *The structure of science.* New York: Harcourt, Brace and World, 1961.

NAGEL, E. and NEWMAN, J. R. *Gödel's proof.* New York: New York University Press, 1958.

NEUMANN, J. VON. The general and logical theory of automata. In L. A. Jeffress (Ed.), *Cerebral mechanisms in behavior.* New York: Wiley, 1951. Reprinted in J. R. Newman (editor), *The world of mathematics,* Vol. 4, New York: Simon and Schuster, 1956.

NEUMANN, J. VON. *Foundations of quantum mechanics.* (orig. 1932) Princeton: Princeton University Press, 1955.

NEWMAN, J. R. *See* Nagel and Newman, 1958.

NEYMAN, J. and SCOTT, E. L. The distribution of galaxies. *Scientific American,* 1956, **195,** 187–200.

O'NEILL, W. M. Hypothetical terms and relations in psychological theorizing. *Br. J. Psychol.,* 1953, **44,** 211–220.

OPARIN, A. I. The origin of life. (tr. Mogulis) New York: Macmillan, 1938.

OPPENHEIM, P. *See* Hempel and Oppenheim, 1948.

OPPENHEIM, P. *See* Kemeny and Oppenheim, 1956.

OSGOOD, C. E. and HEYER, A. W. A new interpretation of figural after-effects. *Psychol. Rev.,* 1951, **59,** 98–118.

PAP, A. *The* a priori *in physical theory.* New York: Kings Crown Press, 1946.

PAP, A. *Elements of analytic philosophy.* New York: Macmillan, 1949.

PAP, A. *An introduction to the philosophy of science.* Glencoe: Free Press, 1962.

PASSMORE, J. *One hundred years of philosophy.* London: Duckworth, 1957.

PEIRCE, C. S. How to make our ideas clear. (orig. 1878) In J. Buchler (Ed.), *The philosophy of Peirce.* London: Routledge, 1940.

PEPPER, S. Emergence. *J. Philos.,* 1926, **23,** 241–245.

PEPPER, S. *World hypotheses.* Berkeley: University of California Press, 1948.

PETERS, R. S. *The concept of motivation.* London: Routledge, 1958.

PITTS, W. and MCCULLOCH, W. S. How we know universals: the perception of auditory and visual forms. *Bull. Math. Biophys.,* 1947, **9,** 127–147.

PITTS, W. *See* McCulloch and Pitts, 1943.

PLACE, U. T. Is consciousness a brain process? *Br. J. Psychol.,* 1956, **47,** 44–50.

POINCARÉ, H. *Science and hypothesis.* (tr. W. J. G., orig. 1905) New York: Dover, 1952.

POINCARÉ, H. *The value of science.* (tr. G. B. Halstead; orig. 1913) New York: Dover, 1958. Also published in Poincaré, *The foundations of science.* Lancaster: The Science Press, 1913.

POINCARÉ, H. *Science and method.* (tr. F. Maitland, orig. 1914) New York: Dover, 1952.

POPPER, K. R. *The poverty of historicism.* London: Routledge, 1957.

POPPER, K. R. *The logic of scientific discovery.* London: Hutchinson, 1959. Also in Science Editions, New York: Wiley, 1961. (orig. *Logik der Forschung,* Berlin, 1935.)

POPPER, K. R. The propensity interpretation of the calculus of probability, and the quantum theory. In S. Körner (Ed.), *Observation and interpretation in the philosophy of physics.* New York: Dover, 1957.

POSTMAN, L. The history and present status of the Law of Effect. *Psycho. Bull.,* 1947, **44,** 489–563.

PRATT, C. C. *The logic of modern psychology.* New York: Macmillan, 1939.

PRIBRAM, K. H. Toward a science of neurophysiology (method and data). In *Current trends in psychology and the behavioral sciences.* Pittsburgh: University of Pittsburgh Press, 1954.

PRIBRAM, K. H. A review of theory in physiological psychology. *Annu. Rev. Psychol.,* 1960, **11**, 1–40.

PRIBRAM, K. H. *See* Miller, Galanter, and Pribram, 1960.

PUTNAM, H. Review of Nagel and Newman: *Gödel's proof. Philos. Sci.,* 1960, **27**, 205–207.

PUTNAM, H. Minds and machines. In S. Hook (Ed.), *Dimensions of mind.* New York: New York University Press, 1960. Reprinted New York: Collier Books, 1961.

QUINE, W. O. Two dogmas of empiricism. In W. Quine *From a logical point of view.* Cambridge: Harvard University Press, 1953.

RAMSEY, F. P. *The foundations of mathematics.* London: Kegan Paul, 1931.

RESCHER, N. On explanation and prediction. *Br. J. Philos. Sci.,* 1958, **8**, 281–290.

RESCHER, N. Fundamental problems in the theory of scientific explanation. In B. Baumrin (Ed.), *Philosophy of Science: the Delaware Seminar,* Vol. 2. New York: Wiley, 1963.

RESTLE, F. A survey and classification of learning models. In R. R. Bush and W. K. Estes (Eds.), *Studies in mathematical learning theory.* Stanford: Stanford University Press, 1959.

RIESEN, A. H. The development of visual perception in man and chimpanzee. *Science,* 1947, **106**, 107–108.

ROSENBLATT, F. The perceptron. *Psychol. Rev.,* 1958, **65**, 386–408.

ROSENBLEUTH, A. and WIENER, N. The role of models in science. *Philos. Sci.,* 1945, **12**, 316–321.

ROZEBOOM, W. W. Mediation variables in scientific theory. *Psychol. Rev.,* 1956, **63**, 249–264.

ROZEBOOM, W. W. Ontological induction and the logical typology of scientific variables. *Philos. Sci.,* 1961, **28**, 337–377.

RUSSELL, B. *Mysticism and logic.* London: G. Allen, 1917.

RUSSELL, B. The philosophy of logical atomism. *Monist.,* 1918. In R. C. Marsh (Ed.), *Logic and knowledge.* London: G. Allen, 1956.

RUSSELL, B. *Portraits from memory.* London: G. Allen, 1956.

RUSSELL, B. *Logic and knowledge.* (Ed. R. C. Marsh) London: G. Allen, 1956.

RUSSELL, B. *See* Whitehead and Russell, 1913.

RYLE, G. *The concept of mind.* London: Hutchinson, 1949.

SARBIN, T. R. The logic of prediction in psychology. *Psychol. Rev.,* 1944, **51**, 210–288.

SCHAFER, R. and MURPHY, G. The role of autism in figure-ground relationships. *J. exp. Psychol.*, 1943, **32**, 335–343.

SCHEFFLER, I. Explanation, prediction, and abstraction. *Br. J. Philos. Sci.*, 1957, **7**, 293–315. Also in A. Adorno and S. Morgenbesser (Eds.), *Philosophy of science*. New York: Meridian Books, 1960.

SCHLICK, M. Is there a factual *a priori*. (orig. 1930) In H. Feigl and W. Sellars (Eds.), *Readings in philosophical analysis*. New York: Appleton-Century-Crofts, 1949.

SCHLICK, M. Are natural laws conventions? (orig. 1938) In H. Feigl and M. Brodbeck (Eds.), *Readings in the philosophy of science*. New York: Appleton-Century-Crofts, 1953.

SCHMIDT, F. O. (Ed.), *Macromolecular specificity and biological memory*. Cambridge: Massachusetts Institute of Technology Press, 1962.

SCOTT, L. *See* Neyman and Scott, 1956.

SCRIVEN, M. A study of radical behaviorism. In H. Feigl and M. Scriven (Eds.), *Minnesota studies in the philosophy of science*, Vol. I. Minneapolis: University of Minnesota Press, 1956.

SCRIVEN, M. Definition, explanation, and theories. In H. Feigl, G. Maxwell, and M. Scriven (Eds.), *Minnesota studies in the philosophy of science*, Vol II. Minneapolis: University of Minnesota Press, 1958.

SCRIVEN, M. The compleat robot. In S. Hook (Ed.), *Dimensions of mind*. New York: New York University Press, 1960. Reprinted New York: Collier Books, 1961.

SCRIVEN, M. Explanations, predictions, and laws. In H. Feigl and G. Maxwell (Eds.), *Minnesota studies in the philosophy of science*, Vol. III. Minneapolis: University of Minnesota Press, 1962.

SCRIVEN, M. Limits of scientific explanation. In B. A. Baumrin (Ed.), *Philosophy of science: the Delaware Seminar*, Vol. II. New York: Wiley, 1963.

SELLARS, W. Empiricism and the philosophy of mind. In H. Feigl and M. Scriven (Eds.), *Minnesota studies in the philosophy of science*, Vol. I. Minneapolis: University of Minnesota Press, 1956.

SELLARS, W. The language of theories. In H. Feigl and G. Maxwell (Eds.), *Current issues in the philosophy of science*. New York: Holt, Rinehart and Winston, 1961.

SELLS, R. L. *See* Weidner and Sells, 1960.

SENDEN, M. VON. *Space and sight*. (tr. P. Heath; orig. 1932) Glencoe: Free Press, 1960.

SEWARD, J. P. The constancy of the I-V: a critique of intervening variables. *Psychol. Rev.*, 1955, **62**, 155–168.

SHANNON, C. E. and WEAVER, W. *The mathematical theory of communication*. Urbana: University of Illinois Press, 1949.

SHANNON, C. E. Presentation of a maze solving machine. In H. von Foerster (Ed.), *Cybernetics. Transactions of the eight conference of Josiah Macy Jr. foundation, 1951*.

SHOLL, D. A. *The organization of the cerebral cortex*. London: Methuen, 1956.

SKAGGS, E. B. Personalistic psychology as a science. *Psychol. Rev.*, 1945, **52**, 234–240.

SKINNER, B. F. The generic nature of the concepts of stimulus and response. *J. gen. Psychol.*, 1935, **12**, 40–65.

SKINNER, B. F. *The behavior of organisms: an experimental approach.* New York: Appleton-Century-Crofts, 1938.

SKINNER, B. F. Card guessing experiments. *Amer. Sci.*, 1948, **36**, 456–458.

SKINNER, B. F. Are theories of learning necessary? *Psychol. Rev.*, 1950, **57**, 193–216.

SKINNER, B. F. *Science and human behavior.* New York: Macmillan, 1953.

SMART, J. J. C. The reality of theoretical entities. *Austral. J. Philos.*, 1956, **34**, 1–12.

SMART, J. J. C. Sensations and brain processes. *Philos. Rev.*, 1959, **68**, 141–156.

SMART, J. J. C. *Philosophy and scientific realism.* London: Routledge, 1963.

SNYGG, D. and COMBS, A. W. *Individual behavior.* New York: Harper & Row, 1949; Rev. ed., 1959.

SPENCE, K. W. *See* Bergmann and Spence, 1941, 1944.

SPENCE, K. W. *Behavior theory and conditioning.* New Haven: Yale University Press, 1956.

SPERRY, R. W. Neurology and the mind-body problem. *Amer. Sci.*, 1952, **40**, 291–312.

STEBBING, L. S. The *a priori. Proc. Arist. Soc. Suppl.*, 1933, **12**, 178–197.

STEBBING, L. S. *A modern introduction to logic.* (6th ed.) London: Methuen, 1948.

STEVENS, S. S. The operational basis of psychology. *Amer. J. Psychol.*, 1935, **47**, 323–330.

STEVENS, S. S. The operational definition of psychological concepts. *Psychol. Rev.*, 1935, **42**, 517–527.

STEVENS, S. S. Psychology and the science of science. *Psychol. Bull.*, 1939, **36**, 221–263.

STEVENS, S. S. Mathematics, measurement, and psychophysics. In S. S. Stevens (Ed.), *Handbook of experimental psychology.* New York: Wiley, 1951.

STEVENS, S. S. The direct estimate of loudness. *Amer. J. Psychol.*, 1956, **69**, 1–25.

STRATTON, G. M. Vision without inversion of the retinal image. *Psychol. Rev.*, 1897, **4**, 341–360, 463–481.

SUPPES, P. *Introduction to logic.* Princeton: Van Nostrand, 1957.

SUPPES, P. *Axiomatic set theory.* Princeton: Van Nostrand, 1960.

SUPPES, P. A comparison of the meaning of models in mathematics and the empirical sciences. *Synthese*, 1960, **12**, 287–300. Also in H. Freudenthal (Ed.), *The Concept and the role of model in mathematics and natural and social sciences.* Dordrect: D. Reidel, 1961.

SUPPES, P. Models of Data. In E. Nagel, P. Suppes, and A. Tarski (Eds.), *Logic, methodology and philosophy of science.* Stanford: Stanford University Press, 1962.

SUPPES, P. and ATKINSON, R. C. *Markov learning models for multi-personal interactions.* Stanford: Stanford University Press, 1960.

SUPPES, P. *See* Estes and Suppes, 1959.

TARSKI, A. *Introduction to logic.* New York: Oxford University Press, 1941, 1946.

TARSKI, A. *Logic, semantics and metamathematics.* Oxford: Clarendon Press, 1956.

TAYLOR, J. G. *The behavioral basis of perception.* New Haven: Yale University Press, 1962.

THOMAS, G. J. Neurophysiology of learning. *Annu. Rev. Psychol.,* 1962, **13**, 71–106.

TINBERGEN, N. *The study of instinct.* London: Oxford University Press, 1951.

TOLMAN, E. C. *Purposive behavior in animals and man.* New York: Appleton-Century, 1932.

TOLMAN, E. C. Theories of learning. In F. A. Moss (Ed.), *Comparative psychology.* New York: Prentice-Hall, 1934.

TOLMAN, E. C. Operational behaviorism and current trends in psychology. *Proc. 25th Ann. Celebr. Inaug. Gr. Stud., Univ. So. Calif.,* 1936, 89–103. Also in M. Marx (Ed.), *Psychological theory.* New York: Macmillan, 1951.

TOLMAN, E. C. An operational analysis of demands. *Erkenntnis,* 1937, **6**, 383–392.

TOLMAN, E. C. Prediction of vicarious trial and error by means of the schematic sow-bug. *Psychol. Rev.,* 1939, **46**, 318–336.

TOLMAN, E. C. Cognitive maps in rats and men. *Psychol. Rev.,* 1948, **55**, 189–208.

TOLMAN, E. C. Principles of purposive behaviorism. In S. Koch (Ed.), *Psychology: a study of a science,* Vol. 2. New York: McGraw-Hill, 1959.

TOULMIN, S. *The philosophy of science.* London: Hutchinson, 1953.

TREISMAN, M. Psychological explanation: the 'private data' hypothesis. *Br. J. Philos Sci.,* 1962, **13**, 130–143.

TURING, A. M. On computable numbers, with an application to the Entscheidung's problem. *Proc. London Math. Soc.,* 1937, **42**, 230–265; 1937, **43**, 544–546. Reprinted in M. Davis (Ed.), *The undecidable.* Hewlett, N.Y.: Raven Press, 1965.

TURING, A. M. Computing machinery and intelligence. *Mind,* 1950, **59**, 433–460. Reprinted as "Can a machine think?" in J. R. Newman (Ed.), *The world of mathematics,* Vol. 4. New York: Simon and Schuster, 1956.

UTTLEY, A. M. The classification of signals in the nervous system. *EEG Clin. Neurophysiol.,* 1954, **6**, 479–494.

UTTLEY, A. M. The conditional probability of neural connexions. *Proc. Roy. Soc.,* 1955, **B144**, 229.

UTTLEY, A. M. Conditional probability machines and conditioned reflexes. *Automata Studies,* 253–275. Princeton: Princeton University Press, 1956.

VERPLANCK, W. S. Burrhus F. Skinner. In W. K. Estes and others, *Modern learning theory*. New York: Appleton-Century-Crofts, 1954.

VOEKS, V. W. Formalization and clarification of a theory of learning. *J. Psychol.*, 1950, **30**, 341–362.

WALTER, W. GREY. *The living brain*. London: Duckworth, 1953.

WATSON, J. B. *Psychology from the standpoint of a behaviorist*. Philadelphia: Lippincott, 1919, 1929(3).

WATSON, J. B. *Behaviorism*. New York: Norton, 1925, 1929.

WATSON, W. H. *On understanding physics*. Cambridge: Cambridge University Press, 1938.

WEAVER, W. *See* Shannon and Weaver, 1949.

WEIDNER, R. T. and SELLS, R. L. *Elementary modern physics*. Boston: Allyn and Bacon, 1960.

WHITEHEAD, A. N. and RUSSELL, B. *Principia Mathematica*, 3 vols. Cambridge: Cambridge University Press, 1913.

WHORF, B. L. *Language, truth, and reality*. (Ed. J. B. Carroll) New York: Wiley, 1956.

WIENER, N. *Cybernetics*. New York: Wiley, 1948.

WIENER, N. *See* Rosenbleuth and Wiener, 1945.

WINCH, P. *The idea of a social science*. London: Routledge, 1958.

WINDELBAND, W. *An introduction to philosophy*. (tr. J. McCabe) London: Unwin, 1921.

WISDOM, JOHN. *Other Minds*. Oxford: Blackwell, 1952.

WISDOM, J. O. *Foundations of inference in natural science*. London: Methuen, 1952.

WITTGENSTEIN, L. *Tractatus logico-philosophicus*. London: Routledge, 1922.

WITTGENSTEIN, L. *Philosophical investigations*. (tr. G. E. M. Anscombe) Oxford: Blackwell, 1953.

WOODGER, J. H. *Biological principles*. London: Kegan Paul, 1929.

WOODGER, J. H. *Axiomatic method in biology*. Cambridge: Cambridge University Press, 1937.

WOODGER, J. H. *Language and biology*. Cambridge: Cambridge University Press, 1952.

WOODWORTH, R. S. *Psychology*. New York: Henry Holt, 1922 (1st ed.); 1929 (2nd ed.); 1935 (3rd ed.); 1940 (4th ed.); 1947 (5th ed.); 1949 (6th ed.). (1949 ed. with D. Marquis.)

YAMAGUCHI, H. G. Superthreshold reaction potential (sEr) as a function of experimental extinction (N) *J. exp. Psychol.*, 1951, **41**, 391–400.

YOLTON, J. W. Philosophy and scientific explanation. *J. Philos.*, 1958, **55**, 133–143.

YOLTON, J. W. Explanation. *Br. J. Philos. Sci.*, 1959, **10**, 194–208.

ZAVALA, A. *See* Gaito and Zavala, 1964.

ZEAMAN, D. An application of *sEr* quantification procedure. *Psychol. Rev.*, 1949, **56,** 341–350.

ZIPF, G. K. *The psycho-biology of language: an introduction to dynamic philosophy.* Boston: Houghton Mifflin, 1935.

ZIPF, G. K. *Human behavior and the principle of least effort; an introduction to human ecology.* Cambridge: Addison-Wesley, 1949.

NAME INDEX

231

SUBJECT INDEX